THE
NELSON
PORTRAITS

Oil by Heinrich Füger, 1800, (102) - the only portrait showing Nelson in civilian clothes

THE
NELSON
PORTRAITS

AN ICONOGRAPHY OF
HORATIO, VISCOUNT NELSON, K.B.
VICE ADMIRAL OF THE WHITE

RICHARD WALKER

MADE POSSIBLE BY THE GENEROUS GIFT AND SPONSORSHIP OF
CLIVE RICHARDS

Published by the Royal Naval Museum.

Endorsed by the
Official Nelson Celebrations Committee

ISBN 0-9526377-5-8

Typeset in Garamond
Design by Michael O'Callaghan
Typeset and produced by CDA Design, Worthing
Printed in Great Britain by Flexiprint

C O N T E N T S

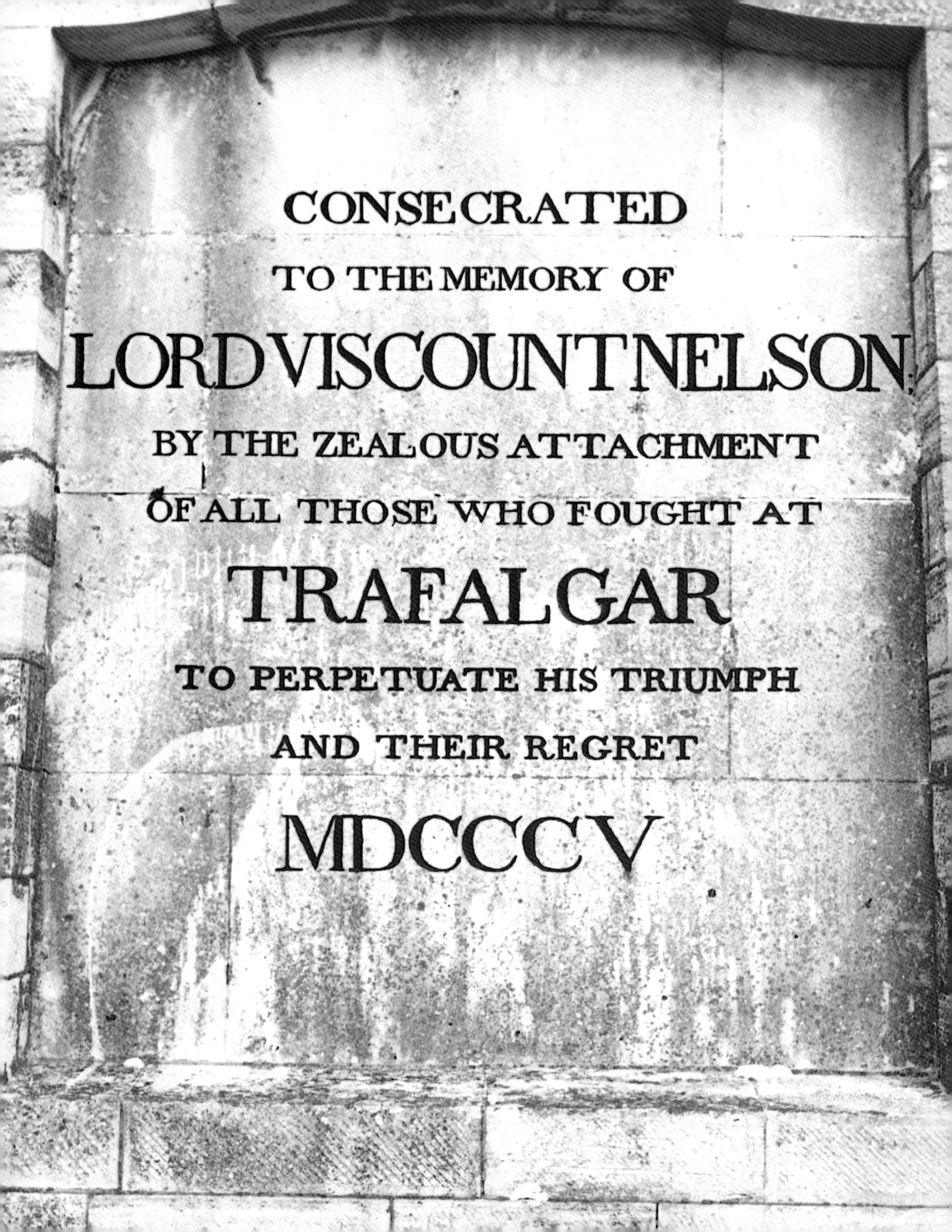

CONSECRATED
TO THE MEMORY OF
LORD VISCOUNT NELSON,
BY THE ZEALOUS ATTACHMENT
OF ALL THOSE WHO FOUGHT AT
TRAFALGAR
TO PERPETUATE HIS TRIUMPH
AND THEIR REGRET
MDCCCV

Among the many treasures on board the Royal Yacht Britannia there is a portrait of Nelson so small that it is easy to miss. What makes it particularly special is that it bears an example of Nelson's right-handed signature. Without flourishes it reads simply 'Horatio Nelson', obviously written before he became a famous hero.

We now know, thanks to Richard Walker's meticulous research, that this portrait is just one of more than 200 likenesses of the great man. You will find them listed in the catalogue section of this book: a remarkable tribute both to Nelson's extraordinary popularity and to Richard Walker's lifelong dedication to his subject.

But this is more than just a catalogue. For Richard Walker uses the evidence of the portraits to tell us more about Nelson the Man: his illnesses, his wounds, even his state of mind, are all fascinatingly examined. By the end of the book, we feel we know Nelson better.

The publication of this book coincides with the preparation of a new exhibition at the Royal Naval Museum, *Nelson: The Hero and The Man*. There too, new insights about Nelson will be offered, based on careful research and scholarship. But there too, as in this book, the aim will be to bring Nelson alive, so that hopefully he can work his extraordinary magic on a new generation.

I hope that this book will bring Nelson alive for you and that it will encourage you to visit the Museum and find out more about our greatest naval hero.

Anne

Opposite: Inscription on the Nelson Monument on Portsdown Hill, above Portsmouth, (227)

For Margot Firebrace
a soldier's daughter

AUTHOR'S PREFACE

New books on Nelson appear relentlessly year after year, and the excuse for yet another must relate to the phenomenon that no detailed account of the contemporary portraits of Nelson has yet been published. Although iconographies of other national heroes - Shakespeare, Pope, Pitt, Blake, Scott, Wellington and Wordsworth - have been written by their admirers, apart from the preliminary work of the late Oliver Warner, Nelson himself so far has escaped.

Iconography, the study of a subject through his portraiture, has somehow not appealed to art historians in this country; or perhaps not to our publishers. The last major investigation into the portraits of Shakespeare, for instance, apart from Sir David Piper's concise survey, *O Sweet Mr. Shakespeare I'll have his Picture*, was published by M.H.Spielmann, a hundred years ago in 1907. This curious anomaly is all the more strange because of, as Sir Roy Strong calls it, The British Obsession: 'for four centuries the British were obsessed by portraiture more than any other European country'. Indeed, although there is no easy explanation for this, most of the great portraits of the world are either by British artists or by foreign artists resident in this country spurred on by the native delight in hanging images of themselves and their friends on the walls of their houses. The proper study of mankind is man, and one way to try to solve this mystery is through his portraiture.

This book originates with the Nelson entry in *Regency Portraits*, written for the National Portrait Gallery and published in 1985, and my first acknowledgement must be to the Director and Trustees at that time for allowing me latitude, and to my colleagues on the Gallery staff for their good-natured patience in tolerating my obsession with the Nelson entry.

My second debt is to Mrs Lily McCarthy CBE, who placed her knowledge of the Nelson iconography, extending over half a century, unrestrictedly at my disposal. Her collection of photographs, her correspondence with museums, galleries and private owners, her library, and above all her personal encouragement, have been a great help.

Thirdly the constant help of the staff of the National Maritime Museum made my labours there a delight. I would specially like to thank Westby Percival-Prescott, Teddy Archibald and Roger Quarm for guidance through the labyrinth of oil paintings, watercolours, drawings and prints; Gillian Lewis and Anne Leane of the Conservation Department for expert technical advice; John Munday, Rena Prentice and Patricia Blackett Barber for help with the busts, medals, Wedgwood medallions and other relics; and the late Dorothy Osbon for her work among the archives where she found and handed over to me a treasure-trove of information about the history and provenance of the National Maritime Museum Nelson possessions. I am delighted that my old friend from National Portrait Gallery days, Richard Ormond, now Director of the National Maritime Museum, should honour me with such a glowing Introduction.

Finally, ending the long search for a publisher, a Nelson enthusiast of long standing, Clive Richards, has come to the rescue and agreed to sponsor and totally finance this project. I am deeply grateful to him for this timely generosity. This vital resource has been largely the responsibility of another Nelson enthusiast, Colin White, Deputy Director of the Royal Naval Museum, Portsmouth, whose determination to ensure that *The Nelson Portraits* celebrates the bi-centenary of the Battle of the Nile, has been the drive behind the book's publication. Nelson had his Guardian Angel in his cabin on the *Victory.* I look on Colin as the spirit of inspiration. I thank him for his endless patience, encouragement, practical advice and ready availability whenever needed. The staff of the Royal Naval Museum have supported him at all times, and I would like to thank especially the Director, Campbell McMurray, Dr Chris Howard Bailey, Michael O'Callaghan, Michael Forder and Chris Arkell for managing the photography, design and publication.

Elsewhere I acknowledge help from Keith Kissack and Andrew Helme of the Monmouth Museum, J.G. Pollard of the Fitzwilliam Museum, Richard Ollard, David and Anne Horatia Piper, Tom Pocock, Michael Nash, and the late Hugh Murray Baillie of the Royal Commission on Historical Manuscripts. The private owners of Nelson relics have with unfailing generosity allowed me to examine, photograph and sometimes even to borrow for long periods their prized possessions. It is not possible to thank them by name but I am most grateful for their kindness and support.

I dedicate this book, with great delight, to my wife Margot. She, like Clemency the General's daughter, 'pulls across with even strokes'. She accompanied me, through driving rain and a force 8 gale, on a pilgrimage to the boulder marking Admiral Sir Cloudisley Shovell's last landfall on the Scillies. But that was a trifle when set against her patience, endurance and encouragement, throughout my voyage in search of the Nelson portraits.

The Nelson iconography is beset with pitfalls. I have tried to take advice wherever possible and, though conclusions have not always synchronised, the final decisions have been my own. *Palmam qui meruit ferat.*

HOW TO USE THIS BOOK

Layout

This book is in two parts.

In the first part, the author reviews all the known Nelson portraits and places them in their historical and iconographic context.

The second part is a detailed Catalogue of all the known original images of Nelson created in his lifetime or immediately after his death: oil paintings, watercolours, drawings, busts and sculpture.

Engravings, prints and other contemporary copies of these images, are listed in the Catalogue, under the entry for the original image from which they are derived.

Numbering and Cross-referencing

Each original image listed in the Catalogue has been given its own unique number.

When the image is referred to in the main narrative, it is followed by two numbers, thus: (000, *p.000*). The first number is the image's Catalogue number; the second is the number of the page(s) on which the image is illustrated.

All the picture captions include the Catalogue number of the image illustrated.

NELSON'S WOMEN

No life of Nelson is complete without a mention of the women
who played such an important role in it.
Here are some lesser-known images of three of the most important.

'A treasure of a woman': Mrs Mary Moutray, who Nelson met while he was serving in the West Indies in 1784/5.
Watercolour drawing by John Downman, 1781.

His Wife: Frances Nelson. Pencil and watercolour drawing by Henry Edridge

His Mistress: Emma Hamilton. Oil by Domenico Pellegrini, 1791

Drawn from Life by S. De Koster Dec.r 8 1800.
Engraved by J.d Stow.

What did Nelson look like?

from top to bottom:

*Oil by Lemuel Abbott (1798): the most
well known likeness of Nelson, which
shows him ill and emaciated after the
loss of his arm.*

*Engraving after a sketch by William
Beechey (1800):
a state portrait painted for the City of
Norwich, which shows Nelson as The Hero.*

*Vignette after a drawing by Simon
De Koster (1800), which Nelson himself
said, '…is the most like me.'*

INTRODUCTION

by
Richard Ormond
Director, National Maritime Museum

Richard Walker and I are both authors of two volume catalogues in the series devoted to the collections of the National Portrait Gallery. He did the Regency, I tackled the Early Victorians, in succession to such luminaries as Sir Roy Strong (Tudors) Sir David Piper (Stuarts), and John Kerslake (Early Georgians). Our aim was not just to document the Gallery's own collection of portraits, but to chart the imagery of each individual represented. To misquote a famous verse you might say 'by their faces shall ye know them'. And it is true that there is a particular fascination in seeing what famous people looked like, in tracing their lineaments and characters through their surviving portraits. Thomas Carlyle the Victorian historian once commented that a portrait was worth a hundred biographies and you can see what he meant. Portraits present historical characters as living persons of flesh and blood, with no third-party intervention. They bring history to life by giving the past a visual reality and the stamp of human authenticity. These people once lived, moved, and had their being in periods that seem remote and inaccessible. And who has not suddenly come on a picture of someone well-known and exclaimed 'goodness is *that* what Sir Francis Drake or Jane Austen really looked like.'

Historians tend to underestimate the role that visual images play in our understanding of the past. Portraits, in particular, have often conditioned what we feel about historical personages, and how we view them. Holbein's majestic picture of Henry VIII, legs astride and arms akimbo, was designed to overawe his subjects, and even now, through debased copies, it has the power to cower us. It is impossible to separate our conception of the King from Holbein's implacable physical image of him. And the same is true of that image of the three Brontë sisters, Charlotte, Emily and Anne by their brother Bramwell: crude, almost like sign-painting, but a haunting likeness of that gifted literary trio, and almost the only visual record we have of them.

Nelson is no exception to this rule. We all have an idea of what England's greatest naval hero looked like, slight, attractive and romantic: not a conventional sea dog, but someone sensitive as well as formidable. And the most familiar image of him is the soft and idealised portrait by Lemuel Francis Abbott which is known through countless versions and replicas. Abbott no doubt owed his primacy among Nelson's portraitists to his marketing skills, for he was by no means the most talented artist to depict the naval hero. Sir William Beechey and John Hoppner, who both portrayed Nelson, were much better painters, and Sir Thomas Lawrence, the genius of the age, never had the opportunity. I remember the excitement at the National Portrait Gallery in 1966 when Beechey's original life study of Nelson was discovered by Hugh Leggatt and lent to the gallery. Here was a naval commander we could believe in, tough, energetic and resourceful, with the wound above his right eye clearly visible, an image startlingly at odds with the weak tea and sugar dished up by Abbott.

As one would expect with a self-publicist as relentless as Nelson he took a keen interest in the production of his portraits. Like Lord Byron, another much painted hero or anti-hero of the age, Nelson presented himself as a man of destiny around whom there hung an aura of greatness. His portraits proclaim him as England's hero long before the battle of Trafalgar that would immortalise him. And these portraits in turn spawned a vast production of prints and popular imagery, in every conceivable medium, that continues to this day. A visit to the Nelson galleries of the National Maritime Museum and the Royal Naval Museum demonstrates how inextricably the Nelson myth is bound up with the appearance of the man himself He even managed posthumously to colonise Trafalgar Square, getting his statue atop the column originally intended to commemorate the victory rather than the victor.

There have been several books written about the portraiture of his contemporaries, romantic poets chiefly it must be admitted, and one slim volume on the Duke of Wellington portraits, but we have had to wait until now for a thorough survey of Nelson's iconography. Richard Walker is well equipped for the task, for he knows the period inside and out, and he has already written the best account of Nelson portraiture in his Regency catalogue. He unravels the complexities surrounding the versions and copies of well-known portrait types, tracks the histories of individual portraits in detail, and bases his conclusions on a careful sifting of the available documentary evidence.

Not the least of the virtues of his new study is the documentation he provides for images of Nelson with which we are less familiar, the bizarre but strangely compelling portraits by the obscure Neapolitan artist Leonardo Guzzardi, for example, or the characterful busts by the Irish sculptor Lawrence Gahagan. He has undertaken a formidable task, with a light hand, never losing sight of his quarry and bringing us back again and again face to face with Nelson.

The answer to the simple question of what Nelson really looked like we shall never know. In the absence of film and photography, and even the camera can lie, we have no objective evidence, except possibly for the life mask. What we are faced with is a daunting array of images that tell us as much about the aesthetic preconceptions of the artists concerned, the attitudes of society, and the manipulation of the media by Nelson himself, as about truth of appearance and physical reality. Each interpretation adds something new to our conception of the great man, draws out some special feature or characteristic, and amplifies our view of him. We know far more about Nelson than any of his famous predecessors and our conception of him as a hero has been shaped more than we realise by the evidence of his portraiture.

Watercolour drawing by Captain Cuthbert Collingwood, 1784, (2)

P R O L O G U E

I remember that, after the Battle of the Nile when quite a child,
I was walking with a schoolfellow near Stonehouse, when a little
diminutive man with a green shade over his eye, a shabby well-
worn cocked hat, and buttoned-up undress coat, approached us...

So said the artist Benjamin Robert Haydon, recalling the encounter many years afterwards. The two boys took off their hats and held them out so that the little diminutive man could not help noticing them and in return he touched his own hat and smiled at them. They boasted of this for months, says Haydon. Many of Nelson's contemporaries described his physical appearance of which a noticeable characteristic seems to have been his stature: his 'diminutive figure' says Clarke and M'Arthur, his biographers, both of whom knew him personally; 'the little Captain of the *Boreas*' said a friend of Fanny Nisbet before his marriage; 'the merest boy of a Captain' said Prince William, a shipmate and finally King of England in succession to George IV. 'Admiral Nelson is little and not remarkable in his person either way' said Cornelia Knight on meeting him in Naples; 'a little man without dignity' said Mrs St George in 1800; 'shrunk and mutilated' said Lord Palmerston, and there are many others testifying to the smallness of his size. Perhaps it was the contrast of fact with expectation. Great men ought to be tall, muscular and well-built, but often they are not and their very absence of inches finds compensation in heroism of spirit. It is not difficult to discover examples but for this very reason it may be that his contemporaries exaggerated his littleness. In fact his nephew, George Matcham who knew and admired Nelson, said that 'he was not as described, a little man, but of the middle height and of a frame adapted to activity and exertion'.[1] A measurement taken of the effigy in Westminster Abbey records a height of 5 feet 5$\frac{1}{2}$ inches, certainly a reasonable size even in these days of 6 feet and over.[2]

A man's stature is not an index of his character though an imposing presence can surely be a help in his passage through the world. His countenance and expression are far more solid witnesses but even these are notoriously unreliable. Sydney Smith and Tom Moore delighted in visiting the studio of the phrenologist, James Deville, solely in order to ridicule the hopeless inaccuracy of his judgements on their friends. Nevertheless a man's face, his voice, the colour and expression of his eyes, even the shape of his head, all help us to assess the value as human beings of our fellows. Artists, with their specially sharpened sensitivity, must provide our only guide-lines to the past, but even they find themselves inadequate to the task. Rembrandt and Cezanne spent weeks and months striving to penetrate into the spirits of their subjects.

The spirit and the body interweave, sometimes one predominates sometimes the other. Nelson, normally a kind, good-tempered and tolerant man, frequently admitted his ill-humour and irritability and this was very often triggered by bouts of ill health. As a young man he suffered from 'an ague and fever which ... has pulled me down most astonishingly', probably the malaria recurring throughout his life.[3] James Kemble, Fellow of the Royal College of Surgeons, in his study of 'The Medical Life of Lord Nelson', considers that the dysentery which ravaged the San Juan expedition was in reality typhoid fever. Nelson was recalled for his appointment to the *Janus* probably just in time to save his life but he was so ill on arrival at Port Royal that he had to be carried ashore in his cot and eventually sent home to England to recuperate in Bath where atrophy of his left arm and leg was a recurrent and alarming symptom. It took him nearly two years to recover and it was not until September 1782 in Quebec that he could write to his father, 'Health, that greatest of blessings, is what I never truly enjoyed until I saw fair Canada'. During the next three years on the West Indies station he was ill again, according to the naval doctors, of tuberculosis, but diagnosed in the light of modern medical knowledge as a chest disorder due to the climate, his malaria, and the chronic stress and worry caused by his situation as a young captain in opposition to the local establishment. James Kemble thinks it unlikely to have been tuberculosis which would almost certainly have killed a man of Nelson's constitution and medical history. The toll taken by the illness, including the loss of his hair, can be seen in the amateurish but revealing portrait by his fellow officer, Cuthbert Collingwood (2; *p.xx*). Scurvy, pains in the chest and lungs, and severe mental depression, all left their marks on his face.

During the five years ashore, spent mainly with his wife and father in Norfolk, Nelson enjoyed good health marred only by the occupational anxiety endured by any normal active man in unemployment. No certain portrait of him at this time is known though claims are made without foundation. A portrait by his fellow East Anglian, Thomas Gainsborough, would be a treasure but out of the question. Gainsborough died in 1788. The next portrait we have is the miniature sent home to his wife from Leghorn at the end of 1794 (3; *p.19 and p.195*). But by this time he had suffered the first of his many wounds, the injury to his right eye at Calvi. The wound was caused by a shot landing at his feet and flinging sand and stone splinters into his face and chest and causing a heavy flow of blood from his head. The actual damage to the eye has never been clinically ascertained; a detached retina is the usual conclusion though a haemorrhagic retinal lesion has also been diagnosed. Nelson's facial appearance after the bruises had healed, was not apparently much altered though he probably minimised the extent of the damage to his wife. The sight of the right eye had gone, he told her, but '...the blemish is nothing, not to be perceived unless told'. However in many of the portraits the blemish can be detected, especially in the corners of the eyes where the formation known as pterygium or wing of flesh can be seen to have grown. Many of his contemporaries have said however that nothing was really noticeable until much later when an opaque membrane could be seen disfiguring the other eye.[4]

Partial loss of eyesight is serious enough to an ambitious naval officer; the loss of an arm as well could easily put paid to his career in the Royal Navy. At Santa Cruz on 25 July 1797 Nelson's right arm was shattered by a musket ball. The flow of blood was checked by a tourniquet applied by his stepson Josiah Nisbet, but he was forced to return aboard to endure the agony of an eighteenth century amputation, in the days before anaesthetics the only relief being a gulp of rum or brandy and a leather pad to bite.[5] The operation was conducted by the surgeon of the *Theseus* and his mate, a French refugee from Toulon, Louis Remonier.[6] The effects were described by Southey:

> His sufferings from the lost limb were long and painful. A nerve had been taken up in one of the ligatures at the time of the operation; and the ligature according to the practice of the French surgeons was of silk instead of waxed thread and the ends of the ligature being pulled every day, in hopes of bringing it away, occasioned fresh agony. He had scarcely any intermission of pain, day or night, for three months after his return to England.[7]

Southey's vivid account conveys some idea of the suffering Nelson endured afterwards though, as James Kemble points out, the trapped nerve theory is a myth perpetuated by Nelson himself from a chance guess spoken by a London surgeon weeks later. The true cause of his suffering was sepsis in the stump and the presence of poison in the wound for over four months. It says a great deal for Nelson's capacity to endure a high degree of pain, without displaying more of his feelings, at a time when he was giving sittings for his portrait to Lemuel Abbott at Greenwich. The Abbott portraits, especially the early ones, are

Detail from oil painting by Leonardo Guzzardi, 1799 (see p. 82)

marked by a severity of expression that can only be due to the prolonged endurance of considerable pain (for example see 13; *p.39*). The pterygia in the inner aspect of both eyes are another distinguishing characteristic of the Abbotts.

Nelson very nearly gave up hope after the Santa Cruz action. 'I am become a burden to my friends and useless to my Country' he declared to Jervis three days later in a letter from the *Theseus* written in an untidy but completely legible hand. Characteristically the subject of the letter was not about himself nor the loss of his arm but the promotion of his stepson Josiah. 'You will excuse my scrawl', he concludes, 'considering it is my first attempt'. Once the stump had healed it gave no further trouble, he never even complained of the phantom sensations often experienced as if located in the missing hand or foot after amputations. A change of weather would cause it to ache sometimes, and under stress he would move it to and fro unconsciously. 'The Admiral is working his fin' they said and kept clear if they could.

The Santa Cruz action took place on the night of 24 July 1797. Almost exactly a year later he was wounded again, at the Battle of the Nile on 1 August 1798. On this occasion he was struck on the forehead above the right eyebrow by a piece of langridge. A large triangular flap of skin was stripped from the skull and fell across and over his left eye so that he could see nothing. 'I am killed', he cried, 'remember me to my wife'. On examination the surgeon assured him it was merely a scalp wound and easily repaired. 'Brought the edges of the wound together and applied strips of Emp. Adhesiv. Pil. anodyn ii. n.s.s,' entered Dr Jefferson in the *Vanguard* medical log. But for weeks afterwards the patient complained of headaches, dizziness, sickness and lack of clarity in his thought, symptoms indicating the modern diagnosis of severe brain concussion. It is not altogether surprising that an artist, invited on board a few days after the action, declined the invitation of the squadron captains to paint Nelson's portrait there and then. 'I dare not risk the attempt' he said, and we can visualise the scene only too clearly. Something of the battle-scarred war-weary visage can be seen in the strange interpretation handed down to us from Palermo by Leonardo Guzzardi (77; *pp. 82 and opposite*). That glory was his at last and that he was acknowledged throughout Europe almost with religious acclaim, coupled with the admiration and tender care blossoming into passionate love lavished upon him by Lady Hamilton, were insufficient to conceal from this perceptive but almost totally unknown portrait painter the malaise that lay hidden not far below the surface. Guzzardi's extraordinary portrait has been regarded with scepticism if not downright disbelief. No Hero could look so pathetic, almost ludicrous, as this forlorn puppet. But gazing back across the expanse of time we can observe a prophetic factor about the Guzzardi portrait. From this time onwards, inherent in the Nelson iconography, lies a deep-seated strain of melancholy that over-rides all the trappings of uniform and decorations. Nelson was barely forty years old, yet he was beginning to look an old man. As he sank deeper into the arms of Lady Hamilton and as his marriage with Fanny receded into the distance and eventually to oblivion, so a transformation can be found in his features and expression. It is as though a metamorphosis were taking place under our very eyes. Some of this change can be attributed to the worry and stress caused by finding himself functioning in the complex field of diplomacy polarised to the relatively straightforward task of running a battle fleet. Some was no doubt caused by his famous 'internal complaint', probably severe and chronic dyspepsia. 'I see but glimmering hopes', he wrote to Troubridge in March 1800, 'and probably my career of service is at an end'. The sense of apathy and depression deepened until on the journey home, through Vienna and Dresden, observers commented on his inability even to smile. This combination of the painful, the ludicrous and the melancholy was recognised by Gillray as early as December 1798 (68; *p.63*). 'In short, my dear Lord', he wrote to the First Lord of the Admiralty in April 1799, 'I am almost blind and so fagged by all things not going on as I wish ... I am out of spirits and with great reason'.[8] And a year later shortly before the start of the overland journey home, 'I am so tired, fagged and worn out, that the Nelson you knew is gone and but a shadow remains'.[9] Similar quotations are not hard to find. No doubt much of this can be put down to congenital self-pity, but the main causes of his unhappiness were assuredly ill-health and disillusion with his own behaviour in the Mediterranean; and most telling of all and the most revealing in his later portraits, was the realisation that his infatuation with Emma and his cuckoldry of one of his most staunch and loyal friends, was bound to lead eventually to doom.

Many worshippers at the Nelson shrine have tried to penetrate into the secret of his charisma. There is a dichotomy underlying his character which can be traced through the whole corpus of his letters and dispatches, and even more so throughout the Nelson iconography, from the humblest miniature portrait and wax profile to the magnificence of the great national monuments in St Paul's Cathedral and Trafalgar

Square. He was fond of mis-quoting *Henry V*, 'if it be a sin to covet Glory I am the most offending soul alive', and indeed the main driving force of his career was the ambition to win renown. The fact that he lived in an age when his ambition could be harnessed towards the destruction of Napoleon was his good fortune. His uniqueness lay in his extraordinary ability to inspire not only respect and admiration in his contemporaries but also to win their affection and even love. They lived in an age before the 'stiff upper lip' had been invented by Arnold of Rugby and his friends. Nelson's compatriots knew the brutality of life at sea with its harsh discipline and miserable conditions. Emotions were allowed to surface with impunity. Manly tears were commonplace and nothing to be ashamed of. Nelson's dual life made him beloved. 'He was Superman with Everyman's weaknesses' says an historian of our own day.[10] 'Love' is the *mot juste* and a word used more than once by weather-beaten old salts to describe their feelings towards The Hero.

NOTES TO PROLOGUE

1. Letter from George Matcham to *The Times*, 6 November 1861. Benjamin Silliman, an indefatigable American traveller, described him as having the balancing gait of a sailor, spare and of about the middle height (*cit.* Hibbert 1994, p. 340).

2. Tanner & Nevinson 1935, p.199.

3. I am indebted to Mr James Kemble FRCS and have drawn extensively on his work, *Idols and Invalids*, for this section. Professor Leslie Le Quesne has also been of great help.

4. Barras 1986, pp. 351-5.

5. Pugh 1968, *passim*.

6. Kemble 1933, pp.134-42; Bosanquet 1952, pp.184-95.

7. Southey 1813, p.115.

8. Letter to Lord Spencer, 17 April 1799 (Nicolas VII clxxix).

9. Letter to Davison, 5 June 1800 (Nicolas VII cxcvii).

10. Pocock 1968, p.126.

Watercolour drawing by an unknown artist, c.1797, (4)

1 THE EARLY PORTRAITS

The numerous 'portraits' of Nelson as a child, a boy, a midshipman and a young man are unsupported by any evidence of identity.[1] Even the melodramatic pictures of the young Horace attacking a polar bear on the Arctic ice-floes are romantic evocations painted years later, one by Edward Orme as an illustration for the first of the popular biographies of Nelson, *Orme's Graphic History of the Life, Exploits and Death of Horatio Nelson*, published in 1806, the other by Richard Westall for the first edition of Clarke & M'Arthur's *Life*, published as a lavish folio in 1809. The incident certainly occurred. It was vouched for by the commanding officer of the *Carcass*, later Admiral Sir Skeffington Lutwidge, who survived till long after Trafalgar and never ceased to delight in recounting the story at great length. But in no sense can such pictures be counted as portraits.

The first authentic portrait we do have is the enchanting three-quarter length oil by Rigaud of the young Captain Nelson, in the National Maritime Museum (1; *p.18*). John Francis Rigaud was born in Turin in 1742, studied in Rome, Parma and Bologna, and came to England in 1771 working for a time in Nollekens's studio as an assistant sculptor. He then turned to decorative work earning a good living at the restoration of mural and ceiling paintings at Greenwich Painted Hall, Marlborough House, Somerset House, Trinity House and elsewhere.[2] He was elected ARA in 1772, RA in 1784, and the Royal Academy catalogues record his classical and history pictures, together with occasional portraits of naval officers, from 1772 to 1801. His son Stephen sketched the funeral in St. Paul's and devised a not very impressive memorial for Nelson in 1806.

William Locker, Nelson's 'sea-daddy' and his commanding officer in the frigate *Lowestoffe*, had been painted by Rigaud with his wife and children in about 1779,[3] and is believed to have commissioned him to paint his young second-lieutenant on joining the ship in April 1777. Nelson was then under twenty and, judging from Rigaud's portrait, very far from Mahan's description of him as 'of florid countenance, rather stout and athletic'[4] Rigaud shows him with a pale boyish complexion and a slight wiry figure but carrying himself with poise and assurance. The tricorne hat and grey powdered hair add tremendous charm and vitality to the youthful face with its innocence and suspicion of immaturity. We can easily see what Prince William had in mind a few years later with his own vivid description of 'the merest boy of a captain I ever beheld'.

HMS *Lowestoffe* sailed a month later before the artist had a chance to finish the portrait, and Nelson served abroad for the next four years during which he was appointed to command the brig *Badger*, promoted post-captain in command of the frigate *Hinchinbroke*, and took part in the mosquito-ridden Fort San Juan expedition as a result of which he became desperately ill with the 'Yellow Jack', returning to England in November 1780. He must have visited Rigaud's studio in Great Titchfield Street in London shortly after his convalescence in Bath. Early next year he wrote to Locker, 'If Mr Rigaud has done the picture, send word in the next letter you write to me, and I will enclose an order upon Mr Paynter'.[5] The uniform had to be changed from a lieutenant's to post-captain's full-dress and the background altered to contain Fort San Juan and the captain's coxswain standing by his boat at the jetty. Rigaud made the necessary modifications and thinned down the chubby boyish face. Most people, and the artist too no doubt, were appalled by the havoc wrought by the fever, and Nelson himself was under no illusions. 'As to my picture', he wrote again to Captain Locker, 'it will not be the least like what I am now, that is certain; but you may tell Mr Rigaud to add beauty to it, and it will be much mended...'[6] Fortunately Rigaud did not

Details from oil painting by Rigaud (see p.18): Fort San Juan (right) and captain's barge (below)

HORATIO NELSON ESQ.ᴿ

now Sir Horatio Nelson, K.B. Rear Admiral of the Blue Squadron.

From an Original Picture in the possession of Wᵐ Locker Esqʳ
— Lieuᵗ Govʳ of Greenwich Hospital. —

Pub.ᵈ as the Act directs Aug.ᵗ 14.1797. by R. Shipster George Street Woolwich.

Stipple engraving by Robert Shipster, after the oil by Rigaud, 1797, (1)

add beauty though x-ray photography in 1995 reveals considerable alterations. It hung in Locker's rooms in Greenwich Hospital and when in 1797 public curiosity was aroused about the intrepid commodore, inventor of Nelson's famous bridge for boarding first rates, who had lost an arm and the sight of his eye in the war against France and Spain, Locker lent the portrait to the engraver Robert Shipster of George Street, Woolwich. Shipster's print was issued in August 1797, an indifferent production which probably did not do much to allay the public interest (see *p.11*). No concession was made to Nelson's change in rank after sixteen years nor to the loss of his right arm; but there is no doubt but that Shipster's 'ageing process' of the features since Rigaud's day records the toll taken by repeated attacks of malaria, the manchineel poisoning afflicting him in the West Indies, the typhoid, the partial paralysis that attacked him in Bath, bouts of scurvy, the mental depression he suffered after his marriage, to say nothing of the wounds he sustained at Bastia and Calvi, the internal bruising at Cape St Vincent and the hideous almost mortal wound at Santa Cruz in July. Shipster's print was published a fortnight before the *Seahorse* landed Nelson at Spithead on 1 September, so there is no question of Shipster having seen the battle-scarred veteran in order that the alterations could be done *ad vivum*. He can only have acted on the advice of Captain Locker and as such the pinched wizened features of his print were probably not very wide of the mark.

Captain Locker, who died in 1800, bequeathed the Rigaud portrait to Nelson's brother and it remained in the family possession until its acquisition by the National Maritime Museum in 1948. It had been looked upon as one of the family's most priceless treasures and used to hang over the fireplace at the end of the large drawing-room in Trafalgar House.[7] Since then it has rightly become one of the most widely appreciated of the Nelson portraits, reproduced almost without fail in every publication that appears in his name.

HMS *Albemarle* was a captured French merchantman converted into a 28-gun frigate in 1781. Nelson took command of her at Woolwich in August, sailing her to the Baltic and, after a sequence of mishaps, escorting a convoy to Newfoundland, capturing an American schooner off Boston Bay and patrolling endlessly up and down the eastern seaboard. It was of this period that Prince William, later Duke of Clarence and King William IV but then a midshipman aboard Lord Hood's flagship *Barfleur*, recollected the singular appearance of Captain Nelson. The *Albemarle's* barge came alongside, and to the sound of the boatswain's pipe, there stepped aboard the youthful figure of Captain Horatio Nelson, only five years older than the boyish lieutenant we know from Rigaud's portrait of the *Lowestoffe* days:

> I was then a midshipman on board the *Barfleur*, lying in the narrows off Staten Island, and had the watch on deck, when Captain Nelson of the *Albemarle* came in his barge, alongside, who appeared to be the merest boy of a captain I ever beheld: and his dress was worthy of attention. He had on a full-laced uniform: his lank unpowdered hair was tied in a stiff Hessian tail of an extraordinary length; the old-fashioned flaps of his waistcoat added to the general quaintness of his figure, and produced an appearance which particularly attracted my notice. My doubts were however removed when Lord Hood introduced me to him. There was something irresistibly pleasing in his address and conversation; and an enthusiasm when speaking on professional subjects that showed he was no common being.[8]

Prince William's verbal portrait is a valuable contribution to the iconography and unlikely to be surpassed. Traditionally an oil in the Norwich Castle Museum belongs to this period but there is no certainty of its authenticity. Indeed though it is of the right date most observers consider it not to represent Nelson at all. Prince William's vivid picture is by far the best we have.

In May 1784 Nelson in command of HMS *Boreas* sailed for Barbados and the Leeward Islands, anchoring in English Harbour in September. 'Collingwood is here'- he wrote to Captain Locker, 'he desires to be kindly remembered'.[9] Collingwood was then captain of the frigate *Mediator* on the Leeward Islands Station and it was at about this time or perhaps a little later that the two young captains exchanged portraits (2; *p. xx*). The story was told by Mrs Mary Moutray, wife of the Commissioner of Antigua who Nelson greatly admired (see *p.xiii*), to Collingwood's daughter when her husband was editing the Collingwood papers:

> Captain Nelson was equally an intimate in the Commissioner's house [English Harbour, Antigua], and among the memorials of those times and of the friendly freedom in which they lived together, Mrs Moutray has in her possession two portraits which were taken under the following circumstances. Nelson had lost his hair from fever, and its place had been so grotesquely supplied by the art of the West Indian perruquier, that Captain Collingwood said to him one day, 'I must draw you, Nelson, in that wig'. He accordingly made a coloured drawing which bears much resemblance to the later pictures of the hero. When the laughter which this created was over, Captain Nelson said, 'And now, Collingwood, in revenge I will draw you in that queue of yours', and produced in his turn an outline drawing in which he has caught with considerable success the features of

13

his friend. 'I believe I am correct in my dates', concludes this amiable lady, 'if eighty-four years have not impaired my memory. Adieu, my dear madam; you have been well fathered! may the same blessings attend you as wife and mother'.[10]

This remarkable account does not occur in the early editions of the book, first published in 1828. The fifth edition came out in 1837 when Mrs Moutray had died and the drawings had passed into the Collingwood family possession. Neither can be classified as great works of art but they are certainly interesting examples of the skill in drawing most naval officers cultivated and often used for outlines of cliffs and headlands for coastal navigation. The fact that Nelson had lost his hair and wore a wig at that time was probably caused by the manchineel poisoning which Prince William believed troubled him for the rest of his life.'[11]

There follows a long stretch of time during which no certain portrait of Nelson is known. In March 1785, still in the West Indies, he met Fanny Nisbet, niece of the President of Nevis, Governor Herbert. 'We have at last seen the little Captain of the *Boreas*', wrote one of Fanny's cousins, commenting on his taciturnity, reserve and sternness of behaviour but unfortunately not describing his appearance. Nelson at this time aged twenty-seven - 'I have the honour, Sir, of being as old as the Prime Minister of England', he crushingly retorted to a crusty old General who had unwisely tried pulling his rank - was deeply involved in the business of scotching the illegal trade with American ships visiting the islands. The Navigation Laws had to be enforced and Nelson endured considerable unpopularity and social ostracism locally. However he married Fanny on 11 March 1787 and a drawing, rather in the manner of Edridge, of two standing figures said to be the newlyweds, hangs in the little museum at Nevis.[12] A few months later the *Boreas* returned to Portsmouth, the ship's company was paid off and Nelson who had come back more dead than alive - 'so ill that it was not expected he could live to reach England, and he had a puncheon of rum for his body in case he should die during the voyage' - spent the next five years on the beach, mainly at home in Norfolk.[13]

In January 1793, much to his relief and delight, he was given command of the *Agamemnon*, 'one of the finest Sixty-Fours in the Service', and shortly afterwards sailed with Lord Hood for Cadiz, Gibraltar and the Mediterranean. The first portrait we know of this period was taken after the incident at Calvi on 12 July 1794 when Nelson's right eye was damaged, '... much bruised about the face and eyes by sand from the works struck by a shot'.[14] A month later he wrote home to Fanny saying that he had nearly lost his sight; '... however the blemish is nothing, not to be perceived unless told ... The pupil is nearly the size of the blue part, I don't know the name'.[15] The nature of the injury has never been established pathologically though the intense pain he experienced points to a detached retina; speculation has included a haemorrhagic retinal lesion (ruptured choroid), retinal detachment and optic atrophy'.[16] Although the sight was impaired and eventually totally lost from the right eye, to all outward appearances it was not noticeable apart from a light film which later on also attacked the left eye. He wore the famous green shade to protect his eyes from the glare, but any suggestion of a glass eye or even a black patch is a popular misconception.[17]

In the autumn of 1794 the *Agamemnon* berthed in Leghorn for a refit. Nelson took the opportunity to commission a local artist (unfortunately of unknown name) to paint his portrait and on 12 December wrote to Fanny: 'I have sent to Mr Suckling a miniature of myself. I don't know it is a strong likeness but I know it will be acceptable. I shall take another opportunity to send Josiah's who is very well and says the picture is not the least like me. Everybody else says it is but I believe he is right.' (3; *p.19*). Curiously enough the letter crossed with one from Fanny herself dated 16 December: 'I wished very much you had sat, for your picture. I am told Italy is the place to have it done. Is it possible? I mean a small one.'[18] The Leghorn miniaturist does not show the enlarged pupil but has quite clearly painted two linear scars near the eyes; they were probably even more noticeable and disfiguring then as certainly no more than three or four months can have elapsed between the dates of the wound and the sitting. Captain Berry seems to have agreed with Josiah. Several years later, Fanny in her first letter as Lady Nelson wrote 'Captain Berry begged to see your picture which he had seen me wear. I showed it but he did not allow it's like you.[19]

The Leghorn miniature became Lady Nelson's most treasured possession and Mahan relates a story told him by her great-granddaughter, Mrs F. H. B. Eccles, the daughter of 'little Fan'. 'The latter years of her life were passed in Paris, where she lived with her son and his family. Her eldest grandchild, a girl, was eight years old at the time of her death. She remembers the great sweetness of her grandmother's temper, and tells that she often saw her take from a casket a miniature of Nelson, look at it affectionately, kiss it, and then replace it gently; after which she would

Mezzotint by Robert Laurie, after the miniature by a Leghorn artist, 1797, (3)

turn to her and say, 'When you are older, little Fan, you too may know what it is to have a broken heart'. This trifling incident, transpiring as it now does for the first time, after nearly seventy years, from the intimate privacies of family life, bears its own mute evidence that Lady Nelson neither reproached her husband nor was towards him unforgiving.'[20]

Captain Berry's visit to Lady Nelson took place a few months after the Battle of Cape St Vincent when Nelson had become something of a national hero. On his return home, after the loss of his arm at Teneriffe, demands for his portrait became peremptory and Lady Nelson handed over the miniature to Robert Laurie who, by altering the captain's uniform to a rear-admiral's, adding the Bath insignia and removing the hero's right arm, produced a tolerable and up-to-date mezzotint for public consumption[21] (see *opposite*). A whole-length version, with suitable alterations was published after the Battle of the Nile (see *p.195*).

The little watercolour drawing in the Monmouth Museum, probably by a fellow officer on board HMS *Theseus*, can be claimed as the last portrait of Nelson we have before the loss of his arm. It shows him drawing up a plan of attack on a land position, because of his apparent age probably Calvi or Santa Cruz. He writes: *F.A.O. The First line to attack - the second will sustain* (4; *p.8*).

One of the first of the many artists to take advantage of the public demand for portraits was Henry Edridge who specialised in small whole-length drawings usually in pencil, chalk or watercolour, and frequently of officers in the uniform of both the Services. A portrait of Nelson was ordered from Edridge by Sir Henry Englefield, a scientific writer, antiquary and collector, elected to the Royal Society in 1778, to the Society of Antiquaries in 1779, and the Dilettanti Society in 1781.[22] According to Englefield's brother-in-law, Richard Bulkeley, an old comrade of Nelson's from the days of the Nicaraguan expedition in 1780, Nelson did sit to Edridge at Englefield's wish. Hoping for a portrait for himself several years later Bulkeley wrote to his old friend reminding him of this former sitting. 'When I was in London I was at Mr Eldridge's *(sic)* in Margaret Street, where I saw some admirable likenesses, well and expeditiously executed. You, I understand, sat once to him for my brother-in-law, Sir Henry Englefield. What the devil tempted you I know not, but I hope that my influence upon the present occasion will not be less than the devil's or the Kt's...'.[23] Bulkeley's application was successful (187; *p.149*),

Oil by John Francis Rigaud, 1777-81, (1)

18

Miniature by a Leghorn artist, 1794, (3)

but the earlier drawing became one of Englefield's treasured possessions and kept till his death in 1822 (5; *opposite*). It appeared in the sale of his enormous collection of coins, vases, books and pictures, at Christie's in March 1823 when it was bought by a son of Nelson's old companion Admiral Sir George Home. It was bequeathed to the Royal Naval School by another descendant, Sir Everard Home.

Edridge's first drawing shows Nelson with his right arm still bandaged after the amputation in July 1797, the ribbons fastening the aperture in the sleeve visible just above the fold. He wears the Naval gold medal for St Vincent which had arrived in the *Theseus* off Cadiz in May - 'we have got our medals but no chains'.[24] The Order of the Bath, of which Edridge shows the riband over the right shoulder and no Star, was invested by the King on 25 September in St James's Palace. This was the famous occasion when the King exclaimed rather obtusely, 'You have lost your right arm'. 'But not my right hand', replied Nelson, 'as I have the honour of presenting Captain Berry'. Edridge's drawing gives him an expression, serious and rather distant, that can easily be imagined to be drawn with pain. The dramatic easing of the wound, when the stitches came away during the night of 30 November, enabled the stump to heal rapidly thereafter and caused an almost instant release from the pain which had been his constant companion since the crude amputation in July. Nelson's note, to the Vicar of St George's Hanover Square, was sent on 8 December: 'An officer desires to return thanks to Almighty God for his perfect recovery from a severe wound...'[25] So we can assume that the drawing was done in October or November 1797 at Edridge's house, 10 Dufour Place, Broad Street, Golden Square, the address given in the Royal Academy catalogue at the drawing's exhibition there in 1798, and well within walking distance of Nelson's lodgings in Old Bond Street.

Two other artists were lucky enough to get sittings from Nelson at about this time, either in their own studios or in his Old Bond Street lodgings - Daniel Orme and Henry Singleton. After the Battle of Cape St Vincent when the news arrived in London of Jervis's destruction of the Spanish Fleet, made even more memorable by accounts of Commodore Horatio Nelson's dare-devil part in the action, Daniel Orme conceived the idea of a large *tableau* to be called 'The Surrender of the San Josef at the Battle of St Vincent, 14 February 1797'. It was finally completed in 1798 (engraved by Orme himself in 1800) and showed the Spanish admiral's sword surrendered by one of his officers on the quarterdeck. The picture is

Pencil and ink drawing by Henry Edridge, 1797, (5)

Miniature after Daniel Orme, signed HHL, (9)

22

Oil by (or after) Daniel Orme, 1798-1800, (8)

Frances Nelson: pencil drawing by Daniel Orme, 1798

in the National Maritime Museum. Orme's slight preliminary drawing for Nelson's head still exists in a private collection in England (6; *opposite*). It has the appearance of being *ad vivum* but there is no record of Nelson having given Orme a sitting, though a miniature portrait of Lady Nelson dated 1798 and exhibited RA 1799, is also at Greenwich (see above); and a watercolour drawing of Tom Allen, Nelson's sailor servant, was on board HMS *Victory*. Orme was primarily a miniaturist[26] and although the drawing is too large for a miniature its final reduction to the oval stipple engraving, published in February 1798 (see *p.196*), at least indicates the existence somewhere of an authentic miniature by him. The absence of the ribbons securing the opening to the sleeve points to a date late in 1797 or even January 1798 by which time the wound had healed enough for the ribbons to be removed, though the sitter's drawn almost haggard

Chalk drawing by (or after) Daniel Orme, 1797-8, (6)

Pencil drawing by Henry Singleton, 1797, (10)

26

expression (not discernible in the engraving) suggests the presence of a good deal of pain.

The engraving, published in February 1798, was a tremendous success. 'Orme must have made a great deal of money', said Lady Nelson; 'the little picture he published of you he has sold beyond description. Mrs Tarleton as soon as she heard you were to be bought, she was determined to have you, but was told by the bookseller he had had a load of Admiral Nelsons but had sold every one of them, that he had written for another load and one should be saved for her'[27].

Henry Singleton had the same idea as Orme. Singleton had been brought up by his uncle, a miniature painter, and exhibited at the Royal Academy from the age of eighteen every year continuously till his death in 1839. His picture in the National Maritime Museum, 'Lord Nelson boarding the Spanish Ships in the Engagement off Cape St Vincent, 14 February 1797' was exhibited there in 1799, but the modest drawing here (10; *opposite*) was probably done in London at the same time as Orme's and several others, in the autumn or winter of 1797 between his landing at Spithead and his sailing for the Mediterranean in March 1798. Singleton was primarily an illustrator and this drawing was doubtless intended as a preliminary sketch for an engraving, possibly for a frontispiece. It was presumably worked up into an oil portrait, now lost but used for Keating's mezzotint (see *p. 28*) published in November 1798 after Nelson had become the hero of the Nile and the demands for his portrait were urgent. *The Times* Correspondent in 1955 described it perceptively:

> ...many may feel that this modest drawing by Singleton, made before Nelson's fame had become universal, before he had become ensnared in the politics of Naples and the affairs of Lady Hamilton, is fit to rank in interest with the best of the full-faced versions. It helps to convey to posterity how the 'affectionate, fascinating little fellow' as his Chaplain called him, seemed to his contemporaries.[28]

Painted by H. Singleton

London Published November, 30. 1798, by G. Keating at Warwick Street, Golden Square.

Engraved by G. Keati

The Right Hon.ble Horatio

BARON NELSON OF THE NILE,

And of Burnham Thorpe, in the County of Norfolk, Rear Admiral of the Blue

And Knight of the most Honourable & Military Order of the Bath

Mezzotint by George Keating, 1798, after Singleton, (10)

NOTES TO CHAPTER 1. THE EARLY PORTRAITS

1. Nash 1985, pp.28-33. Westall's polar bear picture is reproduced in Van der Merwe, p.67.
2. Croft Murray 1970, p.268; Rigaud 1854, pp.25, 65-7, 120-1.
3. Sitwell 1936, plate 104; Rigaud 1854, fig.16.
4. Mahan 1897, I p.15.
5. Letter to Locker, Bath 15 February 1781 (Nicolas I p.38).
6. Id. 21 February 1781 (ib. p.39).
7. Drawing by Hanslip Fletcher in *The Sunday Times*, 14 December 1947.
8. Clarke & M'Arthur 1809, I p.78, from a conversation with the Duke of Clarence at Bushey Park.
9. Letter to Locker, English Harbour 23 November 1784 (Nicolas I p.112).
10. Collingwood (1837), pp.13-14.
11. Kemble 1933, p.117; Pugh 1968, p.3
12. Information kindly given to me by Tom Pocock, but the identification with Nelson and his wife has not been authenticated.
13. Isaacson 1991, *passim*.
14. Journal of the Siege of Calvi, 12 July 1794 (Naish 1958, p.165).
15. Letter to Fanny Nelson, 18 August 1794 (Naish 1958, p.119).
16. Pugh 1968, p.8; Barras 1986, pp.351-5.
17. A single black patch lined with green silk is among the Bridport relics at Greenwich (Munday 1995 p.76).
18. Letter from Fanny Nelson, 16 December 1794 (Naish 1958, p.263).
19. Id. 28 May 1797 (Naish 1958, p.367).
20. Mahan 1897, II, p.54.
21. Robinson 1930, pp.312-3.
22. Article by Warwick Wroth in *DNB*.
23. Letter from Bulkeley, Ludlow 24 December 1801 (Morrison 1893-4, II p.181).
24. Letter to Fanny Nelson, 27 May 1797 (Naish 1958, p.429).
25. Nicolas II p.455.
26. Foskett 1987, p.611.
27. Letter from Fanny Nelson, 6 May 1798 (Naish 1958, p.429).
28. Tom Pocock in *The Times*, 26 April 1955 14e.

Oil by Lemuel Abbott (Lady Nelson's), (14)

30

Oil by Lemuel Abbott (M'Arthur's), (16)

31

Lemuel Francis Abbott: self-portrait, Mezzotint by Valentine Green, 1800

2 LEMUEL FRANCIS ABBOTT

Nelson's legendary disobedience of orders at the Battle of Cape St Vincent was followed by the blockade of Cadiz and his detachment from the Fleet to capture a Spanish treasure-ship at Tenerife; here he was forced to retreat during a night action amounting to a dismal failure. Between these two engagements lay a period of six months seminal in the formation of that extraordinary charisma known throughout the Fleet as 'the Nelson touch'. From 'Nelson's Patent Bridge for boarding first-rates' to the grandiloquent Nelsonian phrases 'Westminster Abbey or Victory' and 'tomorrow my head will be crowned with either laurel or cypress', the seed was sown that was to blossom into the dazzling flower that Nelson coveted most of all - glory. He never made a secret of this. Time and again he wrote home in letters and dispatches that this was his real ambition. Money and prizes were important to an impoverished naval officer but victory and the just recognition of duty truly done infinitely more so.

The public was becoming aware of this strange portent stirring in the Fleet. The two prints by Shipster and Robert Laurie had been published in August and November 1797. But they were both relatively insignificant affairs. The innumerable portraits of Nelson by Lemuel Abbott, perhaps the most widely recognised of the whole Nelson iconography, originate from the desire of his old friend and mentor, William Locker, Lieutenant Governor of Greenwich Hospital, to add Nelson to the collection of his 'younkers' in the dining-room at Greenwich. According to Locker's grandson, the poet Frederick Locker-Lampson, 'this picture was painted by Abbott at my grandfather's as a present from Nelson to my grandfather. He afterwards sat to Abbott for a similar sized picture for Lady Nelson and though Abbott repeated the picture some 40 times or more, Lord Nelson only sat to him twice[1]. Locker already possessed the Rigaud portrait judiciously lent to Shipster for the engraving, but Nelson's exploits, culminating in the loss of his arm at Tenerife, made it imperative that a more up to date portrait should be painted.

The choice of Abbott was a reasonable one, though possibly the young Lawrence might have been more fashionable but certainly more expensive. Abbott had already painted several naval officers of distinction including Hood, St Vincent, Sir Robert Calder, Kingsmill, Roddam Pasley and others, though probably his most perceptive portrait is that of the poet William Cowper, of 1792, in the National Portrait Gallery. His portrait of Locker himself was later engraved by James Heath and dedicated 'to the friends of the late William Locker Esq... as a Tribute of regard to his Memory' (see *opposite*). Abbott's own self-portrait, engraved in mezzotint by Valentine Green (see *p. 32*), shows a stout prosperous-looking artist holding a porte-crayon and a copy of Barnard's immensely popular engraving of Nelson. The expression is faintly smiling, almost complacent, and shows no trace of the meanness, incompetence and eventual insanity, of which we are told about by Edward Edwards in *The Anecdotes of Painting*. In the conduct of his profession, says Edwards, 'he was rather penurious, which prevented him from employing an assistant. This ill-judged parsimony rendered it impossible for him to finish his pictures in any decent time, and he found himself overwhelmed with engagements which he could not complete.' Edwards goes on to describe the domestic disquiet caused by his marriage 'to a woman of very absurd conduct' and his eventual death in a madhouse at the early age of forty-three.[2]

During the autumn of 1797 Nelson was convalescing, from the amputation, with his old friend Locker at Greenwich. Lord Minto describes how he and his wife accompanied Lord and Lady Nelson from London to dine there in October, and how well Nelson looked, 'better and fresher than I ever remember him':

> His arm is, however, by no means well owing to some awkwardness in the operation. The ligature has not come away, and they are afraid that it has taken in the artery or even a sinew. They must wait till it rots off which may be a great while. If they should attempt to cut it (it is two inches up the wound), and they should cut the artery, they would be obliged to amputate again higher up, which is not easy, for the stump is very short already. He suffers a great deal of violent pain, and takes opium every night. He is impatient for the healing of the wound that he may go to sea again. He writes very tolerably with his left.[3]

Abbott was given two sittings at about this time. Captain Locker's daughter, Frederick Locker-Lampson's Aunt Eliza, used to delight in telling the next generation how she helped Nelson on and off with his coat before and after the sittings. Most of the Abbott portraits show the sleeve with its aperture secured by three black ribbons to enable the coat to be eased over the still painful stump. In spite of Minto's description of

Captain Locker: stipple engraving by James Heath after the portrait by Abbott

him looking fresh and well, the wound was still suppurating and extremely painful, and the early Abbott portraits, before the 'adonising' process had begun, show his face lean and drawn and with a severe unsmiling expression.

This brings us to the vexed question of the so-called 'Kilgraston sketch' (12; *opposite*). Abbott is said to have painted something like forty copies and variants of Locker's portrait, but without necessarily using the Locker portrait as the model. In fact the usual practice of portrait-painters was to keep a studio model on which to base future copies. Abbott was no exception and though doubts have been cast upon it lately, the 'Kilgraston sketch' has for long been accepted as the original study. Assisted by the mezzotints of Barnard and Valentine Green it was used for the production of the very variable stream of copies to follow. According to no less an authority than Sir Francis Grant, President of the Royal Academy from 1866 to 1878, his father, Francis Grant, Laird of Kilgraston, Perthshire, who knew Abbott well, was frequently assured by Abbott himself that this was the original sketch from which all the other pictures of Nelson by him were completed.[4] Grant senior longed to possess this sketch but Abbott always declared that no amount of money would induce him to part with it during his lifetime. Then, at the sale of Abbott's effects in 1804,[5] it was withdrawn by private arrangement with the executors, acquired by Grant and hung at Kilgraston where it was well-known to his son, the PRA.

In 1857 it was lent to a British Institution Exhibition by Sir Francis's elder brother John and actually offered to the newly formed National Portrait Gallery at the Trustees' tenth meeting, but declined on the grounds of 'better' versions existing. Towards the end of Grant's life, when Kilgraston had been inherited by his nephew, the Trustees of the National Portrait Gallery were negotiating for Lady Nelson's version and consulted the President who compared it, not unfavourably, with the original picture 'for which Nelson gave two sittings'. Unfortunately the first part of Grant's letter to the Trustees is missing but it presumably repeats the account given on the back of the Kilgraston sketch (see p.199):

> ...to part with it.
> After Abbots death my father bought it from the family -In the list of Abbots pictures sold at Christies many years ago there is in the list a portrait of Lord Nelson - scratched out - that is no doubt the picture- Abbot frequently told my father that every portrait he painted of Nelson was done from that picture-

Oil by Lemuel Abbott, 1797 (Kilgraston sketch), (12)

The portrait at Greenwich Hospital which belonged to Lady Nelson - the head of Nelson is made up from the Kilgraston picture- But there is a cocked hat on it with a diamond aigrette which is done from the real hat - its vigorous handling contrasting with the tame copy of the head -

The Picture sent to the Trustees is undoubtedly the work of Abbot - and a very fair picture - But *it is not the original picture for which Nelson gave two sittings* Yours truly Francis Grant.[6]

Grant, it is true, could be considered an interested witness for it transpired a few weeks later that his nephew had let Kilgraston on a seven year lease and had offered the sketch to the new occupant for £80. She had refused, ostensibly because she needed the space for looking-glasses, but even so one cannot help expressing surprise at the Grant family being prepared to part with such a treasure for so small a sum. One wonders if perhaps, even by that time 1874, possibly 'improved' by Grant himself in order to arrest its deterioration, it was not on the way towards becoming the wreck that it unhappily is now. On the dispersal of the Kilgraston collection a few years later it was acquired by a member of Lord Sands's family in Edinburgh and came to light at the British Empire Exhibition at Wembley in 1924, lent by Lord Sands himself.

Thereafter its movements are well-known. It became the subject of a spirited correspondence in *The Times* in 1932 and a full-page spread in *The Illustrated London News*, and shortly afterwards both the National Portrait Gallery and the National Maritime Museum entered into delicate negotiations with Lord Sands for its future ownership by the nation. And finally during the 1939-45 war it was taken charge of by the National Maritime Museum as a valuable historic document of national importance. In spite of several attempts to come to an agreement with the owner nothing was concluded and eventually it was put up for sale by Lord Sands's younger son, Christopher Johnston, at Sotheby's 23 March 1977 (91a), where it was knocked down to a private buyer for £25. By this time it had been closely scrutinised at both the National Portrait Gallery and the National Maritime Museum where it had been subjected to X-ray and scientific analysis, and a Sotheby's sale room note declared that 'scientific tests on this painting have established that, although the canvas dates from Abbott's lifetime, the portrait itself dates from 20 years after Abbott's death and is painted over another portrait'. This statement was based on a report from the Conservation Department of the National Maritime Museum (see p. 200). There is no doubt that by this time the sketch had become an almost total wreck. Probably it was already far-gone even by Abbott's death in 1803. Abbott has been

Oil by Lemuel Abbott, 1797 (Captain Locker's version), (13)

described as 'penurious' and prone to 'ill-judged parsimony' and it may well be that, for the preliminary sketch made at Greenwich, he simply painted over an old re-primed canvas that had already been used, knowing that he could take more care with future versions. No doubt, twenty years or so later, when the sketch was positively disintegrating, the Laird of Kilgraston arranged for it to be restored and repainted, possibly even by his talented son, the future President of the Royal Academy. The President's repeated assurances that this was the original sketch ought not to be lightly discounted.

If the Kilgraston sketch was Abbott's preliminary study for his famous portraits of Nelson, the next in sequence was Captain Locker's own portrait, commissioned by Locker himself and the prime version of a work of which copies formed the main financial prop for the artist during the last four or five years of his life (13; *p.39*). The Locker Nelson hung in the dining-room at Greenwich together with family portraits of Lockers, Stillingfleets and Parrys, and of St Vincent, Exmouth, Barrington and other naval heroes admired by the Lieutenant Governor. It was not surprising that Nelson should be added to the number. Apart from Locker having been the captain of one of Nelson's first ships, the *Lowestoffe*, of which he was appointed second lieutenant in April 1777 at the age of eighteen, the two had formed a life-long friendship which ended only when the old man died at Greenwich in 1800 and Nelson followed the coffin containing the remains of his 'old sea-daddy' to the family vault in Addington churchyard. Jervis had written to Locker after the Battle of Cape St Vincent to tell him that 'your élève Commodore Nelson received the swords of the Commanders of a first-rate and an eighty-gun ship of the enemy on their respective quarterdecks'[7] and in 1799 Nelson himself, ensnared in the network of love and intrigue in Naples and Palermo, could write

> My dear Friend,- I well know your goodness of heart will make all allowances for my present situation, and that truly I have not the time or power to answer all the letters I receive at the moment. But you, my old friend, after twenty-seven years' acquaintance, know that nothing can alter my attachment and gratitude to you. It is you who taught me to board a Frenchman by your conduct when in the *Experiment*. It is you who always said, 'Lay a Frenchman close and you will beat him'; and my only merit in my profession is being a good scholar. Our friendship will never end but with my life, but you have always been too partial to me... Believe me, ever your faithful and affectionate friend
>
> Nelson.[8]

Fine words perhaps, but it is scarcely surprising that the recipient of such a letter should wish to own a portrait of its author hanging in his house. Indeed the Locker portrait remained in the family collection until the death of his great-grandson, Frederick Locker-Lampson, in 1923. And now, after a short sojourn in America, it has returned home to a private collection in England where there is every hope that it may finally come to rest in one of the national collections. In spite of a good deal of restoration the picture is in excellent condition and conveys probably the best idea of what Nelson looked like during the weeks following his excruciating amputation before the wound healed. The severe unsmiling countenance of a man in pain but governed by an indomitable spirit that allowed no complaint, bequeaths posterity an impression that has never been recaptured even by Beechey or Hoppner. Abbott was not a great artist, sometimes even deplorably bad, but in the Locker portrait of Nelson he achieved an understanding of the great man that he was never able to repeat. All the subsequent versions were softened or sanctified almost beyond recognition. From the image of a dedicated naval commander, suffering intensely from a hideous wound and standing on the threshold of a career that was to transform him into one of the great heroes of our history, his portraits thereafter become those of a charming sweet-tempered country gentleman not far removed from the breed of Norfolk parsons in which his stock was rooted.

The next in sequence to emerge from Abbott's studio after the completion of Locker's version was that belonging to Lady Nelson and now in the National Portrait Gallery (14; *p. 30*). Before its arrival at Lady Nelson's house it spent several weeks in the studio of William Barnard, the mezzotint engraver, who published his two prints on 25 May 1798 (a whole length with Tenerife in the background) (see *p.47*) and 1 November 1798 (a three-quarter length with ships firing in the left background). Nelson himself was interested in their publication and wrote to Fanny from St Helen's on 7 April 1798, '... when my print comes out you must send one to Captain James Macnamara. If directed at Sir Peter Parker's he will be sure to get it, and he is very anxious about it ...,[9] Lady Nelson hoped to see it at the Royal Academy that spring but was disappointed, only Gahagan's bust being there.[10] By June she writes from Roundwood that the prints were out and 'I am to have my picture, your brother writes, in ten days. He does not say a word of the likeness.'[11] It still had not arrived by 9 July; '...Abbot has promised your brother Maurice to send me the picture, which I grow impatient to

Miniature by William Grimaldi after Abbott, (21)

Oil after Barnard, by James Northcote 1813, (36)

have...'[12] Finally by 23 July it had arrived at Roundwood and Lady Nelson wrote:

> My dearest husband, - I am now writing opposite to your portrait, the likeness is great. I am well satisfied with Abbot. I really began to think he had no intention of letting me have my own property which I am not a little attached to, indeed it is more than attachment, it is real affection. It is my companion, my sincere friend in your absence. Our good father was delighted with the likeness. The room is very near 11 feet therefore it stands very well opposite the east window...[13]

This is the last we hear with any certainty of Lady Nelson's version of the portrait. Most historians, following Lady Nelson's own description that 'it stands very well opposite the east window' in a room nearly eleven feet high, have assumed it to be a whole length portrait, or possibly a three-quarter length. This is born out by Barnard's mezzotints, one of which is actually lettered: *From the original Picture in the Possession of Lady Nelson.* However, in spite of a good deal of search, no such portrait has come to light with a good enough provenance, and there is reason to suppose that no such portrait ever existed. The sheet of paper pasted on the back of the Locker portrait (see pp. 200-1) and signed by Frederick Locker in 1872, clearly states that Nelson sat to Abbott 'for a similar sized picture for Lady Nelson'. The likelihood therefore is that Barnard borrowed Lady Nelson's version from Abbott's studio before its delivery and simply added the legs and sword for effect. This would broaden the field to include the better half-length oils, most of which can be accounted for and one of the most likely being the National Portrait Gallery version which, although it has no ships in the left background, came to the Gallery in 1874 with the tradition of having belonged to Lady Nelson and having been bought at her death in 1831 by the Rev Robert Sherson. It must be admitted however that there is a statement in the Gallery archive, signed *RS* (presumably heir to the Rev Robert), that the portrait 'belonged to Dr Sherson who was born in 1736 and died 1821', but there is no record that can be found of chaplain or medical officer named Sherson in the Fleet in Nelson's time. It is clearly one of Abbott's early replicas painted with vigour and understanding but already showing signs of the 'adonised' treatment deplored by M'Arthur, with the features softened and the expression no longer austere and drawn with pain. When it was offered to the National Portrait Gallery in 1874 Sir Francis Grant recommended its purchase, 'for the very reasonable sum of £150 - I think it is the best of the many replicas I have seen done by Abbot - from the original sketch in my nephew's possession'. Grant was of course

Oil by Abbott and Barnard, (35)

still anxious to persuade the Trustees to buy the original sketch and that they should be under no illusion about the difference between the two: 'the picture sent to the Trustees is undoubtedly the work of Abbott - and a very fair picture - But it is not the original Picture for which Nelson gave two sittings'.[14]

Abbott's third version is that painted for Nelson's agent, Alexander Davison, and bequeathed by his son, Sir William Davison, to Greenwich Hospital in 1873. It hung in the Painted Hall until transferred to the National Maritime Museum in 1932. Davison may well have seen either the Kilgraston sketch in Abbott's studio or the Locker portrait at Greenwich during the autumn or winter of 1797, and if not would certainly have seen Lady Nelson's version at Roundwood the next summer. Family tradition claims that Nelson actually gave it to him. Certainly it was his by the end of 1798 when Richard Earlom's mezzotint was published with the lettering: '... from the Original Picture in the Possession of Alexander Davison Esq...'

This portrait was discussed by Professor Callender in a letter to *The Times* 29 October 1932 where he considers the general assumption that Abbott was commissioned to paint a whole-length portrait which was later engraved by Barnard and issued on three separate occasions - after the Battles of the Nile, Copenhagen and Trafalgar. The whereabouts of this whole-length baffled Callender and in the absence of opportunity to study it he concentrated on the half-length then in the Painted Hall at Greenwich and authenticated by its provenance from the Davison family. His conclusion was that the Greenwich portrait was the first copy made by Abbott from the Kilgraston sketch and that all subsequent copies by Abbott were made from the Greenwich copy. The present writer, who has the greatest respect for Callender's judgement, in this case disagrees with the verdict which he considers is based on a misreading of Sir Francis Grant's letter to J C Horsley in the National Portrait Gallery archive. The letter, which refers to the Kilgraston sketch, the National Portrait Gallery copy and the National Maritime later version with hat, is given in full on pages 36 and 38. The relevant passage in Grant's letter is contained in the two paragraphs following his account of the sketch:

> Abbot frequently told my father that every portrait he painted of Nelson was done from that picture-
> The portrait at Greenwich Hospital which belonged to Lady Nelson - the head of Nelson is made up from the Kilgraston picture - But there is a cocked hat on it with a diamond aigrette...

Mezzotint by William Barnard, after oil by Abbott, 1798, (14)

These two paragraphs, which clearly refer to two separate pictures (though Grant confused the issue by treating the versions belonging to Lady Nelson, Davison and M'Arthur as one and the same), were then telescoped by Callender into one sentence: 'Abbott frequently told my father that every portrait he painted of Nelson was done from that Portrait - the portrait at Greenwich Hospital'.[15] It would seem that Callender had not read the original letter but based his argument on a typescript copy sent to him in 1916 and which took no account of Grant's idiosyncratic spelling, punctuation and paragraphing. The issue was thus further confused to suit the theory that Davison's portrait had been used as a model for the many replicas issuing from Abbott's studio. In fact the best that can be said for Davison's portrait is that it is one of the first few copies, probably the third or fourth, made by Abbott from the Kilgraston sketch kept in the studio for that very purpose. Davison, as Nelson's agent and man of business would certainly be entitled to expect an early copy but not before the claims of Captain Locker, Lady Nelson and probably even Nelson himself for the use of his family, had been firmly settled.

Callender's search for a whole-length version of the Abbott portrait was unrewarded but at least two were known to exist; one had been offered to the National Portrait Gallery in 1858, the other slightly smaller, had been seen by Sir George Scharf with the Hon Frederick Byng in the basement of the House of Lords.[16] Scharf's drawings show that they both were of standing figures with hat and sword in the left hand and with the buildings of Santa Cruz, Tenerife, in the background. They both closely correspond to Barnard's mezzotint published on 25 May 1798 and may even have been completed by Barnard himself, Abbott having painted the usual head and shoulders and the various Orders. One of these is probably the portrait described as 'Copy by W. Barnard' bequeathed by Sir Robert Hadfield to the National Portrait Gallery in 1940 but declined by the Trustees in 1943.[17] Another was in the Pierpont Morgan sale at Christie's 31 March 1944 (112), and bought from the Caird Fund for the National Maritime Museum. A third, from the Duke of Westminster's estate at Vale Royal, was bought at Christie's by the Lloyd's Patriotic Fund to mark the opening of the new Lloyd's Building in 1961.[18] None of these is of very high quality and even if the heads are by Abbott the bodies and elongated dancing-master legs verge almost on the ludicrous. By no stretch of the imagination could any of them have pleased Lady Nelson hanging in her eleven foot room opposite the east window. Several other whole-length copies are known to exist but all have a distinctly mid-nineteenth century air, one at least having been painted for the centenary celebrations in 1905. All in all the whole length versions can be discounted as unworthy of even Abbott's mediocre talent.

However a genuine and extremely interesting variant on the Abbott theme is the portrait expressly commissioned by John M'Arthur in 1799 for use in *The Naval Chronicle*, then in its early stages and under his editorship (16; *p.31*). Lemuel Abbott, mentally unbalanced but still turning out replicas and variations of his 1797 portrait, was the obvious choice for the job, using the Kilgraston sketch and adding a cocked hat worn well down over the forehead, unlike the Guzzardi cocked hat which was tilted back to avoid the Nile wound (77; *p.82*). In 1799 Nelson was still in the Mediterranean and no one in England had actually seen the chelengk though he had sent home a drawing and a verbal description with which Abbott, using a little imagination, was able to paint in without much difficulty. The first result can be seen in Roberts's stipple engraving published on 1 April 1800 (see *p.205*). Lady Nelson had already seen the picture in March: 'Mrs M'Arthur has kindly brought me your picture with the Chelengk...', she wrote to Nelson.[19] Unfortunately the rest of the letter is missing but the engraving provides an idea of the picture's appearance at this stage. It was used as an illustration to the Memoir of Nelson in *The Naval Chronicle*. It will be seen that the chelengk does not differ materially from Guzzardi's interpretation, though the Star of the Crescent is shown as circular instead of oval. However on Nelson's return to England in November the artist was able to see the actual orders for himself, repaint them and adjust the assembly of the three brooches, but to M'Arthur's annoyance was unable to resist softening the face - 'to adonize it' in M'Arthur's telling phrase. M'Arthur's letter of 1 December 1800 reads as a sort of *cri du coeur* as he implores Nelson to visit Abbott's Pall Mall studio again before the process goes too far:

> My dear Lord
>
> Mr Abbot while finishing the Orders on your Lordship's Portrait, to my great mortification touched the Countenance thinking the likeness was not flattering enough; but in the Reverend Mr Nelson your brother's opinion and mine he has thereby in some measure taken away from its former likeness. Might I request the favor of your Lordship to look in at Abbots tomorrow or next day at any time most convenient, and if your Lordship could sit for ten minutes it would add to the obligation, as the instant after, I should take the Portrait from poor Abbot's presence, that he might not have an opportunity of making a second attempt to adonize it.

I have the honor to remain
Your Lordship's most devoted
and faithful humble Servant
(signed) Jno M'Arthur.[20]

The final result (16; *p.31*) has been cogently pronounced as being 'Abbott far from his best';[21] but it is surely going too far to claim that because of a certain hardness and brassy coarseness in the later copies these must have been done by another hand. Abbott was certified by the Lunacy Commissioners in June 1801 and died in December 1802; but he was undoubtedly still at work at the end of 1800 and the sworn statement by fifteen witnesses that he had enjoyed no lucid interval since 12 July 1798[22] is clearly modified by M'Arthur's letter quoted above about 'poor Abbott'.

The alterations had to be included in a new illustration for Clarke & M'Arthur's forthcoming *Life*, Roberts's old engraving from *The Naval Chronicle* being out of date and anyway unworthy of the two lavish quarto volumes about to appear, and John Golding was commissioned to produce a new line engraving which in fact followed Abbott's portrait exactly. 'The Portrait', says M'Arthur, 'is considered an animated likeness and Mr Golding the engraver, has succeeded in rendering justice to the Painter, after another eminent Artist had failed to give satisfaction in the execution of his plate[23] (see *opposite*).

Abbott's chelengk portrait remained a valued possession in the M'Arthur household until shortly before M'Arthur's death. In 1846 Clarkson Stanfield, then Curator of the Greenwich Hospital pictures, informed the Board of a subscription being raised to buy the Abbott portrait together with the group of pictures by Benjamin West and Richard Westall which had been engraved for illustrations to Clarke & M'Arthur's *Life*. The subscription was headed by Jasper de St Croix and, early in 1847, enough money raised, the Board gladly accepted an offer of the gift. M'Arthur died early in 1849 and the pictures were delivered to Greenwich in May, Stanfield having insisted that they 'should be dusted and wiped twice a week'. Nelson's uniform coats were hung with them.[24] Next year St Croix himself died, one of his last wishes being that the Hospital should be presented with the copy of Davison's gold medal which Nelson himself had given to St Croix's mother.[25]

The portrait is in the National Maritime Museum and is one of the best known and most popular likenesses of Nelson in existence. An interesting comment on it was made, as we have already seen, by Sir Francis Grant,

LORD VISCOUNT NELSON, K.B. VICE ADMIRAL, &c. &c. &c.

Ætat 43.

Published Nov.r 15th 1805, by T. Cadell & W. Davies, Strand.

Line engraving by John Golding, after the oil by Abbott (16)

himself a distinguished portrait-painter, when Lady Nelson's version was under discussion at the National Portrait Gallery. 'The portrait at Greenwich Hospital', he wrote, 'which belonged to Lady Nelson (Grant's mistake: it belonged of course to M'Arthur) - the head of Nelson is made up from the Kilgraston picture - But there is a cocked hat on it with a diamond aigrette which is done from the real hat - its vigorous handling contrasting with the tame copy of the head...' (see the full text of Grant's letter on pages 36 and 38).

From then the numerous Abbott copies deteriorate into the softened form all too familiar from constant reproduction. Perhaps the earliest and therefore least 'sanctified' are those belonging at one time to Nelson's friend Cuthbert Collingwood (Scottish National Portrait Gallery), to Nelson's nephew Viscount Bridport (now in a private American collection) and to Nelson's lawyer William Haslewood (Knight Frank & Rutley 18 October 1960 lot 13). Another is the mysterious copy about which nothing is known until its acquisition by Huson Morris about twenty or twenty-five years after Trafalgar. Even then, the Morris family being of a retiring disposition, it seems to have lain in almost total seclusion until 1932, apart from a line engraving by Robert Graves published in 1847[26] and its possible appearance at the 1905 centenary celebrations. Following the Nelson portrait correspondence in *The Times* in October and November 1932 Miss M. E. Morris of St Mary Church, Torquay, wrote to Callender drawing his attention to the portrait which since the death of their father in 1913 had belonged to her brother and herself. Callender expressed interest and on the strength of the Graves engraving and a local Torquay photograph, pronounced it to be in his judgement 'an original picture by Abbott. It is not of course the first one he painted... Your picture is a true replica; that is, it was painted by Abbott himself. I have compared it with the picture here (Greenwich) and I consider that it keeps very much nearer to the original than the copy in the National Portrait Gallery, though I would like you to keep this opinion to yourself. I do not desire to undervalue the copy in the National Portrait Gallery'.[27] Nothing further transpired until 1940 when Miss Morris again wrote to Callender saying that she and her brother had sent the picture to Christie's 'as Lord Nelson's posthumous contribution to the present war' but that Christie's had described it as 'probably painted by a student of Abbott'. She asked for Callender's advice. She said that the portrait had been acquired by their grandfather at an uncertain date but that the family possessed a bill for repairs dated 26 August 1831, since when it had remained in their house at St Mary

Church. Callender immediately suggested the portrait should be handed over without more ado to Christie's neighbour, Captain J. J. H. Spink, the National Maritime Museum's adviser on naval pictures, and it was placed on temporary loan at Greenwich. Early the following year, after some consultation, Callender drafted a letter which Miss Morris's brother sent to *The Times* suggesting that the portrait should be offered for sale with the object of presenting it to the Museum:

> We feel at this time that the picture should be used for the benefit of the nation's war effort, and we are sure that this would have been in accordance with Lord Nelson's own wishes... As the Prime Minister has said that the greatest threat to our national existence is the U-boat, it would seem fitting that the purchase money should go towards a special effort against the submarine menace.[28]

After keen competition from the Trustees of the Walker Art Gallery, Liverpool, (who actually sent a cheque for £1250 to Mr and Miss Morris the very day their letter appeared in *The Times* followed by no less than seventy-seven letters to Greenwich),[29] the upshot was the sale of the picture for £1000, paid for by the National Art Collections Fund (£865) and private contributors (£135), and its presentation to the National Maritime Museum in April 1941. Mr and Miss Morris immediately sent the money to the Admiralty and a further benefit from their example was the formation of a Nelson Fund, organised by *The Times* and the Admiralty, amounting in a very few months to over £15,000.

The portrait is by no means one of Abbott's best but the dramatic conclusion of its provenance forms an interesting epilogue to this attempt to disentangle Lemuel Abbott's portraiture of Nelson.[30]

NOTES TO CHAPTER 2, LEMUEL ABBOTT

1. Frederick Locker's inscription on the back of his grandfather's portrait of Nelson is repeated in his book, *My Confidences* (1896), p.39.

2. Edwards 1808, pp.281-2. Some of Edwards's more colourful mis-statements, perpetuated in the *DNB* and Thieme-Becker, are corrected in Sewter 1955, pp.178-83.

3. Minto 1874, III, p.2.

4. The correspondence between Sir Francis Grant and the Trustees of the National Portrait Gallery, through the erratic medium of J.C. Horsley RA, is in the NPG archive.

5. Christie's 16 June 1804 (lot 38, passed).

6. Letter from Grant to Horsley, 27 Sussex Place, Regents Park (NPG archive).

7. Letter from Jervis to Locker, *Victory* in Lagos Bay, 14 February 1797 (RNM archive).

8. Letter from Nelson to Locker, Palermo, 9 February 1799 (Nicolas III, p.260).

9. Letter from Nelson to Lady Nelson, St Helen's 7 April 1798 (Naish 1958, p.391).

10. Letter from Lady Nelson, Kentish Town 6 May 1798 (ibid. p.429).

11. Id., Roundwood 25 June 1798 (ibid. p.436).

12. Id., 9 July 1798 (ibid. p.439).

13. Id., 23 July 1798 (ibid. p.441).

14. Letter from Grant to Horsley, 14 May 1874 (NPG archive).

15. Professor Sir Geoffrey Callender in *The Times*, 29 October 1832.

16. Sir George Scharf's Trustee Sketch Book I, p.34, for the version offered to the NPG by T. Bryant, 30 St James's Street, 8 June 1858; and Scharf's TSB IV p.12 for the smaller version in the House of Lords (both in NPG archive).

17. Hadfield's portrait had appeared in a sale by Hampton & Sons, November 1942 (710), as 'Admiral Lord Nelson by W. Barnard after Abbott'.

18. Christie's 3 February 1961 (42). The Lloyd's Patriotic Fund was founded in 1803. From it grants were made to the next of kin of sailors killed in action, and presentations of silver plate were made to officers who had distinguished themselves in battle. Nelson received two grants of £500 to be laid out in plate after the Battles of the Nile and Copenhagen, and it is some of that silver, the kernel of the collection, from which the Nelson Room at Lloyd's derives its name (*see* Lloyds 1932).

19. Letter from Lady Nelson, Roundwood 4 March 1800 (Naish 1958, p.552).

20. Letter from M'Arthur, 1 December 1800 (Croker Papers, Phillips Collection, NMM archive).

21. Report from Miss G.M. Lewis, of the NMM Conservation Department, when the portrait was examined and treated for blisters in 1977.

22. Sewter 1955, p.179.

23. Clarke & M'Arthur 1809, I, xxxvii.

24. The correspondence between Clarkson Stanfield and the Board of Trustees of Greenwich Hospital is in PRO ADM 67/97-100, kindly passed to me by Dr Peter van der Merwe. The gift is also recorded in *The Illustrated London News*, 10 November 1849, p.316. The death of Jasper de St Croix is noted in *The Gentleman's Magazine*, December 1850.

25. Letter from Clarkson Stanfield to J. Lethbridge, 24 October 1850 (NMM archive).

26. Copy of Graves's engraving in Michael A. Nash Collection, repr. *Trafalgar Chronicle* (1992) p.25.

27. Letter from Callender to Miss M.E. Morris, 10 December 1932 (NMM archive).

28. Letter from A.V. Morris to *The Times*, 26 February 1941.

29. The large correspondence file on the acquisition of the portrait, NMM 1923/2/40, is summarised in the NACF *Annual Report* (1941), no. 1225.

30. See also Walker 1994, pp.79-94.

Nelson wounded at the Nile: oil attributed to Guy Head, c.1798-9, (93)

3 THE NILE

ews of the victory of the Nile was brought to Naples by the hands of Lieutenants Bladen Capel and William Hoste who triumphantly paraded the streets accompanied by Lady Hamilton wearing a head-band inscribed 'NELSON AND VICTORY'. Capel arrived in London on 2 October though rumours had been percolating several days before and as early as 28 September St Vincent could speak of it as 'the almost incredible stupendous victory'. Indeed a victory was much needed as public opinion was becoming restive at what appeared to be the Fleet's inadequacy at coming to grips with the enemy. On 3 October Gillray issued the second of his celebrated Nelson prints, *NELSON'S VICTORY: or - Good News operating upon Loyal Feelings*, showing disconsolate members of the Opposition receiving the news in various attitudes of chagrin and disbelief; Sheridan resolves to stop his big mouth, and Fox wearing a bonnet-rouge hangs by a rope having just kicked a stool from under his feet. Three days later appeared the most magnificent of all Gillray's patriotic and anti-Jacobin satires -*Extirpation of the Plagues of Egypt: - Destruction of Revolutionary Crocodiles: - or - The British Hero cleansing yͤ Mouth of yͤ Nile* (67; pp.62, 216). Nelson strides through the waves brandishing a cudgel marked 'British Oak', and from an iron hook in his sleeve drags ashore a great fleet of crocodiles, transfixed with hooks through their jaws and painted garishly in the tricolour; one in the background belches forth a gigantic wedge of flame representing the explosion of *L'Orient*. News of Nelson's wound had evidently got about though Gillray puts it over the wrong eye. Another vivid print, published 24 October, *JOHN BULL taking a Luncheon*, (69; *p.216*) shows how the British cooks (Admirals Warren, Howe, Nelson, Duncan, Gardiner, Bridport and St Vincent) cram Old Grumble Gizzard with delicious French battleships - fricassée à la Howe, dessert à la Warren and Dutch cheese à la Duncan. Nelson, his scarred face in profile, holds a menu of French ships taken, burnt and destroyed, and hands the insatiable John Bull a dish of fricassée à la Nelson.[1]

Nearer the scene of action Nelson's band of brothers, the Captains of the Squadron, mustered aboard HMS *Orion* two days after the battle, resolving to present him with a sword, its hilt shaped as a crocodile; and 'as a further proof of their esteem and regard, hoped that he will permit his Portrait to be taken and hung up in the Room belonging to the Egyptian Club, now established in commemoration of that glorious day'. Nelson thanked them and agreed to 'direct my Picture to be painted the first opportunity for the purpose you mentioned.[2]

According to Captain Ball, as Rear-Admiral Sir Alexander Ball recalling the event at Merton many years later, the captains

> were desirous to have a good likeness of their heroic chief taken; and for that purpose employed one of the most eminent painters in Italy: the plan was to ask the painter to breakfast and get him to begin immediately after. Breakfast being over and no preparation made by the painter, Sir Alexander was selected by the other Captains to ask him when he intended to begin, to which the answer was 'Never'. Sir Alexander said he stared and they all stared but the artist continued, 'there is such a mixture of humility with ambition in Lord Nelson's countenance that I dare not risk the attempt'.[3]

The name of 'one of the most eminent painters in Italy', at that time possibly with Napoleon's army in Aboukir Bay, has never been established, but in any case nothing further transpired from either of these plans. The members of the Egyptian Club, which does not seem to have materialised either, had to make do with copies of portraits by Guzzardi, Abbott, Beechey, Devis and others. Perhaps it was just as well. Nelson's appearance at this stage, wounded above the eye, bandaged, racked with headache and pain generally, and probably concussed, cannot have been prepossessing. The imaginary reconstruction in the National Maritime Museum (93; *p.56*), possibly by Guy Head, is as near as we shall approach to his battered countenance.

Back at home again Sir Horatio Nelson KB was gazetted Baron Nelson of the Nile and of Burnham Thorpe.[4] He received the thanks of Parliament and more prosaically a pension of £2000 a year for three lives, until in fact it lapsed with the death of the third Earl in 1913. The East India Company voted him £10,000, and perhaps the most prized award of all, among a stream of gifts from potentates at home and abroad, the coffin made from the main-mast of *L'Orient*, devised with wry but affectionate humour as a cautionary tale, by Captain Ben Hallowell of the *Swiftsure*.

Pictures of the Battle of the Nile were painted by Mather Brown, Thomas Whitcombe, George Arnald and Thomas Luny.[5] Engravings were issued and found a ready market. Mrs Hemans's poem, *Casabianca*, containing the famous lines, 'The boy stood on the burning deck / Whence all but he had fled', was not published till 1839, but the great flow of Nelsoniana began immediately - replicas of Abbott's portrait, enamels,

Marble bust by Lawrence Gahagan, 1798, (48)

Plaster bust by Lawrence Gahagan, (56)

miniatures, snuff-boxes, cameos, jugs, mugs, caskets, and so on, in an unquenchable stream still flowing merrily two hundred years after the event.[6] Artists were not slow to seize the opportunity to improve or convert their earlier efforts. Lawrence Gahagan was one of these.

Lawrence Gahagan, an Irish sculptor specialising in small bronze busts and statuettes, claimed to have been given seven sittings at Nelson's 141 Old Bond Street lodgings early in 1798 (48; *p.59*). He certainly exhibited a bust of 'Sir Horatio Nelson' at the Royal Academy of 1798 where it was seen and not specially admired by Lady Nelson: 'the bust is there but too old for you', she reported.[7] Now at Portsmouth, it shows the Hero with a faintly smiling expression and the 'shock head' so shrewdly observed by Lady Minto two years later in Vienna.[8] Versions and romanticised variants from the Gahagan family production line, are at Greenwich, Bath, Plas Newyd and Norwich (56; *opposite*). At the back of the Norwich bust is a tattered label: 'I had seven sittings from Admiral Nelson when he resided in Old Bond Street, London...' This is re-affirmed in a curious literary effusion called *Chalcographimania*, a poem in the manner of *Hudibras* satirising 'gentlemen Collectors and the Printselling Trade':

> Having made mention of a statuary, I will here record the name of G-h-g-n the sculptor, who is bitten with *bust madness*, which he has pursued with unparalleled avidity, not having modelled less than two hundred, nor be it forgotten that in hitting off likenesses, he is particularly fortunate, witness the *Bust of Lord Nelson*, who never sat to any artist but G-h-g-n, whom he attended seven times for that purpose, being most particularly anxious that every lineament should prove the precise type of the original.[9]

The claim is repeated in a Bath sale catalogue: '...Lord Nelson having honoured the Artist with seven sittings in 1798..', omitting the wild statement that Nelson had sat to no other artist.[10]

Nelson's popularity and Gahagan's prolific output resulted in a variety of subsequent busts turned out by the family up to Lucius Gahagan's death in 1839. A low-relief, 'The Death of Nelson', appeared in Lucius Gahagan's sale of effects in Bath in 1840 - probably an entry for the 1832 competition for the National Naval Monument in Trafalgar Square. A curious mezzotint by William Barnard (see *p.64*), from 'Gahagon Model', but bearing very little relationship to any of the known Gahagan busts, was published, strangely enough, on Trafalgar Day 1805 (long before the news arrived in England), and dedicated to the Sicilian Ambassador

Gahagan's Royal Academy marble bust was followed by a black basalt bust by Robert Shout, one of several modellers employed by Wedgwood. This

Detail of James Gillray, Extirpation of the Plagues of Egypt, 6 October 1798 (see p.216)

The HERO of the NILE.

PALMAM QUI MERUIT FERAT.

James Gillray, The Hero of the Nile , 1 December 1798, (68)

63

To His Excellency the Marquis of Circello,

His SICILIAN MAJESTY'S Envoy Extraordinary & Minister Plenipotentiary to his BRITANIC MAJESTY,

This Portrait of ADMIRAL LORD NELSON, BARON NELSON of the NILE, and of

BURNHAM THORPE in the County of NORFOLK, & K.B.

is by Permission Dedicated.

LONDON, Publish'd as the Act directs 21 Oct.r 1805 being the day for commemorating his LORDSHIP'S ever memorable & Glorious Victory over the French, &c.&c.&c.

Mezzotint by William Barnard, 1805. Lettered as 'Gahagon' but the head more like Abbott, the body like Shout, (65)

Wedgwood basalt bust by Robert Shout,1798, (64)

Herculaneum stoneware bust after Shout, c.1805, (66)

shows Nelson with unnaturally tidy hair and was published in July 1798 (64; *above*) with the curious incision NILE in the medal, the date of this battle being 1 August 1798, ten days after the publication date of the bust on 22 July. As Colonel Grant says, 'the explanation probably is that part of the issue was still in the Etruria workshops when news of the engagement came, every remaining piece being then stamped with the name which was in every mouth in the civilised world'.[11] Nelson would of course have been entitled to wear only the gold medal for St Vincent. The grant of the Nile medal was not announced until 7 October and the medal was actually sent to Nelson on 9 January 1799.[12] Either Gahagan's or Shout's bust was that noticed by Lord Palmerston at a visit to Sir William Hamilton's London house in November 1800 - 'his bust is in the room and Sir William says his friendship and connection with him is the pride and glory of his life...'[13] A bronze version, in which Nelson has been promoted from KB to a Knight of the Garter, is a solecism repeated in the Herculaneum copies, and possibly a reflection on the prevailing mood of adulation which swept the country shortly before and after Trafalgar (66; *above*).

An interesting sideline was the use of Shout's Wedgwood bust for the profile in the private medal issued by Alexander Davison (73; *below* and *p.220*). But before we turn to this it is necessary to consider another Wedgwood development. Shout's idea proved too smooth and bland for the popular taste. A more heroic image was demanded and a few months later Wedgwood came up with an alternative that answered the need without question. The Wedgwood Nelson medallion (72; *p.75*) is one of a series made in 1798 and which included Lord Howe the hero of Ushant, Lord St Vincent of the Battle of Cape St Vincent, and Lord Duncan victor of Camperdown.[14] Nelson's victory of the Nile in August 1798 immediately qualified him to take his place among the naval heroes and the same modeller was employed, John De Vaere. De Vaere's receipt, dated 9 November 1798, accompanies his original wax model in the Wedgwood Museum. There is no record of a sitting and indeed, unless he paid a flying visit to Naples, there is no likelihood of there having been one. De Vaere mentions the use of a print which can only have been either Orme's oval stipple published in February or Evans's oval stipple after Edridge's drawing published in May. Neither of these are in profile and De Vaere would have had to make considerable adjustments. Keating's mezzotint did not appear on the market until 29 November though it is possible De Vaere may have seen Singleton's original picture.

The profile is glamourised but there is no mistaking the fierce turned down mouth noticed a year or two later by both Mrs Damer and De Koster but conspicuously absent from the softened portraits of Abbott, Beechey and Hoppner.

Detail from Davison's Nile medal, 1798 (see p.220)

De Vaere's profile of Nelson turned out to be one of Wedgwood's major successes, conforming in most people's imaginations to the intrepid slightly swashbuckling hero attacking two Spanish first-rates, cutlass in hand, ahead of his boarding party. The image acquired a graver implication by the accounts filtering home of the hero's consummate seamanship and flair for a broader strategy, leading to the Battle of the Nile and the total frustration of Napoleon's eastern ambitions. It was used constantly by Wedgwood in various forms, often applied to vases, urns, jugs and other memorabilia. An especially attractive one is on the side of a buff-coloured caneware jug

De Vaere profile from the side of a Wedgwood caneware jug, 'The wooden walls of Old England.'

in the McCarthy Collection in the Royal Naval Museum (*above*). This is a black basalt profile in a beaded oval with a ribbon above lettered *NELSON AND VICTORY*, with anchors at the sides and inscribed along the top *THE WOODEN WALLS OF OLD ENGLAND*. It is a typical but rather classy example of countless objects which have issued in a continuous stream ever since. De Vaere's unmistakable profile of Nelson was used again, apparently without acknowledgement, for the

Copenhagen badge of 1801 (183; *p.256*) and for Turton's memorial medal by Thomas Wyon 1805.

The Wedgwood profile could be used for a variety of decorative purposes, whereas the bust was free-standing and intended as an individual ornament or possibly in a group as a library bust. It came into practical use very shortly after its publication, as the basis for Davison's Nile medal (73; *pp.66,220*). Alexander Davison, contractor, ship-owner and a friend of Nelson whom he first met in Quebec in 1782 and is said to have saved from an injudicious attachment, made a considerable fortune out of government contracts from which he was able to live in some state in St James's Square and to run a house in Northumberland, Swarland Park, into the bargain. Nelson's victory at the Nile, combined with the commission to dispose of the prizes on behalf of the captains, induced Davison to issue a private medal 'as a tribute of my respect and admiration' - gold for the admiral and captains of the Fleet, silver for lieutenants, copper gilt for warrant officers and copper bronzed for ratings.[15] The commission to produce the medal was given to Matthew Boulton of the Soho Mint, Birmingham, and William Budge, Dundas's private secretary, acted as intermediary. The design was roughed out by Davison himself, perfected by Robert Cleveley, and the die executed by Conrad Küchler. The rather insignificant effigy of Nelson on the obverse derives from Shout's Wedgwood bust which had been published only a few days before the battle itself (64; *p65*). A letter from Budge to Boulton, 25 October 1798, says 'you will receive by the night coach a bust of Rear-Admiral Lord Nelson together with a design for a medallion'.[16] Gahagan's first bust had been exhibited at the Royal Academy earlier that year but this had not been mass-produced and the most practical and readily available for dispatch to Birmingham by the night coach would have been the Wedgwood bust. Allowing for the translation from three to two dimensions the likeness is close enough to make this almost a certainty. Budge was advised to consult other artists, such as Nathaniel Marchant, engraver at the Royal Mint, the sculptors John Bacon and Thomas Banks, Henry Tresham, history painter who had been made an RA that year, and Joseph Planta, librarian of the British Museum. One of these (possibly Banks whose sister presented a gold specimen of the medal to the British Museum in 1819) suggested that the hair line should be adjusted to lower the height of the forehead; but there can be no doubt that basically the profile stems from Shout's Wedgwood bust.

Davison's generosity was very much appreciated by all those who had served in the action, especially on the lower deck. It was the first known instance of a private medal being accepted and worn in the Service, though never officially part of uniform, and the profile of Nelson, by this time already well on his way to becoming The Hero, added immensely to its significance. The boxes containing the medals arrived in Palermo in August 1799 and Nelson arranged for their distribution immediately, actually giving his own gold one to Hardy who had been mistakenly excluded from the list. A spare copy he gave to Sir William Hamilton, 'the man that all Europe is obliged to for his encouragement of the Arts', and another copy to the King of Sicily.[17]

No comments on the portrait itself are recorded but, apart from one large Naval gold medal for Nelson himself and thirteen small ones for the captains, neither King nor Parliament considered the Nile action to be worthy of a general award, so Davison's Nile medal with Nelson's portrait on the shield held by Peace was greatly treasured. Many of the recipients had their names and the names of their ships engraved on them at their own expense.

The profile, in reverse, was used again in Boulton's medal made to commemorate the return of the King of Naples to his capital aboard the *Foudroyant*, Nelson's flagship, in July 1799. The design in this case was by Thomas Bingham Richards, the eldest son of a Birmingham silversmith, as chance would have it abroad on his father's business and evacuated from Naples with the Royal Family on 23 December 1798. Richards was given a berth on board the *Vanguard* and was actually able to help with the pilotage into Palermo. He stayed with Nelson for several days and would have had ample opportunity to make sketches for a profile.[18]

Although Davison's medal was officially unauthorised and no ribbon was issued for it by the Admiralty, we are assured by Nelson's great-nephew, the third Earl, that he wore it constantly. 'I believe my great-uncle always wore it, and I have his medal in a red Russian leather case with gold ring through the top of it by which it was hung round the neck.'[19] The third Earl's statement may be true but the only confirming evidence we have from the Nelson iconography is from the foreign portraits - the Turkish version of the Guzzardi portrait (83; *p.225*) where he wears Davison's medal on a dark blue ribbon on his right breast, the Palermo miniature (96; *p.96*) worn on his left breast from the third buttonhole, Füger's oil in the Royal Naval Museum where he wears it partly hidden on his right breast (103; *p.111*), and the Schmidt portrait in pastel, done in Dresden on the way home, where he wears it on the left breast from the second buttonhole (128; *p.116*). Thereafter, in none of the 'state' portraits by Beechey or Hoppner nor in the later Abbott variants, does Davison's Nile medal appear at all. In fact Nelson, although by this time a law unto himself, was obviously uncertain about the exact protocol, and even in the Thaller & Ranson bust the medal appears on his left breast but disguised to resemble a Naval gold medal. Flaxman followed this ruse in the posthumous busts (215; *p.174*).

It is an interesting point to note that in none of the serious portraits painted after the Battle of Copenhagen in 1801 is Nelson shown wearing his full quota of medals. The sittings for the Beechey and Hoppner portraits took place in December 1800; the last portrait to be painted, by Keymer in Great Yarmouth shortly before he sailed in March 1801 (181; *p.86*), shows him wearing his two Naval gold medals for St Vincent and the Nile, but not Davison's. From then, with the possible exception of the little Downman drawing (186; *p.147*), he wears no Naval gold medal at all. Nelson attached great importance to the proper Government recognition for the Fleet's efforts and the omission of this after the Battle of Copenhagen, never satisfactorily explained, was bitterly resented by Nelson and his officers. Parliament voted its thanks to the Fleet, Nelson was created a Viscount, Admiral Graves made a KB, and several promotions were gazetted, but the action was not classified as comparable to the other great naval engagements for which gold medals were issued since the Glorious First of June in 1794. He made his feelings clear among others to Captain Foley, his flag captain on the *Elephant* at Copenhagen, by declaring that 'he would never wear his other Medals till that for Copenhagen was granted'[20] A uniface badge was issued privately, possibly by Davison, examples at Portsmouth (183; *p.256*), Greenwich and Monmouth showing a naval trophy supporting a medallion with a bust of Nelson in a tie-wig and vice-admiral's uniform deriving from De Vaere's Wedgwood portrait of 1798, also used for Davison's Nile medal.[21] But this was no substitute for full Admiralty recognition. No doubt this was an occasion for his favourite Shakespeare quotation,

> But if it be a sin to covet honour
> I am the most offending soul alive,

though he liked to change the word 'honour' to 'glory'.

Late in 1805 small silver boxes were issued containing medals for St Vincent, the Nile, Copenhagen and Trafalgar, but the boxes were scarce and, anyway by then, the Hero was no longer interested in coveting honour.[22]

70

NOTES TO CHAPTER 3, THE NILE

1. Coloured engravings in BM, NPG, NMM and RNM (George 1942, VII, nos 9248-57 etc).

2. Resolution on board HMS *Orion*, 3 August 1798, signed by Jas. Saumarez, T. Troubridge, H.D. Darby, Thos. Louis, Jno Peyton, Alex Jno Ball, Sam. Hood, D. Gould, Th Foley, R. Willett Miller, Ben. Hallowell, E. Berry, T. M. Hardy (Nicolas III, p. 67).

3. *Naval Chronicle* 37 (1817), p. 67.

4. Nelson's was the seventh English peerage to commemorate a foreign achievement, being preceded by Lords Stanhope of Mahon in Minorca, Clive of Plassey, Heathfield of Gibraltar, Amherst of Montreal, Jervis of St Vincent and Duncan of Camperdown (*Complete Peerage* III, p.635).

5. All are in the National Maritime Museum.

6. May 1995, *passim*.

7. Letter from Lady Nelson, Kentish Town, 6 May 1798 (Naish 1958, p.429).

8. Letter from Lady Minto to her sister, Lady Malmesbury (Minto 1874, III, p.147).

9. W. H. Ireland, ('Satiricus Sculptor Esq'), *Chalcographimania* (1814).

10. Chandos House (Miss Fenton) sale catalogue, bound in RA *Anderdon Catalogues* XVI (1816-17), p.166.

11. Grant 1910, pp.170-4.

12. Letters from Lord Spencer to Nelson (Nicolas III, pp.75, 473).

13. Palmerston's Journal 25 November 1800, cit. Connell 1957, p.436.

14. Reilly and Savage 1973, pp. 125, 195, 256, 297.

15. Letter from Davison to Nelson, 18 March 1799 (Nicolas III, p. 321).

16. Letters in Birmingham Assay Office, cit. Pollard 1970, pp. 284-6.

17. Letter from Nelson to Davison, Palermo 15 August 1799 (Nicolas VII, cxc).

18. Westwood 1926, p.6; Brown 1980, p.479a.

19. Note dated from Trafalgar House, Salisbury, 4 May 1890, quoted in Mayo 1897, I p.179.

20. Letter from Admiral Sir Thomas Foley to Rear-Admiral Sir Graham Hamond, 23 February 1828 (Nicolas IV, p.527).

21. NMM *Medal Catalogue* BNM 492; reproduced Hattersley 1974, pp.118-9, and Warner 1958. p.143, enlarged in both cases.

22. Brown 1980, 510, 511.

HAMILTON

Lady Hamilton: engraving by Vincenzo Aloja after Grignion,

72

4 NAPLES AND PALERMO

The Hon Mrs Damer is believed to have been staying in Naples when Nelson arrived from the Nile in September 1798. Her studio 'was a sanctum open only to her closest friends', wrote the Princess Dashkov[1], but she is said to have persuaded Nelson to sit for her wearing the uniform he had worn a few weeks before during the battle itself.[2] No confirmation can be found for this sitting in Naples but it was a very likely possibility and Nelson probably did not need a great deal of persuasion. Certainly he gave her the coat. Her cousin, Alexander Johnston, has left a graphic if possibly hearsay account of the occasion:

> The last time he sat to her, he good humouredly asked her what he could give her for the high honour which she had conferred on him, and for all the trouble she had taken on the occasion. She answered, 'one of your old coats', on which he replied, 'you shall immediately have one, and it shall be the one I value the most highly, - the one which I wore the whole day of the Battle of the Nile, and which I have never worn, nor even allowed to be brushed since, in order that my Naval as well as other friends may know, from the streaks of perspiration and hair-powder which are still to be seen on it, the exertions which I made, and the anxiety which I felt, on that day to deserve the approbation of my King and Country.[3]

The likelihood of Mrs Damer having made a bust of Nelson in Naples in the autumn of 1798 is strengthened by a letter she wrote from Grosvenor Square to the Common Council of the City of London offering to execute a portrait of Lord Nelson, either in bronze or marble, for presentation to the City. The Common Council Journal, for 23 January 1799, records the resolve that 'the Lord Mayor convey the Court's acceptance to her'.[4] Six days later the Lord Mayor laid Mrs Damer's reply before the Court in which she promised her 'utmost exertions' in the task.[5] By April 1799 it was decided that the bust should be placed in the Common Council Room and that was the last we hear of it from the City for several years. But meanwhile Mrs Damer had made good use of the unique opportunity she had enjoyed in Naples. She had joined the select group of sculptors on the fringe of the firm of Wedgwood. Her original model is lost but a painted plaster bust in the Wedgwood

Museum (75; *p.77*) relates closely to her Guildhall bust. This is attributed by the Wedgwood authorities to Papera whose account is among the Wedgwood archives.[6]

Mr Byerley	June 19 1802	
Bought of B Papera		
Figure Maker to Her Majesty		
...One Bust of Mrs Deamour	0.12.0	
One ditto of Lord Nelson	0.12.0	

Papera probably worked from the model in Mrs Damer's studio, possibly as early as 1799 or 1800, and the bust became one of several issued to satisfy the popular demand for portraits of the Hero. A version in plaster painted black, signed and dated *Damer 1801*, was in the Royal Collection at Windsor but destroyed when a shelf collapsed in the 1930s. Another was seen by the diarist Joseph Farington when he visited Versailles with John and Mrs Hoppner in 1802; they noticed in a bedroom 'two Busts, one of Charles Fox - the other of Lord Nelson, both executed by Mrs Damer, not very good likenesses but they might be known'.[7]

Another clear derivation from Mrs Damer is the William John Coffee bust of 1806 at Greenwich (76). Coffee had formerly worked for Mrs Coade at Lambeth but moved north to Derby where he worked as modeller to the china factory, later setting up on his own. His very idiosyncratic bust of Nelson with its austere treatment of the Hero's features, emaciated by wounds and illness after the Nile, probably relates even more closely than Papera's to Mrs Damer's original model made in Naples in the autumn of 1798.

Meanwhile, by July 1803, the City Fathers were becoming impatient and the clerk of the works, George Dance, was ordered to wait on the sculptor to find out when the bust would be ready.[8] Farington records in his Diary for 14 July a visit from Dance on his way to Mrs Damer's house and, a week later, a letter from Mrs Damer was read out to the Court in which she regretted the delay but hoped to finish the bust in six weeks or two months. It was in fact finished that winter and exhibited at the Royal Academy the next spring, receiving lavish praise from *The Morning Post*: '...the fair hand of a female artist remains as yet almost unrivalled in the arduous task of defying every difficulty opposed by the hardest produce of the Parian quarry...'[9] This bust is slightly larger than life and is now in the Nelson Room at the Guildhall (74; *p.79*). A large engraving of it was published by Orme a few days before Trafalgar,

Wedgwood blue dip profile by John De Vaere, 1798, (72)

without acknowledgement to the sculptor - a discourtesy which wounded Mrs Damer deeply, particularly as her work was in some quarters looked upon as amateurish and indeed worse still, it was whispered that she received assistance from 'ghosts'.[10] Orme used a small print of it as frontispiece to his *Graphic History of Nelson* (1806) with Mrs Damer's name credited in capital letters, but the previous omission rankled, and a few years later in October 1809, getting wind of the imminent publication of Clarke & M'Arthur's *Life*, she wrote a special plea to Lady Hamilton asking for her help:

> I must not forget one thing on which I wished to speak to you; that is, that as I understand a fine Edn of Lord Nelson's life is coming out soon (I concluded under the direction of the present Lord and his friends) I have the greatest desire that in some way or other, no matter how shortly or simply said, either in a note or otherwise, my having had the honour I prize so much, of that immortal Hero's having sat to me & to me alone, for a Sculptural Bust, should be mentioned. To you, my Dear Lady Hamilton, & to my kind friend Sir William, you know I owe this favour, & you will not wonder at my ambition, nor my anxiety that such a circumstance, which I know so well how to value; should be recorded in a manner never to be forgotten and that my name should thus be (if I may so term it) joined to the most brilliant Name England ever gave birth to - I think it probable that you may be able to assist, me in this & I am sure you will if it should be in your power.[11]

Lady Hamilton's influence did not prove powerful enough, or perhaps was not even exerted. Clarke & M'Arthur's *Life* was published later that year in two volumes, with illustrations mainly by Westall, Pocock and Benjamin West. Golding's engraving of the Abbott portrait was used as frontispiece. A one-volume reprint came out in 1810 and several subsequent editions appeared later, but nowhere did Mrs Damer's 'Sculptural Bust' adorn the pages. Perhaps the explanation is to be found in a curiously harsh criticism levelled at it by Thomas Hope, 'Furniture Hope of Deepdene', a rich connoisseur and collector wielding a powerful influence in matters of taste at that time. Farington was scornful of Hope's strictures but they seem to have been effective none the less. 'Baker showed us [Farington and others] a criticism of Thos Hope upon Mrs Damer's bust of Lord Nelson, most extravagant & false & ridiculous. It was published in the newspapers & was so ungrateful to Mrs Damer that she had fifty copies of it printed to give away'.[12]

A bust, attributed to Mrs Damer and said to have come from the Deepdene collection, was presented to the National Maritime Museum

Wedgwood bust by B. Papera, based on the one by Mrs Damer 1802, (75)

in 1932 by Sir Bruce Ingram in memory of his son David, but this has the appearance of being a Thaller & Ranson type rather than Mrs Damer's very characteristic work.[13] However the 'Sculptural Bust' seems to have found favour with the City Fathers because for many years it remained prominently in the Council Chamber, garlanded on Trafalgar Day with oak-leaves and laurel. A bronze cast was made for the King of Tanjore in 1826 and another for the Duke of Clarence in 1827. Mrs Damer, by then aged eighty, completed the cast herself a few days before her death; it was delivered to the Duke by her nephew, Lieutenant Johnston of the *Terrible*, and placed in the royal library at Bushey House, a stump of the *Victory* foremast acting as a pedestal. [14]

Mrs Damer may have been the first artist to be given sittings by Nelson on his return from the Nile, arriving in Naples in 'the poor wretched *Vanguard*' on 22 September. The evacuation of the Neapolitan court and the British residents to Palermo took place in December, after a stormy passage during which the *Vanguard* split her three topsails and one young member of the royal family died, it is said in Lady Hamilton's arms.[15] In Palermo a new chapter in the Nelson iconography begins, consisting of the strange portraits by Leonardo Guzzardi.[16]

The Guzzardi portraits stem from the magnificent gifts made to Nelson by the Grand Sultan Selim III for saving the Ottoman Empire from the onslaughts of Napoleon, Aboukir Bay being at that time, at least nominally, under Turkish suzerainty. The gifts consisted of the *Chelengk* taken from the Imperial turban, a scarlet pelisse lined with sable fur, and two thousand sequins to be distributed among the wounded of his ship's company. They were accompanied by a letter in the handwriting of the Sultan himself, dated 3 October 1798, in which he said the Chelengk, or Plume of Triumph, was such as had never before been presented to any but victorious Mussulmans. No Christian had ever received such an honour. The Sultan's mother also sent Nelson a box inlaid with diamonds to the value of £1000. The presents were brought to Naples, via Alexandria, by Abdullah Kelim Effendi aboard HMS *Alcmene* (Captain Hope), arriving on 13 December, though inexact details had startled the London scene at least a fortnight earlier. Gillray's satire *The HERO of the NILE* (68; *p.63*), appeared in the printshops on 1 December, an uncouth ludicrous figure that only Nelson's enormous popularity could have made tolerable.[17]

The following year another present arrived from the Sultan in the shape of an elegant letter enclosing a plan of the Battle of the Nile and a drawing

Marble bust by Anne Seymour Damer, 1798-1801, (74)

of Nelson himself - 'a curious present, but highly flattering to me, as it marks I am not in the least forgotten'.[18] Nelson's effusive message of thanks to the Sultan was conveyed in a letter to the Grand Vizier from Palermo dated 22 December 1799.

Nelson was delighted with the Sultan's gifts especially 'my Order of Merit' as he described the chelengk, He wrote immediately to 'the most Sublime Imperial Grand Signior' expressing his thanks. 'Words are entirely inadequate to my feelings for the exalted mark of approbation bestowed on me by the Imperial Grand Signior, which I must ever attribute to his goodness, not to my deserts'.[19]

It is not clear exactly when Guzzardi was commissioned to paint the portrait to be sent to Constantinople in exchange (83; *p.225*). In any case Leonardo Guzzardi is a shadowy figure who, apart from the Nelson portraits, appears to be unrecorded; not even in Naples or Palermo are there any other portraits by him. His signature on the rim of the shield followed by the word *PANOR^mi* indicates that he was a native of Palermo, Panormus being the Latin name for the modern Palermo. He could conceivably have been the Italian painter asked to breakfast aboard the *Orion* to paint the victor for the Egyptian Club (see p.58). He could have been commissioned by Nelson himself in fulfilment of his promise to his captains. He could have been aboard the *Alcmene* with 'the Turkish Ambassador, interpreters, etc. bringing the diamond Aigrette' mentioned by Miss Cornelia Knight in her journal for 15 December. He could have been simply an artist attached to the Neapolitan Court and thus the most obvious local choice for a return gift.[20]

Guzzardi's portraits of Nelson can be divided into two types differing only in insignia. They all show him in rear-admiral's full-dress uniform, and all display the chelengk prominently in the front of his black cocked hat, tilted backwards to avoid discomfort from the painful wound on his forehead. The versions in the Admiralty, in the San Martino Museum and one of the Greenwich copies (that descending directly in the Nelson family) show him wearing only the insignia of the Order of the Bath and one Naval gold medal. Later copies, including that sent as a reciprocal gift to Turkey, show him wearing, prominently on his right breast, the Star of the Order of the Crescent together with Davison's gold medal, and round his neck, on the regulation blue and white ribbons, are the two Naval gold medals (St Vincent and the newly acquired King's medal for the Nile). This vital difference means that several months must have elapsed between the two types. Davison's gold medal arrived in Palermo

Oil by Guzzardi, 1799 (Earl Nelson's), (79)

Oil by Leonardo Guzzardi, 1799. Originally belonged to Sir William Hamilton, now in the Admiralty Board Room, (77)

82

Unknown miniaturist after Guzzardi, (92)

83

in August 1799, the insignia for the Order of the Crescent in November. Certainly all these *could* have been added later to the various copies of Guzzardi's strange figure but it seems reasonable to assume that the first copies would have been appropriated by Nelson himself, by the Neapolitan royal family who owed their safety to Nelson's decisive action in evacuating them to Palermo in the depths of December, and by Sir William and Lady Hamilton who for obvious reasons could be expected to receive a copy, if indeed they did not actually commission the original.

The next stage in the Guzzardi saga is the overland journey home via Vienna, Prague, Dresden and Cuxhaven, arriving at Yarmouth on 6 November 1800. Here a local artist, Matthew H. Keymer, was instructed to produce yet another copy. This is probably Lady Wright'sversion (81; *opposite*) but is known with certainty from John Young's mezzotint published by Keymer himself, with astonishing dispatch in December, with the lettering: *Painted by M.H. Keymer Yarmouth, from a Portrait by a Celebrated Artist at Palermo...* (see *p. 224*). A feature of Keymer's painting is that it shows the chelengk (following Guzzardi's pattern) but without the star of the Crescent and with only one Naval gold medal.

We can assume therefore that Keymer's copy was made from an early Guzzardi type and probably from the Admiralty Boardroom one, at that time belonging to Sir William Hamilton. However he was not particularly impressed with Guzzardi's interpretation of the national hero and when Nelson next came to Yarmouth, on his way to the Baltic, Keymer painted his own idea, now to be seen in the rather heavy-handed portrait in Great Yarmouth town hall (181; *p.86*).

The story of the subsequent travels of the various Guzzardi portraits is fairly clear. The smaller replicas were distributed among the family (79; *p.81*) and friends. Several were acquired by members of Nelson's 'band of brothers', the captains of the squadron at the Nile. In the summer of 1802, Nelson and the Hamiltons toured the West Country, visiting Milford Haven where Sir William was interested in the dock development, his nephew Charles Greville being the owner of property there including the Packet Hotel where the party stayed. The large Guzzardi portrait (Admiralty Boardroom) was presented ceremoniously to Greville and hung in the assembly room of the hotel - 'Sir William left a fine whole-length picture of Nelson, which had been painted at Vienna *(sic)*, to be preserved for the perpetual gratification of visitors, by the occupier of the New Hotel, where his Lordship and friends resided while

Oil by Matthew Keymer after Guzzardi, 1800, (81)

Oil by Matthew Keymer, 1801, (181)

Oil by Guy Head, 1798-9, (94)

at Milford'.[21] It was seen there again by a writer in *The Naval Chronicle* in 1808: 'The picture is placed over the fireplace and has the following motto in large Italian capitals:

Mi Lord Orazio Nelson, erva del secol nostro, a ninno secondo, forte, invetto, terore de' rebelli, destrutore degli empi, difensor de' re, a tutti caro, questa cittude e il regno, l'ama, loda ed ammira - Lord Horatio Nelson, hero of the age, surpassed by none, unconquered, a terror to the rebellious, destroyer of the perverse, defender of kings, dear to all, this city and the whole kingdom, love, praise and admire him.[22]

It was noticed again by the head messenger of the Admiralty shortly before the Lords Commissioners redecorated the Boardroom and were looking for a portrait to balance the Beechey of William IV acquired in 1847. The circumstances are described in a graphic memorandum drawn up by Admiral Baillie-Hamilton, second secretary of the Admiralty from 1845 to 1855:

It was in the summer of either 1845 or 1846 when the Board was away on their annual visitation, that the opportunity offered for cleaning and redecorating the Admiralty Board Room.

At that time the picture of William IV was where it now is, and the opposite end of the room was hung with charts on rollers, fixed to the door of a large closet containing globes etc.

It was while debating how to make the two ends of the Board Room agree with each other that Laplume - the then Head Messenger, a man of much intelligence and a valuable servant of the office - reported having seen a picture of Lord Nelson in the Assembly Room of the Hotel at Milford Haven, where the Board in former times, used to lodge when on visitation, and this picture he thought would balance the William IV.

Laplume was accordingly directed to communicate with the Mistress of the Hotel and it was ascertained that the picture was still in existence but dismounted and laid aside.

Upon this I communicated further with the Landlady who referred me to Colonel the Hon R F Greville and to the Trustees of the Greville property of which the Hotel and its furniture were a part. Accordingly I wrote to the acting Trustee - Mr James Garrard - and it appearing to that gentleman that the picture was in the way of being worthily disposed, he rendered every assistance.

I wrote also to Colonel Greville, with whom (and with whose generous disposition) I was well acquainted, and the result was the presentation by him of the picture to the Admiralty.[23]

In order to fit into the panel, Guzzardi's portrait had to be enlarged slightly. This was done by a restorer, John Peel of Golden Square, recommended by the Earl of Aberdeen, then foreign secretary. Peel added strips of canvas round each side - a large strip at the top containing background painting only, another large strip down the right side containing extra ships in the background and completing the back of the chair, and narrow strips down the left side and along the lower edge with the addition of some cannon balls. Peel's letter, dated 27 June 1849 and enclosing his account, is preserved among the Admiralty records.

Part of the agreement with Colonel Greville was that before the portrait were handed over to the Admiralty a copy should be made for the hotel. This was done by an artist named Beetham and the whole transaction is recorded in the Admiralty Board Minutes for 11 August 1849:

> The Nelson Picture.
> Mr John Peel's account amounting to eighty-six pounds one shilling and twopence for restoring the Nelson Picture, enlarging it to fit the panel and for a copy by Mr Beetham of the said Picture, to be presented to the Hon. Robert Fulke Greville - to be paid and charged to the contingencies of the Office.[24]

Another copy is said to have been painted by Beetham as part of his fee but this copy is untraced at present.[25] Guzzardi's original was duly hung in the Boardroom and approved by two members of the Board who had actually served with Nelson and remembered him clearly, Admiral Sir George Cockburn and Vice-Admiral Sir William Gage. They agreed that there was a *likeness* though they were disposed to quarrel with the complexion which appeared to them to be too highly coloured and flushed.[26]

Beetham's first copy was hung in the Packet Hotel as arranged and was seen there by a visitor in 1856, by then renamed the Nelson Hotel. At Greville's death in 1867 the hotel copy passed to his nephew, Edward Hatton Finch Hatton. It was bought by Sir Robert Harmsworth at the Finch Hatton sale in 1916 and presented to the Britannia Royal Naval College, Dartmouth, where it still hangs (90).

One further copy was made, that in the National Portrait Gallery, resulting from Sir Charles Dilke's visit to Turkey in 1887 and sent as a gift to the British Government by the Sultan in 1888 (91; *p.90*). This is clearly of the second Guzzardi type displaying the full complement of decorations including the Star of the Crescent prominently placed on Nelson's right breast.[27]

Oil by L. Acquarone after Guzzardi, 1888, (91)

90

Guzzardi's portrait shows Nelson lean, almost emaciated, sickly in colour, his strange hat with the chelengk thrust unbecomingly back on his forehead to avoid the painful wound over the right eye, his attitude wooden and stiff. He is something of a puppet or actor on the boards of a provincial Italian stage. 'Bizarre' is a word often used to describe it though, as we have seen, Nelson's battered appearance was probably fairly bizarre too at this time. However, at about the same moment another more romanticised interpretation was in progress. If there is something sinister about Guzzardi's portrait, Guy Head's fine upstanding Englishman is the very opposite and the sort of clean-living Admiral we might expect on the cover of the *Boys' Own Paper* (94; *p.87*).

Guy Head was the son of a butcher and born in St Cuthbert's parish of Carlisle in 1760. He entered the RA Schools in London, was noticed by Reynolds, and then travelled in Europe settling for a time among the artist colony in Rome. He finally set up a studio in Naples where he made a living copying Old Masters and painting portraits of visiting English and prominent residents like Lady Hamilton, and indeed the King and Queen of Naples themselves.[28] He was certainly there in September 1798 when Nelson, with the *Vanguard* in tow, arrived from the Battle of the Nile. He would almost certainly have made sketches of the Hero, one of which may have been the dishevelled bandaged and bloodstained romance given by Nelson to Lady Parker and now in the National Maritime Museum (93; *p.56*). 'Anthony Guy Head, Portrait of Nelson at one sitting', was in Peter Coxe's 3-day sale of Head's unsold works, 11-13 April 1810 (Lot 95).

In December of that year Naples was threatened by Napoleon, Nelson evacuated the royal family to Palermo, and on 8 May 1799, in a Fleet Order from the *Vanguard*, he ordered Captain Burlton of HMS *Haerlem* to receive on board 'Guy Head Esq. and his family, with his pictures, books, prints, and other materials, and give them a passage to England, victualling them at two-thirds allowance'.[29] The family arrived in Newcastle on a visit to Guy's brother in October 1799; the following year his health broke down and he died in December 1800. Two months later Nelson wrote to Lady Hamilton from the *San Josef* in Torbay: 'Pray have you got any picture from Mrs Head's. I hope Mr Brydon has executed the frames to your satisfaction; the bill he is directed to send to me.[30]

Guy Head's scene is fanciful of course. The Battle of the Nile was fought during the darkness of an August night; the French admiral's sword was brought to Nelson shortly after midnight, not by a midshipman but by the *Vanguard's* first lieutenant; and Nelson himself had been wounded above his right eye, was bandaged, bloodstained, haggard and exhausted, and a long way from the polished officer standing at ease in his best clothes on Guy Head's quarterdeck.

Tradition has it that Head was actually commissioned to paint it by King George III though it is more likely that the order came from King Ferdinand of Naples. The *Vanguard* lay refitting in Naples Bay until the French troops forced the evacuation to Palermo that winter, so Head would have had plenty of opportunity to go aboard and make drawings of the deck fittings, gunports and rigging details, though irregularities can certainly be detected in the prize ships in the background. The uniforms, correct in every detail, were no doubt borrowed for the purpose. Nelson's sword, with an oval side ring hilt, corresponds with the type of sword he would have been wearing at the time.[31] Admiral Blanquet's sword had been sent by Nelson to the lord mayor of London with a letter from the *Vanguard* dated 8 August 1798. They are both in the Guildhall Library. [32]

The identity of the midshipman is not known. The tradition that he was Nelson's stepson, Josiah Nisbet, can be ruled out completely, Josiah having been promoted master and commander in August 1797. Another tradition names him as Charles Fielding, but no midshipman of this name can be traced in the Fleet at the time. And why a midshipman instead of the first lieutenant should be shown presenting the sword is also a mystery. Another legend, that he was the artist's son, Horatio Nelson Head, Nelson's godson and later a naval officer himself, can also be rejected on the grounds of age. He was born either in Palermo that year or on the passage home. His passing certificate as lieutenant is dated Portsmouth 3 January 1821.

The probability is therefore that the picture was painted in Naples or Palermo during the winter and spring of 1798-99 and accompanied the artist and his family to England in the *Haerlem*. According to an old tablet on the frame it was 'painted from life by Head and presented to Lady Hamilton by Lord Nelson'. No doubt it hung at Merton and then in Emma's house in Blackheath. After her flight to Calais it was taken over by Alderman Smith who had bailed her out of prison more than once and financed her exile abroad. After the death of the alderman's widow it was acquired by an upholsterer of Golden Square, Richard Phillips, who offered it to the newly-formed National Portrait Gallery;

it was turned down, migrated to Scotland and remained in the same family collection until finally it came to rest in the National Portrait Gallery again in 1976.[33]

Shortly after the arrival of Nelson and the royal party at Palermo there appeared on the scene two adventurers from Rome, Robert Fagan and Charles Grignion. Fagan was a diplomat and portrait-painter chiefly remarkable for his acquisition between 1794 and 1798 of the cream of the Altieri Palace collection of works of art. Grignion, 'poor old Charles Grignion' as Nollekens called him, was at that time a thriving member of the artistic colony in Rome where he made a comfortable living painting and dealing in Old Masters for the English market. The romantic story of how these two, in the teeth of the advancing French armies, managed to smuggle the Altieri Claudes to Naples, Palermo and finally Falmouth, has often been told. They were two of the most marvellous works of art in existence and the fact that they have survived can in some measure be attributed to Nelson who arranged for HMS *Tigre* to escort them home in convoy. 'Grignion', Nelson exclaimed when the artist told him of his anxiety for the safety of these priceless pictures, 'this is a national concern' and immediately sent off an order to the Governor of Gibraltar detaching a polacca. The two Claudes (heavily over-restored) are now in the National Trust Collection at Anglesey Abbey. The story is not supported in the Nelson letters but originated in George Cumberland's memoir of Grignion in *The Monthly Magazine* where he continues with an account of Grignion dining with Sir William Hamilton and being given a sitting by Nelson:

> On the 7th Feb 1799, Mr Grignion had the honour of Lord Nelson's sitting for his portrait at Palermo in Sicily; the pencil high-finished study for which picture is now in his brother's possession [Thomas Grignion, a watchmaker in London] and is accounted one of the most dignified and expressive likenesses of that brave Admiral. With this there are two exquisite drawings of Lady Hamilton in attitudes the most noble that can be imagined.[34]

The fact that the drawing is something of a caricature (95; *p.95*) is not surprising; Grignion, though also a portrait and miniature painter, practiced caricature a good deal. He sent home to his brother an album of caricatures (comparatively inoffensive according to Cumberland) representing members of a 'sort of Club' of artists in Rome, and in his *Rules for Executing Caricaturas* he says 'it is best to begin by making a harsh likeness of the person', then emphasising any remarkable feature, long faces should be made longer, smooth faces polished, rugged faces made into 'rock-work'; if the subject usually looks grave, his caricature should have a still more solemn aspect'.[35] The element of caricature is not far off in Grignion's drawing of Lady Hamilton, engraved by Vincenzo Aloja and probably done at about this time (see *p. 72*). Her hair, decorated with rosebuds, cascades over her shoulders admirably setting off the slightly vacuous face. The drawing of Nelson is possibly a study for an oil. Grignion had painted a portrait of Captain George Farmer in a similar pose but holding a naked sword. Farmer had rated Nelson as a midshipman and had also been one of the signatories to Nelson's certificate of competence as a lieutenant in 1777. In addition to this drawing and to the two drawings of Lady Hamilton 'in attitudes the most noble', Grignion had seized the chance to paint Sir William Hamilton too, miniatures of him at Lennoxlove and in the Royal Naval Museum (see *p.98*), having the same tranquil, rather melancholy expression. It is possible therefore that Grignion had intended the drawing of Nelson to be worked into a miniature, though a larger oil portrait is more likely.[36]

If we were to judge by Nelson's hair-style in this portrait the assumption would be that it was drawn before or immediately after the Battle of the Nile. In portraits after this action Nelson usually wore his hair brushed forwards to conceal the Nile wound over the right eye. But there must have been an interim period during which he wore it brushed back, and George Cumberland's evidence appears to be incontrovertible, placing it in February 1799 six months afterwards. Guzzardi also shows us a bare forehead with the hat pushed back to avoid a painful wound.

Grignion's perceptive drawing of the relaxed Nelson, absorbed in his own gloomy reflections and even concealing the Star of the Bath with his left hand, can be offset with startling effect by another drawing and a group of miniatures of about the same date by an unknown Palermo artist. It is difficult to believe that they are in fact the same man. It is also uncertain which is the original though the probability is that the first is the hatless drawing in the Mackintosh collection (96; *p.96*). This is inscribed in Emma's flourishing handwriting: *Admiral Lord Nelson Duke of Bronte painted from the Duke of Bronte at Palermo 1799 from Lady Hamilton to her friend Mrs Nelson.*[37] It was given by Emma to her sister-in-law Sarah, later Countess Nelson. Another drawing, with hat and a strange variation on the chelengk, was given by Nelson to Hardy and is still in the

Pencil drawing by Charles Grignion, 1799, (95)

Admiral Lord Nelson Duke of Bronte
painted from the Duke of Bronte at palermo 17
from Lady Hamilton to her friend Mrs Nelson

Chalk drawing by a Palermo artist, 1799, (96)

Red chalk drawing by the Palermo artist, 1799 (Admiral Hardy's), (98)

Miniature of Sir William Hamilton by Grignion with (right)
Emma Hamilton's annotation,

98

possession of his descendants (98; *p.97*). Family tradition claims that Nelson gave the original to Hardy with instructions about framing, and ordered copies to be made for his friends. Presumably one of these copies belonged to Captain Savage of the Marines (afterwards Major-General Sir J Boscawen Savage) who lent it to Thomas Burke for the engraving to be made, published in August 1800 and lettered *from an Original Drawing taken at Palermo...* Hardy's copy is briefly mentioned in a letter to his legal adviser and brother-in-law, dated 7 January 1801 aboard the *San Josef* at Hamoaze:

> Dear Manfield... I am happy the prints please. A Register Stove & Carpet, with the Hero of the Nile's Picture (which J^no Brown of course will get) cannot fail to make it the Handsomest Drawing Room in Dorchester. The King of Naples's Picture will follow from Mr M'Arthur...[38]

Both these pictures were in the Hardy Manfield collection at Portishall House until 1925 and now belong to a collateral descendant. Variants are in the Monmouth Museum (100; *p. 230*) and the Royal Naval Museum (97; *p. 229*).

Hardy himself may have been pleased with the portrait but one of his nephews certainly was not. His sister's son, John Manfield, a midshipman aboard the *Ambuscade* in the Mediterranean in 1804, was occasionally invited by his uncle aboard the *Victory*. In his diary for 5 August he says, 'I dined with Lord Nelson, Admiral Murray and Captain Hardy and I assure you your picture is not the least like his Lordship'.[39]

The insignia of the Orders vary slightly in each version but they all show him wearing the two Naval gold medals, Davison's Nile medal, and the Turkish Crescent. In none of them does he wear the Neapolitan Order of St Ferdinand and Merit, instituted by the King of Naples on 1 April 1800. However they all have one characteristic in common, shrewdly observed by his nephew, the total unfamiliarity of the Admiral's countenance, the shape of his head, the colour and style of his hair, and even his expression when compared with his other portraits. There is an Italianate cast to his features which find an echo in the proverb, *Inglese italianato, Diavolo incarnato*, though this is perhaps too emphatic for this ponderous and rather ludicrous figure. A nearer assessment is given by a modern correspondent in *The Times* who says, 'the artist in this case has turned Nelson into a complete macaroni.[40]

NOTES TO CHAPTER 4, NAPLES AND PALERMO

1. *Memoirs of Princess Dashkov* (trans. and ed. Kyril Fitzlyon 1958), p.177.

2. Noble 1908, p.157.

3. Nicolas VII, pp.347-8, note 8. The Nile coat was presented to Greenwich Hospital by the Duke of Clarence in 1828. It was enclosed in a box with a silver tablet engraved:
    THIS BOX / containing the Naval Uniform which the late / VISCOUNT NELSON / wore on the 1st of August 1798, at the / Battle of the Nile / is presented by / H.R.H. PRINCE WILLIAM HENRY / Duke of Clarence & St Andrew & Earl of Munster, / the Lord High Admiral / to / The Royal Hospital at Greenwich, / which Uniform His Royal Highness received as a legacy from the late / The Honble Mrs Damer. / This Lady, the daughter of the late Marshal Seymour, / executed the Bust of the late Viscount Nelson; / and in the Identical Uniform / did his Lordship on that occasion sit / to the Honble Mrs Damer / Bushy House, July 6th 1828.
    For the Trafalgar coat *see* Munday 1995, pp.58, 68, and reproduced Van der Merwe, p.111.

4. Common Council Journal 78, f.159b, 23 January 1799.

5. Ibid. Mrs Damer's letter was addressed from Grosvenor Square.

6. Papera's Wedgwood account has been kindly sent to me by Dr Ian Fraser of Keele University. There is no further evidence of Mrs Damer's employment by Wedgwood.

7. Farington 11 September 1801; also noted in *The Diaries of Sylvester Douglas* (Lord Glenbervie), ed. Francis Bickley (1928), I p.338.

8. Committee of City Land Journals 95, ff 109b-111b and 120-121b. Common Council accepted Dance's report on 27 July 1803.

9. *The Morning Post* 5 May 1804, cit. Noble 1908, pp.160-1.

10. Sir Leslie Stephen in *DNB*.

11. Letter from Mrs Damer to Lady Hamilton, 31 October 1809 (NMM class mark AGC/33: 49/209).

12. Farington 14 February 1808. Hope's quite reasonable article had appeared in *The Times* 5 May 1804.

13. NMM 32-78 and presented to the Naval College, Esquimault, Vancouver. Mrs K.A. Esdaile, in a report to the NMM, attempted the attribution to Mrs Damer but without much conviction.

14. Account by Sir Alexander Johnston, Nicolas VII, p.348. The stump of the *Victory* foremast is now in the NPG, supporting Chantrey's posthumous bust of Nelson.

15. Nelson's graphic letter to St Vincent, Palermo 28 December 1798 (Nicolas III, pp.210-3).

16. Walker 1985/1, pp.186-8.

17. George 1942, VII no. 9269. He wears the Sultan's scarlet sable-lined pelisse, not a peer's robe as stated in the BM Catalogue.

18. Letter from Nelson to Lord Spencer, Palermo 18 December 1799 (Nicolas IV, pp.145-6). Nelson also wrote to J. Spencer Smith, secretary of the British Embassy, Constantinople, saying that 'a handful of diamonds comes naturally from the hand of a great monarch, but this drawing, made probably for the occasion, could only come from an affectionate, amiable disposition' (Nicolas IV, p.157).

19. Letter from Nelson to the Grand Signior, Naples 16 December 1798 (Nicolas III, p.202). For details of the chelengk (see Appendix I, p.279).

20. The entries for Guzzardi in Thieme-Becker and Bénézit are unhelpful, nor is information forthcoming from Naples and Palermo.

21. Harrison 1806, II p.391.

22. *Naval Chronicle* XX (1808), p.111.

23. Admiral W.A. Baillie-Hamilton's memorandum of 15 April 1875, quoted by Sir Eric Geddes (NMM archive).

24. Admiralty Board Minutes for 11 August 1849 in PRO.

25. Callender/Bonham-Smith correspondence in Callender Papers.

26. Admiral Baillie-Hamilton, *op. cit.*

27. Walker 1985/2, p.361.

28. Edwards 1808; Waterhouse 1981, p.166; Walker 1977, pp.393-4.

29. Order Book, *Vanguard*, Palermo 8 May 1799 (Nicolas III, p.349).

30. Letter from Nelson to Lady Hamilton, *San Josef* 8 February 1801 (Nicolas IV, pp. 284-5).

31. Bosanquet 1955, p. 239.

32. Letter from Nelson to the Lord Mayor, *Vanguard*, mouth of the Nile, 8 August 1798 (Nicolas III, p.95).

33. Walker 1985/2, p.360).

34. George Cumberland, 'Memoir of Charles Grignion Esq', *Monthly Magazine* 1 November 1809, p.551; Waterhouse 1981, p.151; Walker 1986, pp.986-8.

35. Unsigned letter in *Monthly Magazine* 1 November 1809, p.377.

36. Miss Turner's lithograph and the RUSI Catalogue both date this drawing to Naples 1797, and Lionel Cust, in the *DNB* article on Grignion, to Palermo 1798, but the place and date, Palermo February 1799, were established by W.T. Whitley, quoting Cumberland's Memoir in Whitley III, pp.224-5. Whitley's notes, with the relevant newspapers cuttings, are in ten bound volumes in the BM Print Room.

37. Oliver Warner, 'Two Drawings of Nelson' in *Country Life* 2 August 1956, p. 244. Lady Mackintosh kindly allowed me to borrow this drawing for study at leisure.

38. Broadley 1906, p.60. 'The King of Naples's Picture' is presumably the pencil profile of 1799.

39. John Manfield's diary (NMM archive and microfilm).

40. Tom Pocock, *The Times* 26 April 1955 14e.

Marble bust by Thaller & Ranson, 1801, (107)

102

5 HOMEWARD BOUND

Early in 1800 Nelson had the good fortune to capture the *Guillaume Tell*, Villeneuve's flagship which had escaped at the Battle of the Nile. Berry went on board to receive the surrender of the French admiral's sword and her flag was sent home to the Admiralty on 12 May. Some extra verses parodying Cornelia Knight's 'National Anthem' verses, were sniggered in London when the news arrived shortly afterwards:[1]

> Nelson, the flag haul down,
> Hang up thy laurel crown,
> While her we sing.
> No more in triumph swell,
> Since that with her you dwell,
> But don't her William tell
> Nor George, your King.

A few days later Ferdinand IV, in order to celebrate the Restoration of his kingdom, issued an amnesty to political prisoners, the gallows were removed from the central square in Naples, and the Tsar of Russia, General Suvorov and Nelson himself were presented with the Grand Cross of St Ferdinand and Merit. In exchange Nelson asked the King to 'permit me to lay on your table a Gold Medal' - presumably a copy of Davison's Nile medal.[2]

The Grand Cross consisted of a gold and silver Star containing the figure of St Ferdinand holding a naked sword and a laurel crown surrounded by the motto *Fidei et Merito*, and worn with a broad blue riband with a red border over the right shoulder, suspending the Badge of the Order at hip level.[3]

As it happened both Nelson and Sir William Hamilton were recalled at about the same time, Hamilton with many regrets after thirty-six years service *en poste* at the Court of His Sicilian Majesty, Nelson after two years service in the Mediterranean beginning in glory at the Nile and ending with the near fiasco of the blockade of Malta. He had received a frosty and much-quoted letter from the First Lord of the Admiralty warmly recommending his recovery to health and strength in England rather than an inactive situation at a foreign court. He hoped to be allowed to sail home in the *Foudroyant*, badly in need of a refit, taking the Hamiltons and others with him, but as it turned out they were only able to sail in her as far as Leghorn where they arrived on 14 June, 'the Ships overflowing with the Queen's retinue', and then proceed overland to Vienna, via Arezzo, Ancona and Trieste. The journey, already made hazardous enough by Napoleon's armies having crossed the Alps once again, was not improved by the coach overturning at Castel San Giovanni. But apart from the discomforts, and the news of the defeat of the Imperial armies at Marengo, the journey was a triumphal progress. 'Lord Nelson', says Cornelia Knight, 'has been received with acclamations in all the towns of the Pope's States'. From Ancona they were escorted across the Adriatic in a Russian squadron to Trieste ('illuminations and many *Viva Nelsons* prepared') and then overland again to Vienna.[4]

According to a note in the *Allgemeine Zeitung* both Nelson and Lady Hamilton sat to Heinrich Füger shortly after their arrival in Vienna on 19 August.[5] Crowds had flocked to the studio to be introduced to the Hero of the Nile, the only man in Europe apparently able to stand up to the invincible Napoleon with any degree of success. A banker's order, signed Bronte Nelson of the Nile and dated Vienna 23 September 1800, directed Mr Hertz the banker to pay Füger the sum of £250 for one full length of the Queen of Naples, one full-length of Lady Hamilton and one-quarter-length of Lord Nelson of the Nile. The two full-lengths appeared at Christie's in 1860.[6] The quarter-length is presumably the uniformed version in the Royal Naval Museum (103; *p.111*). This is one of the three known Füger portraits. It shows Nelson in rear-admiral's full-dress uniform and the insignia of the three Orders of Chivalry to which he was entitled at this time: the Bath awarded after the Battle of Cape St Vincent, the Turkish Crescent awarded after the Nile, and the Neapolitan Order of St Ferdinand and Merit awarded barely three months before. The two Naval gold medals hang from his neck and Davison's Nile medal. Lady Minto, the wife of the British ambassador in Vienna, wrote home of Nelson's 'shock head ... He is a jig from ribands, orders and stars', but the famous charm captivated her again; 'he is just the same with us as ever he was', she said.[7] But there is a totally different atmosphere about this portrait than is to be found in any other before or since. Füger was primarily a miniaturist but because of failing eyesight had up to this moment not practiced much on a larger scale.[8] It is interesting to note how his hand, trained in the exacting technique of miniature painting, had detected something in Nelson's expression that no artist had hitherto attempted - a ruthlessness, a capacity for total absorption, a streak almost of cruelty, all of which were undoubtedly part of his genius. There is no indication of any flaw in the eyes which are both equally bright and normal, though the colour is a distinct hazel instead of the usual clear blue. But there is something here of Nelson's ill-health and no doubt of his submerged feelings of guilt. 'My health is better but you will see an old man', he wrote home to Davison.[9] This possibly explains the mysterious disappearance of this portrait for over a hundred and fifty years; neither Nelson nor his family could tolerate this cold psychological analysis by the Viennese miniaturist, uncloyed by the prevailing hero-worship.

The history of the National Portrait Gallery version of Füger's portrait is clearer (102; *p.ii*). This is the only image to show Nelson out of uniform. He is dressed informally in a dark blue coat and neckcloth and a light blue jersey. The thin-lipped unsmiling expression is the same but the eyes are grey. Whether it is Füger's first attempt, later bedecked with stars and medals for the more resplendent version, or whether it was painted afterwards for the artist's own interest, is uncertain. Füger's son thought the former. In an affidavit sworn before witnesses in Vienna on 14 February 1859, Füger's son declared that his father had painted the portrait in 1800 on Nelson's arrival in Vienna, and that the Admiral had sat for it in person. He had painted it for his own interest (*aus Interesse für den grossen Mann*) and it had hung in his studio till his death in 1818. It was not a copy and in 1823 he had disposed of it to Moritz von Tschoffen.

The affidavit was legalised by the Austrian minister for foreign affairs and certified by Augustus Hopper, the British ambassador in Vienna; but that was sixty years after the portraits had been painted and it is possible Füger's son had become confused. However the portrait then made its way to Leipzig where, in another affidavit sworn before the British consul-general on 3 March 1859, von Tschoffen solemnly stated that it had never been out of his possession since 1823 and that no copy had ever been made. The original certificates are in the National Portrait Gallery archive (see Appendix II p. 283). At this point or shortly afterwards, in Leipzig, it was bought by a firm of music importers, Ewer & Company of 390 Oxford Street, London, who sold it to the National Portrait Gallery as one of its earliest acquisitions. In spite of von Tschoffen's assertion that no copies had ever been made (possibly he meant during his ownership or perhaps he considered the uniformed version not to be strictly a copy), at least two copies do in fact exist - the miniature formerly in the collection of Sir Edmund Gosse and the large oil version at Portsmouth.[10]

Lady Hamilton as Britannia. Engraving by Thomas Baxter, 1805, showing her leaning on a copy of the Thaller & Ranson bust.

The sittings in Füger's studio were not the only contacts with artists Nelson enjoyed in Vienna. The strange party was entertained for four days at the Schloss Esterhazy where Nelson was introduced to Franz Joseph Haydn who dedicated to him the 'Nelson Mass' (the Missa in angustiis). He also accompanied Emma singing Miss Knight's 'Nelson Aria'. Haydn's features were portrayed in wax by a Viennese sculptor, Franz Christian Thaller, who also had a sitting from Nelson. The result was the well-known Thaller and Ranson bust, now in the National Maritime Museum, incised on the back: *Franz Thaller et Matthias Ranson / Viennae Austr. MDCCCI*. Thaller was a distinguished local artist known, apart from the wax of Haydn, for sculpture done for the Emperor at Schönbrunn and for the City of Vienna itself [11] (107; *p.102*). Matthias Ranson, apart from this inscription, is otherwise unknown and may have been a sculptor working in Thaller's studio, possibly a student. I have not been able to find any record among contemporary newspapers of the sitting though there is every probability Nelson gave him one in view of his evident delight in the sessions in Füger's studio, which became a place of pious pilgrimage for all who wished to pay their respects to the Hero of the Nile. The earliest evidence we have is the 1801 Latin inscription. But both Füger's oil painting and the Thaller and Ranson bust show Nelson wearing a rear-admiral's uniform as was in order for him at this time; he was promoted to vice-admiral on 1 January 1801, therefore although the marble is clearly dated 1801, the sittings can only have taken place a year earlier. At some time during the first five years of the century it was brought to England and to Merton House where it stood in the drawing room. A version appears in Edridge's drawing of Lady Nelson (see *p.xiv*), and it was quite popular, copies being turned out by Turnerelli, Nollekens and other sculptors, including probably Bertolini in Florence. Flaxman's memorial in St Paul's Cathedral is based on it (219; *p.177*). It was used with dramatic effect in the engraving by A.R. Burt after Thomas Baxter, 'Britannia Mourning Nelson', 5 December 1805 (see *opposite*).

A certain amount of mystery shrouds the origins of this bust but an illuminating inscription in small print at the bottom of a commemorative 1805 engraving by the calligrapher, P. W. Tomkins, below a bust of Nelson flanked by Victory and Fame, tells us that 'Lord Nelson when at Vienna permitted a Cast to be taken from his Face by Thaller: from that Cast this likeness is taken and perfected from the life'.[12] This statement opens up a whole new range of hypothesis. If Nelson submitted to the unpleasant process of having his life mask

Life masks, 1800 - possibly done as models for the Thaller & Ranson. From the collections of The Royal Naval Museum, (105), (right) and The National Maritime Museum, (104), (above).

108

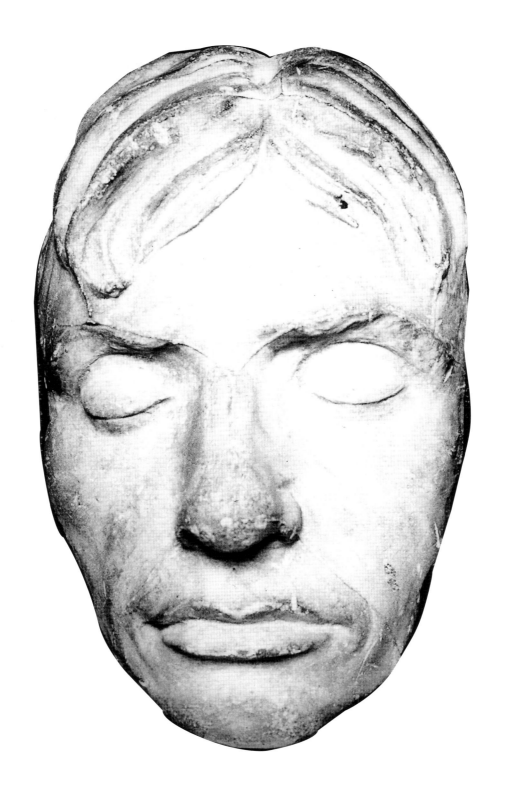

109

made in Vienna this might explain the long delay between his visit there for a few weeks in August and September 1800 and the date of 1801 on the back of the marble. It would have taken weeks if not months to transfer the cast into a bust. It might also throw light on the identity of Matthias Ranson who could have been a practitioner in the technique of taking life masks.[13] Unfortunately very few letters home from Vienna survive if they existed at all, and Nelson kept no journal. Cornelia Knight's journal does not mention it either and one would certainly expect from her a highly coloured account of so interesting an experience. However at the time of the Trafalgar medal, when various designs were being discussed (see pp. 166-170), it was known that Nelson had at some time previously had a life mask made. Sir William Beechey, called on to advise on a profile for the medal, mentions a bust in the Royal Collection and concludes, '...the Bust, tho it was done from a cast from his face is very deficient; he pursed up his chin and screwed up his features when the Plaster was poured on it, the nose is very like and so is the mouth, the chin not at all; the latter was thin and flat in a front view, in the Bust it is pointed; the breadth of the face is like but too thin ...'[14]

These two statements, from PW Tomkins and Sir William Beechey, point to the existence of a life-mask of Nelson, made possibly in Vienna in August-September 1800. No such life-mask is known to have survived unless consideration is given to the vexed question of the two so-called death-masks, one with the eyes open at Greenwich (104; *p.108*), the other with eyes closed in Portsmouth (105; *p.109*). Unfortunately neither of these can be convincingly authenticated. The Greenwich version has an impressive pedigree first published in the Catalogue of the Royal Navy Exhibition, Chelsea, in 1891:

> 3164. Post-mortem mask of Lord Nelson; taken after death on board the Victory, for his sister Mrs Matcham. On the death of Mrs Matcham it became the property of her daughter, the wife of Captain Blanckley; from whom it passed to his second wife and widow, and from her to her sister, Miss Naylor, who gave it to the present owner's father.
> Lent by J G Tasker Esq.

But the pedigree goes back no further than 1891 and on examination cannot be corroborated. In the first, place there is no record that Mrs Matcham ever owned the mask and according to the third Earl Nelson none of her family ever remembered it in her possession. Secondly Mrs Matcham survived her daughter by four years dying in 1842; unless therefore she gave it to her daughter before her death it could not have passed in this way into the Blanckley family. Thirdly and

Oil by Heinrich Füger, 1800, (103)

perhaps more vitally, Nelson's physician, Dr William Beatty, in his minutely particularised account of Nelson's death and its aftermath, mentions no mask being taken - surely a dramatic affair worthy of record; nor did Beatty ever mention it in his frequent conversations with the third Earl whom he visited every year till his death in 1842.[15]

The Portsmouth mask, with closed eyes (105; *p.109*), has even less of a pedigree. It was bought by HM Queen Mary in 1924 from an antique shop in the Isle of Wight and presented by her to HMS *Victory*. It had a similar hearsay provenance which was valiantly defended by Professor Callender when it was exhibited at Spinks, St James's, in 1928.[16] At a later exhibition, held at the Royal Naval Hospital, Haslar, in 1967, both masks were exhibited, together with a third lent by Mrs M.E. Weekes, patently a squash from one of the Thaller & Ranson busts. The help of a technical adviser from Madame Tussaud was drawn in at this point, his opinion being that they could have been genuine death-masks but the 'downward drag' of the soft tissues of cheek and neck was a feature of both life and death masks.[17]

The general outcome of all this uncertainty is the probability that a death-mask of Nelson was never made; that a life-mask was almost certainly made in Vienna in 1800; and that the Thaller & Ranson marble bust was built up during the course of that year and the next, using as a guide the two casts now at Portsmouth and Greenwich. I personally believe that the casts are genuine life-masks made in Vienna in August or September 1800, possibly by Matthias Ranson, and used by Franz Christian Thaller for the production of his marble bust. This view was upheld at a symposium in Portsmouth in 1993.[18]

After their stay in Vienna Nelson and his party continued their journey to Prague and then down the river Elbe to Dresden where they lodged at the Hotel de Pologne. Here the Court painter, Johann Heinrich Schmidt, commissioned by the British minister, Hugh Elliot (Lord Minto's brother), produced pastel drawings of Emma and Nelson himself. They are both in the National Maritime Museum (128; *pp.116, 117*). Schmidt specialised in pastels and had already drawn many distinguished men of the time, including Napoleon, and was delighted to have the opportunity of a sitting from Nelson, though his actual appearance seems to have disappointed the Saxons. A Lutheran pastor, Thomas Kosegarten, then living in Leipzig, described him minutely:

> Nelson is one of the most insignificant figures I ever saw. His weight cannot be more than 70lbs. A more miserable collection of bones and

wizened frame cannot be imagined. His bold nose, steady eye and the solid worth revealed in the whole face betray in some measure the great conqueror. He speaks little, and then only in English, and he hardly ever smiles. I have no doubt of his high ability, but one cannot look without astonishment at his slender body, although this of course, can have no immediate connection with a great soul. ...He was almost covered with orders and stars. As his right arm is missing, the coat-sleeve was fastened to his breast. As a rule Lady Hamilton wore her hat... She behaved like a loving sister towards Nelson: led him, often took hold of his hand, whispered something into his ear, and he twisted his mouth into the faint resemblance of a smile ... She did not seek to win hearts, for everyone's lay at her feet.[19]

Schmidt seems to have agreed with Kosegarten. He no doubt had imagined the admiral as a conquering Viking but beneath the thatch of grey straggling hair the pastel shows a melancholy face, the expression unsmiling, the uninjured eye bold and clear with perhaps too intense a blue, the blinded one darkened and set awkwardly under the brow on which the Nile wound is clearly apparent; the nose is slightly bulbous at the tip. With hindsight we can say that it is the face of a man, sick in body and mind, conscious that his precious career is in jeopardy, and conscious too that he is approaching home to a wife to whom he has been blatantly unfaithful, and accompanied by a friend whom he has openly cuckolded. The knowledge that Lady Hamilton was carrying his unborn child cannot have added to his peace of mind. But as Lord Minto wrote home, 'it is hard to condemn and use ill a hero, as he is in his own element, for being foolish about a woman who has art enough to make fools of many wiser than an Admiral'. Schmidt's portrait takes some account of this network of constrained emotion and guilt. There is small wonder that at this moment Nelson hardly ever smiled. The only bright aspect of the portrait is the blue of the uniform which is better preserved than in most of the oil portraits; and we can understand Mrs St George's malicious pleasure in describing Nelson in Dresden as a perfect constellation of stars and orders:

Oct. 5 - Went by Lady Hamilton's invitation to see Lord Nelson dressed for Court. On his hat he wore the large diamond feather, or ensign of sovereignty given him by the Grand Signior; on his breast the Order of the Bath, the Order he received as the Duke of Bronte, the diamond star including the sun or crescent given him by the Grand Signior, three gold medals obtained by three different victories, and a beautiful present from the King of Naples. On one side is His Majesty's picture, richly set and surrounded with laurels which spring from two united anchors at bottom, and support the Neapolitan crown at top; on the other is the Queen's cypher, which turns so as to appear within the same laurels, and is formed of diamonds on green enamel. In short Lord Nelson was a perfect constellation of stars and orders.[20]

Schmidt's portrait and its companion of Lady Hamilton (see *p.117*) were favourites of Nelson. The pastel of Lady Hamilton, during his later campaigns, he kept on the bulkhead of his cabin near his desk, and referred to as his 'Guardian Angel'. Indeed, in Emma's scrawling handwriting on a tattered paper fixed to the backboard of the frame, is the inscription:

> This Portrait of Emma Hamilton was in all the Battles with the virtuous, gallant and heroic Nelson. He called it his Guardian Angel and thought he could not be victorious if he did not see it in the midst of Battle. He used to say under his Banner. I grieve (or lament) the fatal 21st of October, when he gloriously fell and ordered Captain Hardy to bring it to me.[21]

The pair of portraits was no doubt, in view of Emma's inscription, included among Nelson's possessions delivered by Hardy to Lady Hamilton after Trafalgar - 'Pray let dear Lady Hamilton have my hair, and all things belonging to me' - though it is difficult to reconcile this with the provenance through Hugh Elliot's descendants. Schmidt certainly painted copies, and probably the pair was divided, the 'Nelson' remaining in Dresden until the end of Elliot's term of office, the 'Emma' accompanying Nelson as his 'Guardian Angel'.

NOTES TO CHAPTER 5, HOMEWARD BOUND

1. Connell 1957, p. 417.

2. Letter to the King of Naples, Palermo 2 June 1800 (Nicolas IV, p. 244).

3. The Cross of Knight Commanders of the Order, awarded to Hood,
    Troubridge and Hallowell, was worn round the neck like the Order of St Anne
    (letters in Nicolas IV, pp. 250, 293, and VII, pp. cxcvi, cxcvii).

4. The rigours of the journey were described by Cornelia Knight in letters to Captain Berry
    (Knight 1861, pp. 319-23).

5. *Allgemeine Zeitung* 1 September 1800 (copy at Colindale).

6. Christie's (Phillips sale), 13 July 1860 (239-40).

7. Minto 1874, III pp. 114, 147-50.

8. Alfred Stix, *H. F. Füger* (Vienna 1925), but containing no reference to Nelson portraits.

9. Letter to Davison, 20 September 1800 (Nicolas VII, cxcviii).

10. Walker 1985/2, p. 362.

11. Thieme-Becker XXXII, p. 577.

12. Stipple engraving 'Drawn Engraved & Published by P.W. Tomkins Engraver to Her
    Majesty, Nov 21 1805, No. 49 New Bond Street London' (O'D 1908-25, 70).

13. The lurid process of taking life-masks is described in B.R. Haydon's Diary for 5 May
    1821, and *The Phrenological Journal*, January 1845. Nollekens's technique of taking a
    death-mask is described by Farington, 19 September 1806 (C.J. Fox), and (of Lord Lake)
    in J.T. Smith, *Nollekens and His Times* (1920), I, pp. 367-8.

14. Letter from Beechey to J.F. Tuffin, 31 December 1805, cit. Pollard 1970, p. 304.

15. *Windsor Magazine* (1904), pp. 513-21.

16. 'The Death Mask of Lord Nelson', *Society for Nautical Research, Annual Report* (1928).
    The subject is discussed further in Walker 1980, pp. 319-27, and Nash 1993.

17. Pugh 1968 pp. 39-42.

18. Nash 1993, *passim*.

19. Kosegarten 1801, cit. Callender 1943 and Keigwin 1985.

20. Mrs Richard Trench, *Journal kept during a Visit to Germany 1799-1800*, p. 77.

21. Lady Hamilton's almost indecipherable inscription is rendered intelligible in Callender's
    transcription (Callender 1943, p. 314).

Pastel by Johann Heinrich Schmidt, 1800, (128)

Lady Hamilton: Pastel by Johann Heinrich Schmidt, 1800
This picture, which Nelson called his 'Guardian Angel', hung in his cabin in HMS Victory,

Stipple engraving by Robert Cooper, 1815, after an oil sketch by Beechey, (132)

118

6 STATE PORTRAITS AND OTHERS

The journey from Dresden through North Germany included Magdeburg where a local observer, von Dalwick, noticed nothing abnormal about Nelson's sightless right eye, and ended in a misunderstanding at Hamburg where a frigate was expected to convey the Hero home. No frigate was waiting and, after a few days of the customary fêting and jollifications, Nelson and his companions lost patience and boarded the *King George* mail-boat at Cuxhaven. Their arrival at Yarmouth on 6 November 1800 was recorded by Rowlandson who shows, in a superb watercolour-drawing, a giant Admiral landing from an improvised gangway amid the rapturous welcome of his pigmy Norfolk compatriots.[1] Crowds harnessed themselves to his carriage and drew it to the Wrestlers' Inn where the landlady asked his permission to rename it the Nelson's Arms. 'That would be absurd,' said her guest cracking one of his few recorded jokes, 'for I have but one'. Here the Hamiltons handed over one of the Guzzardi portraits to be copied by a local artist, Matthew Keymer (81; *pp.84-5*).

The cortège, amid continuous rejoicing, fireworks, trumpet fanfares and a cavalry escort, proceeded through Ipswich to Colchester, where at his new home, Roundwood, another misunderstanding awaited. The house was empty and cold, the travellers being expected in London. They carried on south to arrive finally in London, Nelson after an absence of nearly three years abroad, in the midst of the worst thunderstorm since 1703. It provided a suitably sombre backcloth to the inevitably catastrophic encounter between Lady Nelson and Lady Hamilton. Nelson's marriage lasted a few more weeks, then crashed. He cannot have failed to foresee this and indeed had already written to the Admiralty, 'I trust that my necessary journey by land from the Mediterranean will not be considered as a wish to be a moment out of active service'. And no doubt he relished the irony of Halliday's medal, struck in honour of his return and inscribed: *HAIL! VIRTUOUS HERO, THY VICTORIES WE ACKNOWLEDGE AND THY GOD.* In London the Hero's welcome continued. There had been no opportunity for popular rejoicing since the storming of Seringapatam on 4 May 1799. Napoleon's armies had been depressingly victorious. Rear-Admiral Nelson, hero of St Vincent, victor of the Nile, one-armed and partially blind, slight of figure but of clearly, indomitable virility, sparked off the one hope of salvation. The fact that he was flouting the conventions of society, in any case becoming out-moded by the exploits of the Prince of Wales and his royal brothers, added interest and colour to the grey wartime scene. Once again the horses were removed from his carriage, this time at Blackfriars Bridge, and Nelson was drawn by the London crowds to the Guildhall where the Lord Mayor presented him with a sword voted by the City of London.[2] Two days later, at a levée in St James's Palace, he and Hamilton were cruelly snubbed by the King.

Apart from a few days in Salisbury and with Hamilton's friend Beckford at Fonthill, Nelson spent his leave in London until his departure on 13 January 1801 for Plymouth and the Baltic campaign, culminating at the Battle of Copenhagen. During those eight weeks or so Nelson sat to about seven artists - Beechey for the City of Norwich, Hoppner for the Prince of Wales, possibly Mrs Damer for the City of London though she may have made use of the sittings she had two years earlier in Naples (see p.73), and an assortment of minor artists including Catherine Andras, Robert Bowyer, De Koster, an unknown sculptor for Mrs Coade and possibly Richard Cosway. Lord St Vincent's uncharitable cut, 'that foolish little fellow Nelson has sat to every painter in London' may carry some weight;[3] but among the Royal Academy portrait painters could be numbered the President himself, Benjamin West, and Angelica Kauffman, Lawrence, Northcote, Opie, Russell, Shee, Westall and Zoffany, not to mention the miniaturists Burch, Cosway and George Engleheart, and the sculptors Banks, Flaxman, Nollekens and Rossi. None of these are known to have had sittings from Nelson, so St Vincent's jibe can be largely discounted, though a portrait from the hand of Lawrence, then at the height of his powers, or by the ageing Zoffany, would have been a treasure indeed.

Up to this point the various portraits by Lemuel Abbott had dominated the scene. The small half-lengths painted for Captain Locker, Lady Nelson and others, had been enlarged and engraved in mezzotint for a wider and no less avid public. Now the City of Norwich stepped into the breach, deciding that Beechey should be the artist. Nelson was probably the most distinguished man Norfolk had ever produced and Norwich felt that the least it could do was to honour the Hero with a portrait. Nelson himself had presented the City with the Spanish admiral's sword surrendered at Cape St Vincent in 1797 and had been awarded the Freedom of the City in return. Beechey was an Oxfordshire man but had married a Norfolk wife and moreover had already painted Nelson's father, the subject of a touching letter from Lady Nelson to her husband then in Palermo:

> I think you will be surprised when I tell you our good father is sitting for his picture. Sir W. Beechey is the fortunate man, You must know it is a profound secret. I was [to go] to Sir W.B. ask his price, look at his pictures and then enquire whether he would go to an invalid. The answer 'No' puzzled me, however I said sometimes general rules were broken thro'. Sir W. finding I was rather anxious about this picture, said that really he never went to any person excepting the King and the Royal Family; the Duke and Duchess of York had that instant left the house. I knew that. 'But Madam may I ask who is the gentleman?' 'Yes Sir, my Lord Nelson's father.' 'My God, I would go to York to do it, yes Madam directly.' He was as good as his word and has been here twice. I think the likeness will be an exceeding good one. I don't know whether the picture is for you or me.[4]

The portrait of the Revd Edmund Nelson was brought from Earl Nelson by the National Maritime Museum in 1948 and is now at Greenwich.[5] The portrait of Nelson himself was commissioned by the chamberlain of Norwich in 1800 and presented to the City 'in Remembrance of the signal Services to his King and Country, and the Splendid Victories obtained under his Command by the Union of the most Undaunted Valour and the most Consummate Skill, in which the Superiority of the British Navy was decidedly manifested'. It was begun by Beechey between Nelson's arrival in London on 9 November 1800 and his promotion to Vice-Admiral on 1 January 1801. The finished whole-length portrait was exhibited at the Royal Academy in May, and two hundred guineas (and a further £2. 17s for the packing case) paid by the Chamberlain of Norwich at Michaelmas 1801.[6]

Beechey's whole-length portrait (137; *p.123*) is specially interesting because of the brownish coloured eyes, the right one dimmed, the presentation sword leaning against the cannon, and the thirteen rays on the chelengk representing the enemy ships at the Nile (see Appendix I p.279). But it did not seem to find favour at the Academy where the colouring of the face was criticised as being preposterously high and the whole effect 'more like a caricature than a portrait of the Hero of the Nile';[7] and according to a later critic in *The Athenaeum*, referring to

Oil sketch by Sir William Beechey, 1800, (132)

122

Oil by Sir William Beechey, 1801, (137)

Wellington's copy at Apsley House, Beechey's three-quarter length is 'inferior to the portraits of the same hero by Abbott and Hoppner'.[8] *The Quarterly Review* was even more outspoken: 'The pencil of Sir William Beechey was, however, altogether unequal to the man of Trafalgar - poor in point of art, his piece is unlike in form and expression; the spare war and weather Admiral is swelled into an overgrown figure-head. The burning fire which animated his fragile frame is extinguished in the painting of the feeble academical knight'.[9]

However the citizens of Norwich were satisfied and provided an elaborate gilt frame of carved wood surmounted by Nelson's armorial shield; the City of London ordered a three-quarter length copy for the Guildhall, the Drapers' Company a copy for their Hall, and Nelson and Beechey themselves struck up a friendship, Nelson standing as honorary godfather to one of Beechey's children (Charles, later to become a naval officer himself) and giving him the cocked hat he wore at the Battle of the Nile. 'He parted with it', he said, 'as an old and tried friend, for he had worn it in many battles'.[10]

Recalling the sittings several years later, at the time of the Trafalgar medal (see pp. 166-170), Beechey said 'his cheek had rather an Infantine plumpness'. This is noticeable in the Abbott portraits of 1797-8 but markedly less so in the post-Nile portraits by Guzzardi, Grignion, Füger and others, where the face has a lean, drawn aspect, the result of illness and guilt. In fact it is surprising that Beechey should make this comment, made all the more curious by his observation of Nelson's eyes as being light brown in the National Portrait Gallery sketch, and mid-brown to blue-grey in the National Maritime Museum sketch. Apart from the witness of other artists, we have Nelson's own word for it that his eyes were blue. 'The blemish is nothing not to be perceived unless told', he wrote home after the Siege of Calvi, 'the pupil is nearly the size of the blue part'.[11] But in spite of the carping treatment of the critics Beechey's portrait is a remarkable achievement with an immediacy that is specially noticeable in the sketch of the head which he kept in the studio and eventually handed on to Nelson's godson (132; *p.122*). Here, in spite of the unusual colouring of the eyes, there is an altogether convincing closeness of observation handed down to posterity by an artist, by no means in the first rank certainly, but with a skill and integrity that assures us that this image of the great Admiral is as close and faithful as we shall ever see. The Nile scar clearly to be seen above the right eyebrow, the film over the right eye itself, even the strange alteration to the shape of the head, combine to give an air of quiet self-confidence that is missing from all other portraits.[12]

Beechey is usually thought of as a prosaic portraitist, a bluff countryman not much at home in London society. 'He is not very polished', said Northcote, but in spite of his rather offhand treatment of royalty (he is said to have offended the King in an argument about Reynolds's use of red in trees) Beechey's work was admired by the King who, on hearing that he had been defeated by Sawrey Gilpin in the Royal Academy election of 1797, remarked acidly that it was 'because he is the best painter'.[13] Apart from the rising Lawrence, Beechey's rival in the field of portraits was John Hoppner who was commissioned, not surprisingly by the Prince of Wales, to paint the second of the 'state portraits' of Nelson, now in the Royal Collection with many copies elsewhere. (146; *p.127*). Hoppner had been born in London of German parents (some said a natural son of George III), was working for the royal family by 1785, and perhaps because of his slightly flashy bravura, became Principal Painter to the Prince of Wales in 1793 though he had already painted for him an excellent portrait of Josef Haydn in 1791. Portraits of Admiral Payne and Admiral Keith, Nelson's commander in chief in the Mediterranean, followed later. The state room in Carlton House contained an array of portraits of men of action of the day, successors to the heroes of the Seven Years' War, and all fitted into special frames carved with dolphins, anchors, coral and sprigs of oak.[14] Nelson's portrait was commissioned by the Prince probably shortly after the arrival of the news of the Battle of the Nile. Hoppner's first sketches in the Royal Naval Museum (145; *p.126*) and the National Maritime Museum (144; *p.242*) show Nelson in rear-admiral's uniform and therefore done from a sitting in December 1800 before his promotion on 1 January. The finished whole-length in St James's Palace shows Copenhagen in the background though he is still in rear-admiral's uniform. Hoppner, usually a copious exhibitor at the Royal Academy, sometimes sending in as many as a dozen portraits, exhibited nothing in 1801 and only a portrait of a girl in 1802, though Farington noted in his *Diary* for 25 March 1802 that Hoppner was planning to exhibit a whole-length of Nelson that year. Turner's very popular mezzotint of January 1806 has the background altered to show Trafalgar. Lane's copy for King's Lynn was delivered in 1807 but the Prince did not see his own picture till after Hoppner's death in 1810. Hoppner's widow delivered it to Carlton House in April 1810.

Oil sketch by John Hoppner, 1800, (145)

126

Oil by John Hoppner, 1801, (146)

Hoppner, we are told by Northcote, 'was a finer portrait-painter than any now living'. His technique in obtaining a likeness, at least of women, was described graphically by Northcote himself: 'he used to make as beautiful a face as he could, then give it a likeness to the sitter, working down from this beautiful state until the bystanders should cry out, 'Oh! I see a likeness coming!' whereupon he then stopped and never ventured to make it more like'.[15] No contemporary account of the reactions to Hoppner's portrait have come down to us though, judging from the immense popularity of Henry Meyer's stipple engraving and Turner's mezzotint, it seems to have been more widely appreciated than the many variations on Abbott's portrait painted after the loss of Nelson's arm. Nelson's chaplain, Dr Scott, considered it to be, apart from De Koster's little profile, the best likeness of him that had ever been painted,[16] and it was thought of highly enough for Catherine Andras to use it as the basis for her wax effigy in Westminster Abbey (214; *p.168*). The modern assessment of Hoppner's portraiture is that he veered to and fro between the styles of Reynolds, Romney, Lawrence and Raeburn, and that his most appealing work is to be found among his portraits of pretty women and sweet little children. Stripped of its paraphernalia of chivalry and war, Hoppner's Nelson, with its coyly tilted head and sugary expression, has an effeminacy distasteful to this hard-bitten age.

Early in December 1800 Nelson arranged a display of his trophies at Admiralty House. These would have included the crocodile-hilted sword given him by his captains at the Nile, the gifts from the Sultan of Turkey, the chelengk, the sable pelisse, the gold-hilted scimitar, the jewel of the Order of the Crescent, a jewelled rose believed to be from the Sultana herself, various diamond-studded boxes from the crowned heads of Europe, a miniature of himself from the mad Tsar, Paul I, the star and badge of the Sicilian Order of St Ferdinand and Merit together with jewels and brooches given by the Queen of Naples and the patent of the Dukedom of Bronte, Davison's gold medal, the dress sword from the Lord Mayor of London, and no doubt many others. The scene was described by the second Viscount Palmerston in a letter to his wife:

> I have been this morning visiting Lady Spencer whom I found at home with quite a levée of people coming in and out. What I thought myself in luck was in meeting Lord Nelson with all his fine presents of every kind which he had brought there to show. It is melancholy to see him, himself so shrunk and mutilated. The worst is that his only eye is so weak as sometimes to give great alarm.[17]

Most of these can be seen at Greenwich though a number, including the chelengk, were stolen in two burglaries and never recovered. (see p.281)

The exhibition seems to have been not too exclusive and it is reasonable to assume that a number of artists were invited. Certainly Abbott was able to alter his version of the chelengk by examining the original. Among the visitors may have been Simon De Koster, a Dutch artist who had studied under Thomas Gaal at the Middelsburg Academy, settled in London and had become a well-known if not specially fashionable portrait painter with a house in George Street, Adelphi. His portrait of the Prince of Wales had been engraved by S W Reynolds in 1794, that of Prince Frederick Augustus in mezzotint by himself, and others had followed including one of George Manby, the inventor of a mortar apparatus for throwing a line from the shore to a shipwreck. His portrait of Nelson (164; *p.130*), according to James Stow's engraving published a few weeks later, was drawn from the life on 8 December 1800; according to De Koster himself it was done at Merton for Lady Hamilton 'a few days before he sailed for Denmark', though De Koster, recalling the sitting many years afterwards, was mistaken about Merton which was not bought until the autumn of the following year.[18] A copy, possibly by John Whichelo, had on the back of the frame a paper inscribed: 'This is a very accurate copy from a Sketch taken by an eminent artist while His Lordship sat at a public dinner in London...,'[19] Nelson himself certainly seems to have liked it best of all his many portraits and gave a copy of one of the engravings to his ADC, Captain (later Major-General) Peter Fyers, after Copenhagen, remarking that he thought it a better likeness than any other.[20] This is confirmed by a letter he sent to another admirer, Thomas Forsyth in February 1802 - 'I rather think a little outline of the head sold at Brydon's Charing + is the most like me.[21]

Lady Hamilton had another copy made of the drawing but Nelson's friends did not think it as good as the first, and De Koster himself said all subsequent copies, both paintings and prints, were made from this first drawing. Lady Hamilton produced her copy, from a locket round her neck (165; *p.164*), when the profile for the Trafalgar medal was being discussed and Nelson's opinion was confirmed by Sir William Beechey at that time. De Koster's original drawing was borrowed for a fortnight and taken to Harley Street where Beechey magnanimously declared it to be 'the most correct likeness he had ever seen', superior even to his own. Nelson's chaplain agreed: 'he (Scott) repeatedly assured me', says Tuffin,

Pencil drawing by Simon De Koster, 1800, (164)

Oil by Simon De Koster, (167)

'it is the strongest likeness ever taken of him & that the next to it is Hoppner's picture'.[22] One unfinished copy, now at Greenwich, was made for Nelson's sister Susannah; a miniature copy, now in the Norwich Castle Museum, hangs in a walnut case with others of Mr and Mrs Maurice Nelson, his other brother William later first Earl Nelson, and a gentleman of the Nisbet family; an 'improved' copy in pastel in the Scottish National Portrait Gallery is adorned with cocked hat, chelengk, and stars of the Bath, Crescent and St Ferdinand; a silhouette painted on plaster by John Miers, with gold contours added by Field, is in the Peyer Collection of silhouettes in the British Museum, clearly based on De Koster's drawing; Whichelo's profile, done at Merton in September 1805, undoubtedly owes quite a bit to De Koster; and on his own admission Tassie used one of the engravings for the medallions and brooches on which he was working to satisfy the immense demand after Trafalgar (220; *p.153*). A black chalk copy by B. R. Haydon at Tyninghame (Earl of Haddington) is signed and dated 1843 and inscribed with an appropriate line from one of the Chorus speeches in Shakespeare's 'Henry V': *NELSON / a little body with a Mighty Heart.*

Two other artists managed to get sittings at this time, the wax-modeller Catherine Andras and her adoptive father, the miniaturist Thomas Bowyer. Bowyer had been a pupil of John Smart and a regular exhibitor at the Free Society and the Royal Academy from 1782. He succeeded Meyer as miniature painter to the Royal Family in 1789 and painted the Duke of Clarence in about 1797.[23] The Duke had given away the bride at Nelson's wedding in the West Indies, the register being signed with the princely 'William' and he may well have recommended Bowyer as an artist to be trusted.

A relevant piece of information was given by a descendant of the miniaturist, Charlotte Wolstencroft of Cambridge, in a letter to *The Times* during a correspondence about the Nelson portraiture begun by Professor Callender.[24] 'I have in manuscript', she writes, 'some reminiscences of Robert Bowyer, his home and work, told by my grandmother, who was a niece and adopted daughter of Mr and Mrs Bowyer. In these reminiscences there are references to two portraits of Lord Nelson which may throw light on the subject. The first refers to the early days of Mr Bowyer's career as a portrait painter, when he had received a diploma from George III which aided his profession by introducing him to many distinguished characters, and about this time he painted Lord Nelson

Detail from line engraving by W. H.Worthington after Bowyer, 1808 (see p.253)

and all the Lords of the Admiralty'.[25] Bowyer's diploma was the result of his miniature of the Marchioness of Salisbury, painted in 1789 and so pleasing to the King that 'unsolicited he sent him a diploma conferring on him the honour of being his own miniature painter on which occasion he was presented at Court in his bag wig and robe'.[26] Bowyer's portraits of the Admiralty Lords are scattered in various collections but assembled in Smirke's triumphant engravings of the Naval Victors published by Bowyer himself in 1803. The miniature of Nelson has lately been located in the Royal Collection at Windsor Castle[27] (175; *p.138*). It was formerly only known from Smirke's Naval Victors and from engravings published after Trafalgar. The best of these, by Edward Scriven (see *opposite*), published in December 1805, shows the oval miniature set amid storm clouds and the smoke of battle (possibly even intended to represent the explosion of *L'Orient* in Aboukir Bay) an uroboros above, a naval engagement below. The whole print is intended as a posthumous glorification of the national hero, published a month before the state funeral held on 8/9 January 1806. The portrait shows Nelson in rear-admiral's undress uniform wearing the riband and Star of the Bath and no other decorations except for one Naval gold medal. The hair is dishevelled and brushed forwards to hide the Nile scar, a certain indication that the miniature was painted late in 1800, though the omission of the Nile medals and the Turkish and Sicilian Orders can only be ascribed to artistic licence on the part of Bowyer himself.

Shortly before Trafalgar Bowyer was able to paint a second portrait of Nelson, treated in the next chapter together with the famous wax profile by Bowyer's niece, Catherine Andras. But meanwhile Catherine Andras had modelled an earlier wax profile probably at the same sitting that Nelson gave to her uncle. Catherine Andras began her wax modelling career in Bristol making dolls in 'coloured wax elaborately finished with eyelashes and eyebrows of the finest hair or fur'. Lady Dorothy Neville says she probably perfected her technique under James Tassie.[28] Among her early subjects were John Wesley and the Polish General Kosciuszko, and in order to have an engraving made of the Polish General she came to London to seek the professional help of her uncle Robert Bowyer. Mr and Mrs Bowyer had her to stay and became so taken with the seventeen year old girl's 'peculiarly lovely appearance and gentle refinement of manners' that she remained with them for the rest of their lives - nearly forty years.[29] Her first exhibit at the Royal Academy was a wax portrait of Bowyer himself in 1799. Princess Charlotte, then a child

Line engraving by E. Scriven, after Bowyer, 1805, (175)

of five, was brought to her studio in 1800, and she had the sitting from Nelson probably in December. For these two models, 'Her Royal Highness Princess Charlotte and Lord Nelson, taken from Life', she was awarded the Greater Silver Pallet by the Royal Society of Arts which had first considered her entries in March 1801.[30] The wax of Nelson was exhibited at the Royal Academy of 1801 in a frame containing portraits of Nelson's agent Alexander Davison, Dr Webster and a lady, all of which have now disappeared.[31] The profile would have shown Nelson as rear-admiral, with a single crown on the shoulder-strap. A crude wax at Stanton Harcourt, sometimes tentatively ascribed to Catherine Andras but surely not of Nelson himself, has been claimed as the missing portrait for which she was awarded the Silver Pallet.

Coade Stone was an interesting and important accompaniment to the development of late Georgian architecture, being a substance pliable in its early stages and with the great advantage of being resistant to fairly rigorous weather conditions. Its first market name was 'Coade Stone' or sometimes 'Mrs Coade's Stone', after Eleanor Coade who had set up business in Lambeth in 1769. It was also for a time called 'Lithodipyra' in explanation of the fact that part of the ingredients had been twice fired and then moulded into shape. Her products - urns, keystones, voussoirs, capitals, pedestals, friezes, river-gods, mermaids and so on - were supplied to the architects of the day, Adam, Chambers, Capability Brown, Soane and Nash, all using them copiously. Mrs Coade published lists and catalogues of her wares in 1784 and 1799 and these included a quantity of busts for both indoor and outdoor use, sometimes covered with a special coat of greenish-black paint known as 'bronzing'. They were intended either for use in gardens or on building façades, or as library busts, among the 1784 group being copies of the Wedgwood busts of Homer, Cicero, Marcus Aurelius and Antoninus Pius among the classics, and Queen Elizabeth, Matthew Prior and Lord Chatham for the moderns. The 1799 list included the Reverend Rowland Hill, George III, the Dukes of York and Clarence, Mrs Siddons as Ophelia and the connoisseur Dr Mead. They usually cost five guineas each and subscriptions were collected at the Lambeth Gallery. The busts were delivered when orders amounted to fifty or more. Mrs Coade, like Wedgwood, employed the best sculptors, men like John Bacon senior, Panzetta, Bubb, Flaxman, De Vaere, Rossi, and John Sealy who became her partner in 1783. Nelson was a favourite subject and it is interesting to note that at least four of the sculptors named above at one time or another did make busts of Nelson. Eleanor Coade was certainly among the Nelson admirers; 'he is better represented among the Coade firm's works than anyone else'.[32]

Moulds have not been discovered but at least four Coade Stone busts of Nelson exist, one found lately in a private collection near Dorking (177; *p.255*). It is clearly dated 1800 and shows Nelson in rear-admiral's full-dress uniform with the usual medals and orders including Davison's gold medal for the Nile. The sculptor is not known though it derives distantly, especially in the treatment of the uniform and Orders, from the Thaller and Ranson bust made in Vienna. The rather dismal expression of sombre gloom is akin to Mrs Damer's Guildhall bust, but Mrs Damer, being both vociferous and articulate, is unlikely to have let slip an opportunity to inform the world of an achievement of this magnitude. John Flaxman is another possibility. His more heroic effigy in St Paul's Cathedral has an affinity with this bust but here again there is no record among the Flaxman papers and numerous sketches and drawings. Catherine Andras's background was Nonconformist, as was Mrs Coade's, and for this reason co-operation was a likely possibility.[33] There is a distinct similarity between her wax profile of 1805 (190; *p.151*) and the Coade Stone bust. Another possibility is Joseph Panzetta, a pupil of Joseph Wilton and a constant supplier of stone work for Mrs Coade, including, after Nelson's death, the statue in Montreal and the Nelson pediment at the Royal Naval College, Greenwich.

There was time for one more portrait before the Battle of Copenhagen. On 18 January, amid cheers from ships anchored nearby, Nelson hoisted his flag in the *San Josef* off Plymouth, with Hardy as his captain. They transferred to the *St George* a fortnight later, and apart from a flying visit to see his newly-born Horatia, every moment was consumed in preparations for the Baltic campaign. When Nelson joined Admiral Sir Hyde Parker in Yarmouth Roads on 6 March, in his innocence he expected to sail immediately. He was not aware however that Parker had lately married again and was in no hurry to leave the shelter of Yarmouth for the cold east winds of the Danish waters. 'Consider how nice it must be', he wrote impatiently to Troubridge, 'laying in bed with a young wife, compared to a damned cold raw wind.'

Within a few days a sharp note arrived from the Admiralty ordering the Fleet to sea, but during that time Nelson gave sittings to Matthew

Miniature by Robert Bowyer, 1800, (175)

Above: Oil painting by Simon De Koster , (173)

Below: Miniature after De Koster by unknown artist, (174)

Keymer, the local artist who had copied the Guzzardi portrait after Nelson's arrival there in November 1800 (see p. 84). Keymer had already decided that Guzzardi's strange portrait did not do justice to the Hero and asked for sittings for a portrait of his own. Nelson, impatient but at a loose end, obliged and two of the sittings were witnessed in the Wrestlers' Arms by a Yarmouth silversmith, Samuel Higham Aldred, who 'continued to speak of this unforgettable experience to the end of his days'. Keymer's portrait was never engraved so it did not achieve a more than local publicity, but Charles Palmer, a Norfolk solicitor and antiquary, considered it 'a capital likeness' and recorded Aldred's evidence in his *Perlustration of Great Yarmouth*.[34] (181; *p.86*) Today not even the most dedicated East Anglian would claim it as an inspired image and indeed one is astonished that so heavy-handed an artist could have managed as accurate a copy of the Guzzardi portrait as we see in John Young's mezzotint. Wooden and stolid it may be but it does carry an air of misgiving absent from the 'state portraits' by Abbott, Beechey and Hoppner, where the Admiral is shown self-confident and heroic. Quite apart from the irritating suspense caused by Parker's procrastination and indecision, and apart from the knowledge that his marriage was wrecked, Nelson was a sick man. He complained frequently of pains and illness. He had been severely wounded four times. His eyesight was a constant worry and only a few weeks earlier he had written to St Vincent to say that his eyes were so bad that he could scarcely see anything. St Vincent was not too sympathetic. 'Nelson was very low when he first came here the day before yesterday', he wrote to Nepean. 'Poor man! he is devoured with vanity, weakness and folly; was strung with ribbons, medals, &c and yet pretended that he wished to avoid the honour and ceremonies he everywhere met with upon the road...'[35] Nelson himself wrote more fully to Lady Hamilton:

> My eye is very bad. I have had the physician of the Fleet to examine it. He has directed me not to write (and yet I am forced this day to write to Lord Spencer, St Vincent, Davison about my lawsuit, Troubridge, Mr Locker, etc. but you are the only female I write to), not to eat anything but the most simple food; not to touch wine or porter; to sit in a dark room; to have green shades for my eyes - (will you, my dear friend, make me one or two? Nobody else shall) - and to bathe them in cold water every hour. I fear it is the writing has brought on this complaint. My eye is like blood; and the film so extended that I only see from the corner farthest from my nose.[36]

He ends this letter (where the green shade is mentioned for the first time) with the characteristic words, 'What a fuss about my complaints!', but he was clearly suffering from strain and, in the psychologist's jargon, from 'effort syndrome' caused by long years of working and living beyond his physical capacity. All this is reflected in Keymer's unfamiliar figure which may indeed have been a 'capital likeness' (181; *p.86*).

After Trafalgar Keymer presented the portrait to the Yarmouth Society of Friends who provided the frame surmounted by cannons, flags and three wreaths of bay and oak leaves. The gift is recorded in the Society's Minutes for 16 January 1806. The Society of Friends was disbanded in about 1807 and shortly afterwards the portrait was acquired by Great Yarmouth itself and hung in the Town Hall.[37] A small copy of it, by Charles Hayter, was intended for a miniature but never got further than a watercolour drawing on tracing paper (182).

NOTES TO CHAPTER 6, STATE PORTRAITS

1. Rowlandson's drawing is reproduced in Pocock 1968, p. 86, and Hattersley 1974 (full-page spread). Curiously enough The Hero appears to have his right arm intact, his left in a sling, and to be walking the plank.

2. *Annual Register*, Chronicle 10 November 1800.

3. Lady Elizabeth Foster's Journal, 14 February 1801, cit. D.M. Stuart, *Dearest Bess* (1955), p. 90.

4. Letter from Lady Nelson, St James's Street, 4 March 1800 (Naish 1958, p.552).

5. Trafalgar House Inventory no.6, and NMM no.BHC2881.

6. Norwich Chamberlain's Accounts for the year Michaelmas 1800-01, kindly sent to me by Mr R. Bamford of the City Hall, Norwich.

7. Whitley III, p. 22 cit. a contemporary newspaper.

8. *The Athenaeum*, 8 January 1853, p. 50.

9. *The Quarterly Review* XCII (1853), p. 469, in a long article on Apsley House, newly opened to the public.

10. Alaric Watts in *Cabinet of Modern Art*, p.102, cit. Roberts 1907, pp. 75-6, and possibly the battle-stained cocked hat now in the Castle Museum, Norwich, presented by Mrs P.E. Baker.

11. Letter to Lady Nelson, *Agamemnon* 18 August 1794 (Naish 1958, p.119).

12. Walker 1985/2, p. 363.

13. Farington 14 August 1797; *Northcote* 1901, pp.151-2.

14. Millar 1969, pp. xxxi, 54, 104.

15. *Northcote* 1901, p.190.

16. Dr Alexander Scott in conversation with J.F. Tufton (Pollard 1970, pp. 305, 308).

17. Connell 1957, p. 440.

18. See Elizabeth Maudsley's note on the back of the original drawing, (see p. 248); this can scarcely be accurate as the purchase deeds for Merton Place are dated 18 September 1801.

19. PRO Warner file B, with transcript in NMM 35-18.

20. Letter from Fyers's grandson, Major E.W.H. Fyers, in *The Times* 5 November 1932.

21. Nelson's letter to Thomas Forsyth, (see p. 248).

22. Letters from J.F. Tuffin to Matthew Boulton, 17 and 26 January 1806 (Pollard 1970, pp. 305, 308).

23. Exh RA 1797. Article by Walter Hepworth in *DNB*, and Foskett 1987, pp.310, 497.

24. *The Times* 29 October to 19 November 1932.

25. *Bowyer Memorials*, (see Abbreviations p. 293).

26. Ibid. p. 2. Bowyer's miniature of Lady Salisbury, at Hatfield, was engraved by Caroline Watson and published by Bowyer himself in January 1790.

27. Walker 1992, pp. 315-6.

28. Lady Dorothy Neville, *Reminiscences* (1906), p. 244.

29. *Bowyer Memorials* pp. 4-6.

30. RSA Committee of Polite Arts, 13 March 1801, pp.166, 168 (MS in RSA library); *Transactions of the Society of Arts* XIX (1801), p. 376.

31. RA Catalogue 1801 (1030).

32. Kelly 1990, pp.139-40.

33. Mrs Coade, a native of Lyme Regis, is known to have been a passionate dissenter and, as she was buried in Bunhill Fields, probably a Baptist. Catherine Andras spent most of her life with Mr and Mrs Bowyer, both ardent Baptists with an Evangelical school of their own at Byfleet.

34. Palmer 1872, I p. 363.

35. St Vincent to Nepean, 17 January 1801 (*Naval Miscellany* II (1912) p. 332).

36. Letter to Lady Hamilton, 28 January 1801 (Nicolas IV, p. 279).

37. Oliver Warner in 'An Unrecorded Nelson Portrait', (*Mariner's Mirror* XLIV (1958), p. 75), describes a portrait he attributes to Matthew Keymer belonging to Captain Cooper. This is in fact a memorial variant *c.*1905 of a portrait at Greenwich (BHC2899) and was sold at Sotheby's 19 November 1969 (Lot 43). Neither of these has the remotest connection with Keymer's Yarmouth portrait, which is discussed at some length by Callender in *The Times*, 21 October 1930.

Oil by John Rising, 1801, (184)

144

7 AFTER COPENHAGEN

Nelson arrived back in Yarmouth on 1 July 1801 and remained ashore, except for special service in the Channel, until the declaration of war in May 1803 and his appointment as Commander in Chief Mediterranean. A. C. Gow's famous picture of the Vice-Admiral descending the steps at the Sally Port, Portsmouth, leaving England for the last time, was painted almost exactly a hundred years later and is therefore outside the scope of this work.[1] Over two years elapsed during the interval between these events but although there must have been innumerable opportunities for sittings there were in fact very few, and of these none of the results is very striking. Possibly the least interesting of all the Nelson iconography was perpetrated by John Rising shortly after his arrival home from the Baltic. Rising had an unenterprising but extensive portrait practice in London, among his former subjects being Admiral Marriott Arbuthnot, distinguished mainly for his lower deck language, and the Right Hon. Henry Dundas, Treasurer of the Navy for over seventeen years, responsible for protecting the simple seamen from land-sharks by forming a system of regular payments to their families, but known to a wider public as Viscount Melville, impeached by the House of Lords for embezzlement of public funds. Rising's portrait of Nelson, signed and dated 1801, is at Greenwich (184; *opposite*). It is almost inconceivable that the artist even set eyes on his subject let alone had a sitting. Despite the naked sword and lurid backgrounds it is hard to imagine this anaemic figure resolving on the destruction of the Russian Fleet in the Baltic.

An even more feeble image is the chalk drawing by John Downman, inscribed coyly:

> HORATIO NELSON 1802
> Admiral Lord Nelson of the Nile,
> Who conquered foes with wondrous spoil.

Downman is said to have known the Hamiltons in Rome when he was a young man though no portrait by him is known either of Sir William or Lady Hamilton. It is quite possible that Downman might have come to Merton early in 1802 when Hamilton was ill there and before he moved to London to die in his own house. Williamson however says that Nelson visited Downman's house in Piccadilly shortly before the artist's departure for Kent in 1804 though he gives no authority for this statement.[2]

There seems therefore no particular reason to doubt the date 1802 inscribed on the back of the picture. Downman's drawing, idealised almost beyond recognition, achieves 'a faint fragrance of character exactly suited to his almost evanescent medium';[3] but it must be admitted it adds very little of value to the Nelson iconography (186; *opposite*).

In October 1801 Nelson had written to the prime minister to say the Order of St Joachim wished to nominate him a Knight Grand Commander.[4] The King's permission for him to receive the honour was granted in February 1802;[5] and the Insignia of the Order arrived at Merton in June. Nelson's letter of thanks tells the Grand Master he was actually wearing it.[6] It consisted of a moss-green ribbon with a laurelled cross *patée* which can be seen as the lowest of the Stars on the coat worn by Nelson's effigy in Westminster Abbey (214; *p.168*).[7]

The Order of St Joachim can also be seen in the drawing by Edridge in the National Portrait Gallery (187; *p.149*), probably done at Merton when Nelson and the Hamiltons had returned from their tour of the West Country. Henry Edridge painted Nelson on two occasions. The first after the Santa Cruz action during his recuperation in the Bond Street lodging late in 1797. This was commissioned by Sir Henry Englefield, exhibited at the Royal Academy in 1798, and is described on pages 17 and 20 (5; *p.21*). The second was drawn in 1802 and is National Portrait Gallery number 879. This drawing originated with a letter from Richard Bulkeley, an old comrade from the Nicaraguan expedition of 1780, who wrote to Nelson on Christmas Eve 1801 asking him to sit for Edridge - 'two sittings will be sufficient if you have patience to sit an hour each time, and *three* if you can't confine yourself to a chair for such a length of time in one day...'[8] The request was successful and the next record appears in Farington's *Diary*, 6 August 1802, noting Edridge's presence at Merton with the Hamiltons and Nelson himself. Presumably the drawing was made then but by the end of August Bulkeley was complaining that he had not received it. 'Sir, My Lord Nelson who is with me, has expressed surprise at not finding the excellent portrait which you have been, so successful in, and he apprehends that you have mislaid my address...'[9] It is not known whether this well-worn device for dunning an artist was successful and whether Bulkeley ever received his drawing. Edridge, who often made copies of his work, usually kept the original as a master-copy, and the National Portrait Gallery drawing, which has descended from his studio through the artist's family, is almost certain to be one of these master-copies. Several

Chalk drawing by John Downman, 1802, (186)

versions are known to exist and the delay in dispatching Bulkeley's copy was probably due to the original being in the hands of Anthony Cardon for engraving.[10]

Shortly before Trafalgar, George Rose 'entreated' Nelson to sit again to Edridge which Nelson promised to do 'if he were not ordered to sea *very very* soon'. On writing to Edridge later on Rose learned that a sitting had not been managed. He then wrote to Lady Hamilton asking if he could borrow one of hers to be copied. In a dramatic postscript he added, 'I have this instant a letter from my incomparable & ever to be lamented Friend, in which (when he was hourly expecting the action) he says "I verily believe the Country will soon be put to some expense on my account, either a monument or a new pension"'.[11] Rose may not have had his drawing, but he did get something far more precious, one of Nelson's last letters written on the eve of Trafalgar.

Another admirer of Nelson, his biographer Robert Southey, was more fortunate and had his own portrait taken by Edridge in 1804. Shortly afterwards, Lady Nelson herself was drawn by Edridge, sitting in a chair with Trafalgar legs and with the Thaller and Ranson bust on a table beside her (see *p.xiv*). It came from an album originally in the Locker family possession and probably at one time belonged to Edward Hawke Locker, a son of the Captain and founder of the Naval Picture Gallery at Greenwich Hospital.[12]

By this time Nelson's health had seriously deteriorated and only his indomitable spirit kept him going. In a letter to an old friend, Robert Kingsmill, he wrote:

> I am sorry to tell you that my health, or rather constitution, is so much shook that I doubt the possibility of my holding out another winter... but my dear Kingsmill, when I run over the undermentioned wounds - Eye in Corsica, Belly off Cape St Vincent, Arm at Teneriffe, Head in Egypt - I ought to be thankful that I am what I am...[13]

However, Emma had transformed 'Paradise Merton' into a shrine. Visitors were astonished, even disgusted: 'the whole house, staircase and all, are covered with nothing but pictures of her and him, of all sizes and sorts... an excess of vanity which counteracts its own purpose'[14]

Time was now running short but there was space for three more portraits, a miniature by Bowyer, a wax profile by his adopted daughter Catherine Andras, and a small but significant drawing by Whichelo. Bowyer has already appeared in the Nelson canon with a miniature

Pencil and watercolour drawing by Henry Edridge, 1802, (187)

149

painted for Smirke's *Naval Victors* (175; *p.138*). The *Bowyer Memorials* mention a second portrait, rather confusingly placed among the royal family and a number of distinguished subjects - 'Lord John Russell, William Wilberforce, James Watt, Lord Nelson, Lord Brougham and others'. This group was painted from sittings given when Bowyer was over seventy, had taken up painting after a long interval devoted to philanthropic work, and had to have 'recourse to both spectacles and eyeglass'.[15] Nelson of course was long since dead but the date of this particular sitting was indicated in a paragraph in the *Monthly Magazine* for January 1806:

> From Mr Bowyer's last Advertisement it appears that he is in possession of a miniature picture of Lord Nelson for which his Lordship sat to him at a very recent period and which the dearest friends of Lord Nelson have uniformly declared to be the most correct likeness of his Lordship ever painted. Of testimonials of this fact, should they be wanting, Mr Bowyer has abundance to produce.[16]

The words 'at a very recent period' presumably mean shortly before Trafalgar, the only available time after his two years' service at sea, being August and September 1805. Nelson landed at Spithead on 18 August, spent his few weeks' leave either at Merton or in London, and boarded the *Victory* for the last time on 14 September. This was about the time when George Rose was hoping Nelson would sit to Edridge. Bowyer and Catherine Andras were luckier, enjoying a sitting together which occasioned another of Nelson's few recorded jokes, faithfully entered in the *Bowyer Memorials*:

> When Miss Andras was working at the medallion of the Hero, the celebrated miniature painter Robert Bowyer happened to be painting the other side of the great Admiral's face, upon which Nelson laughingly remarked that he was not used to being attacked in that manner starboard and larboard at the same time.[17]

Catherine Andras's medallion became an immediate success (190; *opposite*). Bowyer's miniature is missing but, like the first, it can be reconstructed from engravings, the first published in 1809 to celebrate the fourth anniversary of Trafalgar, the second in 1823 to illustrate Edward Brenton's *Naval History of Great Britain* (see *p.152*). It is very different from Bowyer's earlier portrait. Lord Nelson is now cast in heroic mould, a towering figure with commanding expression, the vice-admiral's full dress uniform decorated with ribbons and stars, though St Joachim is missing and there is still only one Naval gold medal. Nothing can

Wax relief by Catherine Andras, 1805, (190)

Mezzotint by Charles Turner after Bowyer's lost drawing (1809), from Captain Edward Brenton's Naval History of Great Britain *(1823),* (176)

152

replace Abbott's portrait as the definitive image of Lord Nelson but if Bowyer's second miniature were to be found this might provide a very convincing alternative.

Catherine Andras's wax profile proved popular and casts from it are plentiful, some dated 1805 others 1812. Many of them are inscribed on the back 'Portrait of Lord Nelson modelled from the life by Miss Andras Modeller in Wax to Her Majesty 87 Pall Mall Historic Gallery'. Lady Hamilton herself considered it a striking resemblance and strongly recommended it as a basis for Boulton's Trafalgar medal (see pp.167 and 170):

> She showed me the inclosed Wax Profile which she declares is the most striking likeness that has been taken, & much more so than our little drawing or print by Mr Da Costa...[18]

Indeed so successful was Catherine Andras's medallion that the Dean and Chapter of Westminster Abbey commissioned her to make and set up the effigy to act as a counter-attraction to the tomb and funeral-car drawing crowds away from the Abbey to St Paul's Cathedral early in 1806. Tassie's very popular medallion also owes a considerable debt to the Andras profile (220; *right*).

If the Bowyer-Andras sitting took place early in September, a young man was fortunate enough to be given a sitting at about the same time. This was John Whichelo (1784-1865) at the age of twenty-one becoming known as a promising marine artist and probably visiting Merton in that capacity. He had painted a number of harbour scenes, had just published *The Select Views of London,* and was to exhibit a large canvas, 'The Battle of Trafalgar' at the British Institution in 1811. The Whichelos (or Whichellos) were a naval family serving on the lower deck until 1815 and there was an R. M. Whichelo as a clerk aboard *Britannia* at Trafalgar.

Whichelo's drawing is in chalk and shows Nelson in profile to the left with greyish-white hair, a grey eye and leathery weather-beaten skin (195; *p.155*). On the back is a paper written in ink by the artist himself probably many years later: 'This Head was sketched from the Hero, during

Paste medallion by William Tassie, 1805, (220)

153

his short stay at Merton the beginning of September 1805 by me John Whichelo'. Apart from this legend there is no other known reference to his visiting Merton.

The marked similarity between the Whichelo and the De Koster drawing (164; *p.130*) can perhaps be explained by Nelson's known liking for it; but De Koster's portrait had been done five years before and, though doubtless the face had aged in the interval, it was still thought to be one of the best likenesses and certainly a more realistic image than the glamourised 'state portraits' by Abbott, Beechey and Hoppner. Nelson kept the De Koster drawing at home together with the numerous prints which he liked to give away as presents; he probably encouraged the young Whichelo to produce something similar. He was killed at Trafalgar a few weeks later and Whichelo kept the drawing for over thirty years - a marvellous relic of a memorable day at Merton in 1805. In 1838 Whichelo agreed to give drawing lessons to the son of one of Nelson's old shipmates, Admiral Sir William Parker. On the day of the first lesson he sent the drawing as a gift accompanied by the following letter:

> 26 Charles Street, St James's Sq^{re} 5th July 1838
>
> Mr Whichelo most respectfully begs to send Sir Wm Parker the Head of the Late Illustrious Nelson. Drawn by him from the Hero during his short stay at Merton the beginning of September 1805 - & trusts Sir Wm Parker will approve the simplicity of the Frame.
> Mr Whichelo will do himself the pleasure of waiting upon Sir W^m this evening relative to beginning his Lessons to Mast^r Parker should it be required-
>
> To Rear Adm' Sir Wm Parker K.C.B.   Admiralty.[19]

The drawing became a treasured possession in the Parker family and was used some years later as a model for a bust by Joseph Pitts, reproduced in parian marble with the incision: *JOS^h. PITTS. Sc / LONDON / 1853 / Model^d under the direction of / Admiral Sir William Parker K.C.B. / from the Painting by Whichell in his possession.* The busts were published and proved extremely popular (238; *p181*). Polychrome versions bear the same inscription. They were intended to form a pair with a similar parian marble bust of Wellington published the previous year. Curiously enough, in spite of the legend, there is very little resemblance between these busts and Whichelo's drawing. Flaxman's posthumous bust has a closer relevance.

The name 'Whichelo' is said to be the subject of another of Nelson's scarce jokes. In 1913 there was a correspondence in *The Observer* about

Chalk drawing by John Whichelo, 1805, (195)

155

this unusual name and containing a letter from F. Whichelo which ends: 'There is a story in the family that the two ls were reduced to one as the result of a characteristic comment by Nelson - that one l was good enough for him and should be for anyone else'.[20]

Whichelo's drawing was the last serious portrait of Nelson before Trafalgar. But there was time for one more sketch, a moving and evocative drawing, possibly by one of Nelson's fellow officers, showing the great commander explaining his plan of attack in the state cabin of the *Victory* at a birthday party on 29 September, a few weeks before the actual battle (196; *p.261*). Nelson wears the uniform cocked hat; the captains, bareheaded, surround him in various attitudes of comprehension and admiration. Nelson described the occasion in one of his last letters to Emma: 'When I came to explain to them the *'Nelson touch'* it was like an electric shock. Some shed tears, all approved - "It was new - it was singular - it was simple!" and, from the admirals downwards, it was repeated - "It must succeed, if ever they will allow us to get at them! You are, my Lord, surrounded by friends whom you inspire with confidence".[21] Not much is known at present about this drawing. It was probably done on the spot, or immediately afterwards from memory, by one of the captains, then worked up by William Marshall Craig, a miniature painter who did portraits of George III, Queen Charlotte and several of the princes and princesses. Coloured engravings of it by J. Godby, were published by Edward Orme in January 1806 with a key naming 'the GALLANT HEROES who Commanded on the 21ˢᵗ Octʳ 1805'.[22]

NOTES TO CHAPTER 7, AFTER COPENHAGEN

1. Gow's *Sally Port* (Royal Exchange Collection) reproduced in colour, Hattersley p.177.

2. G.C.Williamson, *John Downman* A.R.A. (1907) xxix, where the author also says that the drawing was exhibited at the Royal Academy seven years later; there is no trace of it in the RA catalogues.

3. Downman's style of portraiture is neatly summarised in Waterhouse 1953, pp. 232-3.

4. Letter from Nelson to Addington, *Amazon* 13 October 1801 (Nicolas IV, p.510).

5. Letter from Nelson to Baron von Eiker und Ekoffen, Merton 22 February 1801 (Pettigrew 1849, II p.665); *London Gazette* 15 July 1802.

6. Letter from Nelson to Graf von Leiningen-Westerburg, Merton 9 June 1802 (Pettigrew II, p. 666.)

7. The Order of St Joachim seems to have been a mystery in England, sometimes credited to Leiningen, sometimes to Sardinia or Malta. P.W. Tomkins gets the title right but puts the date at 3 April 1798 (memorial print 21 November 1805), and in another large memorial print, written and engraved by J. Girtin and published by Ackermann 24 December 1805, Nelson is credited as 'Knight of the Maltese Order of St Joachim'. The Order was founded in 1755 by a group of Bohemian noblemen in emulation of religious associations like the Knights of Malta and the Teutonic Order, but later fell into disrepute and was forbidden by the Tsar and other monarchs. The principal authority is Levett Hanson, *An Accurate Historical Account of all the Orders of Knighthood at present existing in Europe* (1803) I, pp. 32 ff. but I also acknowledge help on the subject from the late Hugh Murray Baillie.

8. Letter from Bulkeley to Nelson, 24 December 1801 (Morrison 1893-4, II p.181).

9. Letter from Bulkeley in Ludlow to Edridge, 63 Margaret St. London, 29 August 1802 (MS in library of City Museum and Art Gallery, Stoke on Trent).

10. Cardon's stipple engraving was published in 1802 and again, for Clarke & M'Arthur, in 1810.

11. Letter from Nelson to George Rose passed on to Lady Hamilton, 17 November 1805 (Morrison 1893-4, II pp.271-2).

12. Details of the Locker family album are in Christie's catalogue, 4 June 1974 (9-16). McCarthy 1995, p.34, no.3 and colour plate p.116.

13. Letter to Admiral Sir Robert Kingsmill, 4 August 1804 (Nicolas VI, p.134).

14. Letter from Lord Minto, 22 March 1802 (Minto 1874, III p.242).

15. *Bowyer Memorials*, p.17.

16. *Monthly Magazine* January 1806, cit. Robinson 1930, p.327.

17. *Bowyer Memorials*, p.27.

18. Letter from Tuffin to Matthew Boulton, 26 February 1806 (Pollard 1970, p.307).

19. Wichelo's letter to Sir William Parker is pasted on the backboard of the picture; copy in NMM archive.

20. An extract from *The Observer*, 1 October 1913, was sent by Percy Whichelo to Sir William Parker of Llangattock on 1 May 1950. I am grateful to the late Sir Alan Parker for the loan of his family papers and for allowing me to borrow the drawing itself.

21. Letter to Emma Hamilton, 1 October 1805 (Nicolas VII, p.60).

22. Nelson's plan of attack was first propounded to Captain Richard Keats at Merton, shortly before his final departure from the Sally Steps at Portsmouth. It was explained to the captains at two meetings immediately after his arrival with the Fleet and formally issued in a secret memorandum on 9 October. The tactics are brilliantly described by the late Oliver Warner in *Trafalgar* (1959).

Detail of 'The Death of Nelson' by A W Devis, 1807 (see p. 265)

158

8 AFTER TRAFALGAR

The day after the Battle of Trafalgar Nelson's body was examined superficially by the *Victory* surgeon, Dr William Beatty, the musket ball that had killed him located near the spine but not extracted, the hair cut off and his body stripped to the shirt.[1] A leaguer, the largest cask on board, was prepared for the body and filled with brandy, replaced with spirit of wine when the ship made Gibraltar on 28 October after four days of violent gales. The spirit was drawn off several times on the way home and refilled, though on one occasion 'there was a disengagement of air from the Body to such a degree that the sentinel became alarmed on seeing the head of the cask raised' and the leaguer had to be spiked. The voyage to England took nearly five weeks, the *Victory* with the Vice-Admiral's flag and the White Ensign at half-mast anchoring at Spithead on 4 December, though the news had arrived in London exactly a month before. The newspapers had of course been full of lurid and inaccurate accounts of the victory, though most reports echoed Lieutenant Lapenotière, the captain of the schooner *Pickle* bearing the dispatches, whose laconic words, 'we have won a great victory but lost Lord Nelson', were more eloquent than all the panegyrics and funeral orations that were to follow.

A more practical step however was taken by Josiah Boydell with an advertisement for a picture of 'The Death of Nelson', the prize to be five hundred guineas.[2] The picture was to be engraved and clearly was visualised as a follow-up to Benjamin West's classic 'Death of Wolfe', engraved by Woollett and the source of a fortune for its sponsor, Boydell's uncle John. Benjamin West himself entered the competition and finished the work in six months, taking immense pains to get the details right with first hand information, employing a technical adviser and portraits of the chief actors in the drama, though as far as is known, not actually of the main character himself.[3]

An artist however who took even more trouble was Arthur William Devis.[4] Devis had been taught to paint by his father, Arthur Devis, and specialised in portraits and historical subjects. In 1804 he had been imprisoned for debt but on reading Boydell's advertisement had managed to persuade the King's Bench authorities to give him leave to visit the

Victory at Portsmouth and give him a chance to pay off his creditors. The result of his labours, a vast machine nine feet long, is at Greenwich (211; *opposite, pp.158, 265*) with sketches in the Royal Collection and in the *Victory* herself.[5] Devis arrived on board while the *Victory* was riding at Spithead waiting for orders, introduced himself to the first lieutenant and was given the freedom of the wardroom.[6] He stayed aboard for a week while the Flagship lay at anchor, making drawings of the ship's company and of the cockpit itself, and finally sailing with her up-channel, round the Foreland and into the Thames Estuary to Greenwich. He was on board for about three weeks but it was during the final stage of Nelson's last voyage that Devis was able to paint the portrait. As soon as they sailed out of the Solent Dr Beatty carried out an autopsy. The body was removed from the leaguer of spirits which had preserved it since Gibraltar and found to be in excellent condition and completely plastic, says Beatty. 'The features were somewhat tumid from absorption of the spirit but on using friction with the napkin they resumed in a great degree their natural character.'[7] This was Beatty's account written for publication. In a private memorandum describing embalming details he says 'it will be right to apprise his Lordship that the features of his departed brother cannot at this distant period from his demise be easily traced...'[8] A week later, in a letter to the chaplain, he advised against embalmment because of the danger of the skin coming off the body when the bandages were removed. 'The features being lost', he continued, 'the Face cannot with propriety be exposed during the time which the body may lay in state...'[9] There would have been plenty of witnesses to the condition of the body and without doubt, if it had been at all possible, this would have been the moment for a death mask to be made; but nowhere in any of the memoirs and letters of the time nor in Dr Beatty's meticulous narrative, is such a thing mentioned.

This would also have been the moment for Devis to make his sketches for the portrait which had been commissioned by Beatty himself and was used in a modified form for 'The Death of Nelson'. Indeed the third Earl Nelson states that Beatty, who used to visit him every year until his death in 1842, employed Devis to make him a good likeness 'with hints and by allowing him to see the dead body'.[10] Devis would have had ample opportunity. He assisted at the autopsy and his drawing of the musket ball with pieces of Nelson's coat, gold lace and bullion from the epaulette still attached, was later engraved and used as an illustration in Dr Beatty's *Authentic Narrative of the Death of Nelson*, published two years later. The ball was handed to Hardy who had it set in crystal and silver and

Detail of 'The Death of Nelson' by A. W. Devis, 1807 (see p.265)

gave it back to Beatty as a precious relic and memento of an unforgettable experience. It is now in the Royal Collection at Windsor Castle. Devis would have seen the face with his own eyes and members of the ships company would certainly not have been backward in advising him exactly how their commanding officer wore the hat and green eyeshade. Doubtless many preliminary drawings were made. One such, of the cockpit, is in the National Maritime Museum. An unfinished oil was probably Beatty's own copy, perhaps the first, and used for the frontispiece in his *Authentic Narrative*. Scriven's drawing for this engraving has turned up lately in a private collection in Hampshire (199; *p. 262*). Copies were made for Captain Page, Captain Capel, Lady Hamilton and others, and no doubt Devis kept one himself as a model for future copies. Captain Page's copy, according to the third Earl, is the uninscribed Halliday version (197; *opposite*) but it may be more likely that it was the Mentmore version, a miniature inscribed on the back: *Painted for Captain Page in 1805 by A. W. Devis*, but otherwise lacking any convincing provenance. Captain Bladen Capel's version was last heard of as an engraving illustrating Pettigrew's *Life of Nelson*. Lady Hamilton's version is said to have been lost overboard with a box of Nelson relics on the way to Calais. According to the third Earl she had persuaded Beatty to lend her his original but, not trusting her too far with so precious a possession, he probably lent her a copy dated September 1806 which was later acquired by Joshua Smith's wife, with other Emma relics, and was last seen by Sir George Scharf in 1871 in the house of Mrs Smith's daughter, Princess Gonzago.[11]

Devis's humble little portrait is less unassuming than is apparent at first glance. It is the only contemporary image showing Nelson wearing the green eyeshade recommended by Thomas Trotter, shortly before Copenhagen, to protect his eyes from the glare of the sea. 'My eye is very bad', he wrote to Emma:

> I have had the Physician of the Fleet to examine it. He has directed me not to write ...not to eat anything but the most simple food; not to touch wine or porter; to sit in a dark room; to have green shades for my eyes - (will you, my dear friend, make me one or two? - nobody else shall) - and to bathe them in cold water every hour.[12]

One of the shades, for he had several, can be seen with the undress cocked hat in a case near the effigy in Westminster Abbey.[13] Another interesting point is that the portrait clearly indicates the Star of the Crescent inverted, showing that even Nelson himself was uncertain how it should be worn. The Westminster Abbey uniform coat and the two

Oil by A.W. Devis, 1805, (197)

Pencil and watercolour drawing by Simon De Koster 1800, mounted in a locket that belonged to Emma Hamilton, (165).

It was one of the likenesses used as the model for the Boulton Trafalgar Medal (see opposite).

The Boulton Trafalgar medal, 1805 (obverse), (213)

coats at Greenwich all have the Star sewn on upside down. Devis's portrait confirms that this is how he wore it and there is no question of a Victorian repairer having sewn it on wrongly to deceive posterity.

It is not difficult to imagine Devis at his gruesome task as assistant at the autopsy. In his portraits of Nelson there is a livid colouring and a cadaverous air of decay that conforms closely to Beatty's vivid description in the *Authentic Narrative* and his misgivings to Scott. Devis has transferred this with great effect to 'The Death of Nelson' (211; *p.158*) which for this reason gains immeasurably over West's interpretation. West, as President of the Royal Academy and champion of a bygone tradition, set out to paint the scene as an epic composition, an evocation 'of what might have been, not of the circumstances as they happened'.[14] Devis, from his more lowly position as a debtor released on sufferance from the King's Bench, took a more realistic standpoint. He told Farington, when the work was finished in 1807, of the 'care he had taken in painting the death of the Hero to represent everything faithfully'.[15]

Devis's portrait was interesting as *memento mori* and attained a fairly wide circulation through copies and through Scriven's engraving, but a more heroic effigy was needed. News of a great Naval victory over the combined French and Spanish Fleets at Trafalgar had arrived at the Admiralty early in the morning of 6 November, a month before the autopsy. The Prime Minister had been unable to go back to bed on hearing it. It had meant release from the menace of invasion by Napoleon's armies mobilised along the Channel coast. Public rejoicing was ecstatic and promotion in the Fleet was speedily recorded in the *London Gazette*, Collingwood to Vice-Admiral of the Red, Northesk to Rear-Admiral of the Red, Captains Harvey and Grindall of the *Temeraire* and the *Prince* were awarded their Flags, and other officers were promoted. As at the Battle of the Nile Naval gold medals were awarded to flag officers and captains of ships (and to the two lieutenants commanding *Ajax* and *Thunderer*.[16] Collingwood's portrait by Charles Lonsdell in the Mansion House, Newcastle-on-Tyne, shows him wearing the three Naval gold medals for St Vincent, the Nile and Trafalgar.

However the injustice of this award was resented by junior officers and ratings who very reasonably considered that their share in the triumph should also be recognised. This feeling was appreciated by Matthew Boulton of the Soho Mint, Birmingham, who announced in the newspapers in December his intention to bestow medals on all seamen and marines who had served in the action, eventually calculated at some

14,000 in all. As Davison had previously done for his Nile medal, Boulton approached Conrad Küchler for the design, though many hands were employed and several sources drawn on for the final production. The profile of Nelson himself seems to have presented the greatest difficulty, at least three attempts being made[17] (213; *p.165*).

The first attempt involved the help of Sir William Beechey. Lady Beechey, no inconsiderable artist herself, had provided the original drawing as a basis for Küchler to work on. She had seen and talked to Nelson shortly before he sailed on his last voyage in September, perhaps saying goodbye to his godson, and had noticed how much plumper and younger he looked than when he had sat to her husband during the winter of 1800-01 for the Norwich portrait (137; *p.123*). Beechey himself said that 'his cheek had rather an Infantine plumpness at this time'. Besides her own observation of her subject Lady Beechey had used a 'Busto' from the Royal Collection (probably one of the Thaller & Ransons),[18] one of Beechey's own portraits (possibly the sketch in the National Portrait Gallery), and one of the Hoppner portraits or perhaps more likely Meyer's stipple engraving published in November (Charles Turner's mezzotint did not appear till January 1806). Lady Beechey's effort was shown to Nelson's family and to Lady Hamilton for their comments. They all rejected it immediately.[19]

Küchler's second attempt was based on the De Koster drawing of 8 December 1800 (164; *p.130*). This was suggested by Lady Hamilton who produced a copy from a gold locket in her bosom (165; *p.164*) saying 'it was the best likeness ever taken from him'. The original drawing was borrowed from the artist himself and shown to Beechey who instantly pronounced it to be 'in all respects better than Lady Beechey's drawing'. But Küchler's efforts to convert it into a medal profile were equally condemned. Lady Hamilton declared 'the nose too long & too perpendicular, the eye brow too regularly arched, the mouth too brought down at the point next the cheek, & the chin too double'. Her strictures were confirmed by Lady Beechey and the whole of the Nelson family.[20]

Boulton and Küchler's patience was finally rewarded at the third attempt to find an acceptable portrait. Once again the source was a suggestion from Lady Hamilton who, during a conversation with Tuffin about the inadequacies of the earlier experiments, produced Catherine Andras's wax (190; *p.151*), describing it as *'the most striking likeness that has been taken'* and much more so than even the De Koster drawing. Being a relief profile and approximately of the required size it proved an easier model

Wax effigy by Catherine Andras, 1806, (214)

Mezzotint by Charles Turner, 1806, after Hoppner, (146)
Note how closely Catherine Andras followed Hoppner's portrait in the pose for her wax figure.

to work from, Küchler evidently experiencing difficulty in the transfer from drawings.[21] The likeness to the Andras profile is unmistakable and, though there is no mention of any formal acknowledgement in the Boulton papers in Birmingham, she is almost certain to have received some sort of recognition, not the least being the commission to execute the effigy for Westminster Abbey.

Boulton's medal, though his generosity was appreciated, was not an unqualified success. It was finally issued in silver to captains and first-lieutenants, and in pewter to junior officers and ratings, with a few bronze copies. Three gold copies are known, probably made for Nelson's brother, Collingwood and Northesk, though this is uncertain. We are told that the sailors were disgusted at the pewter copies and either gave them back or threw them overboard. Furthermore, although Boulton had obtained approval to issue the medal, the Admiralty refused to sanction it as part of uniform. This rankled in the Navy especially after Waterloo when Army personnel who had served in the action were allowed to wear the Waterloo awards.[22] As late as 1837 a polite request from Lieutenant J. C. Gill who had served at Trafalgar in HMS *Achille* was met with a terse retort written on the back of his letter, 'Their Lordships cannot sanction the wearing of a private medal'.[23] The Naval General Service Medal with a Trafalgar clasp was all that junior officers and ratings were allowed to wear, but not until 1847.

Boulton's medal may not have been a total success though it certainly gave pleasure and was worn with pride by many who had taken part in the action, in spite of the Admiralty veto. An altogether more dramatic portrait appeared at about the same time, one which has a fair claim to being the most striking and lifelike image of the Hero ever to emerge from an artist's hand. This was Catherine Andras's wax effigy in Westminster Abbey (214; *pp.168, opposite*). As we have seen Catherine Andras's miniature wax profile had enjoyed an instant success immediately after its production shortly before Trafalgar. Indeed so successful had she become that the Dean and Chapter seized the opportunity and gave her the commission to construct the first effigy to be set up in the Abbey since that of the great Earl of Chatham. This intention was wholly laudable and in tune with popular sentiment. The Nelson charisma after Trafalgar had attained an intensity beyond anything achieved before or since, even by such national heroes as Marlborough, Wellington, Montgomery, or Sir Winston Churchill. So the decision of the Westminster Abbey authorities was not surprising. It must be admitted however that it was not wholly disinterested. The aura surrounding Nelson's name culminated in the

Detail from the wax effigy by Catherine Andras, 1806 (see p 168)

funeral cortège to St Paul's Cathedral. The funeral car, in the shape of the hull of the *Victory*, was escorted by a procession so long that when the heralds arrived at the west doors the tail had not even left the Admiralty. This led to a major tourist attraction which, even in a cold winter and spring, drained off a large proportion of the lucrative stream of sight-seers from Westminster Abbey.

The effigy of which the body is made of wood, the head and left hand delicately modelled in wax, joined the strange and melancholy company of monarchs and their consorts amongst which the only other figure, outside royalty, is that of Chatham. Catherine Andras had the honour of being chosen to make the new effigy, partly because the other major competitor in the field, Madame Tussaud, was away in Ireland, but more perhaps because of the success of her wax profile of Nelson and because of her having had sittings from which no doubt drawings still existed.

The effigy was set up early in 1806 and seen by Lady Hamilton who, on being asked 'in what features the model so closely resembled Nelson as she had declared, said in the direction & form of the nose, mouth and chin, that the general carriage of the body was exactly his, and that altogether the likeness was so great that it was impossible for anybody who had known him to doubt about or mistake it...'[24]

The Times for 22 March 1806 has a brief note:

> The Wax Figure now put up in Westminster Abbey is a very striking resemblance of the late Lord Nelson, in full uniform, and decorated with all his Orders, modelled from a smaller one, for which his Lordship sat. It has been seen by an illustrious personage and several of the Nobility and Gentry, and is considered by them to be a strong and exact representation of the features and person of our departed Hero.

The 'illustrious personage', was presumably either the Prince of Wales or Nelson's old comrade the Duke of Clarence who, as Prince William, had served with him on the West Indies Station and had given away the bride at his wedding (see p.132). The smaller model 'for which his Lordship sat' was probably the model 'taken from Life' for which Miss Andras had been awarded the Greater Silver Pallet by the Royal Society of Arts in 1801. It has since disappeared. No doubt she had made use of the wax profile too. The main source however was undoubtedly Hoppner's portrait painted for the Prince of Wales, begun late in 1800 but not actually delivered till 1810. However Meyer's stipple engraving had been published in November 1805 and, a much more likely source, Charles Turner's mezzotint published by Colnaghi on 6 January 1806 (see *p.169*). The uniform in Hoppner's portrait has been altered to that of a vice-admiral and Nelson's own cocked hat (with eyeshade and James Lock's trade label) was provided by the family. The effigy follows Turner's mezzotint closely apart from minor adjustments to uniform and decorations - notably the vice-admiral's stripes on the cuff, the Star of St Joachim awarded in September 1801, and the absence of the two

Naval gold medals, a bronze cast of Davison's Nile medal only being worn.[25] The face itself and the tilt of the head follow Hoppner closely and even the rocky background has been neatly transferred as a support.[26]

The reaction of contemporary visitors to Westminster Abbey is well-recorded. Elizabeth Foster, later Duchess of Devonshire, said 'it is as if he was standing there'.[27] Nelson's nephew, George Matcham, 'always said that the Abbey wax effigy was far more like him than any of the portraits'.[28] Perhaps the most remarkable testimony is that of Lady Hamilton herself, as recounted by an Artillery Officer escorting her round the Abbey in 1806:

> Horatia, the late Lord Nelson's *adopted* daughter, was very anxious to visit Westminster Abbey; accordingly, Lady Hamilton and our two selves went thither. After going through the usual routine, the guide, little guessing whom he addressed, said, 'Perhaps, Madam, the young folks would like to see the waxen image of the late Admiral Nelson; it has only been put up these two days'.
>
> Her Ladyship was much agitated but bowed assent; the man led the way to a glass case in which stood the effigy of her idol and the nation's pride.
>
> Tears flowed down her lovely face; she stood gazing intently upon this very faithful portrait; and when her emotions permitted her to speak she told the man that the likeness would be perfect if a certain lock of hair was disposed in the way his Lordship always wore it: this she offered to arrange. The guide refused to let anybody touch the figure.
>
> 'I am sure', she said, with that bewitching grace with which she was pre-eminently gifted, 'when I tell you that I am Lady Hamilton, you will not refuse me.'
>
> The man fixed his gaze upon her. 'Lady Hamilton!' he repeated; 'what, Lord Nelson's Lady Hamilton! Oh Madam, who could refuse you?' He hastened to open the case, the lock of hair was adjusted; she would have kissed the lips, but like the cautious Paulina, the guide assured her the colour was not dry.[29]

Some allowance needs to be made for the Artillery Officer adding colour to his story, especially as he was writing thirty years after the event, but it is interesting that Lady Hamilton should have made no comment on what some observers have thought to be an error in Catherine Andras's effigy, namely a defect in one of the eyes. Nelson lost the sight of his right eye at the siege of Calvi in 1794. To the casual observer nothing appeared to be amiss but several artists, notably Bowyer, Schmidt and Beechey, were careful to dim the lustre of this eye in their portraits.

Marble bust by John Flaxman, 1805, (215)

174

In Hoppner's sketch and in the Andras effigy the defect can plainly be seen in the *left* eye. So explicit a statement is not hard to account for, especially in the work of such a meticulous an artist as Miss Andras. The explanation is that despite the use of the green eyeshade Nelson was losing the sight of his other eye and indeed had he lived for a few years beyond Trafalgar many students have believed that he would have become totally blind.[30] As early as 1801 he was worrying about it and had complained to Emma.[31] By 1804 a Fleet medical report states that 'a thick opaque membrane' could be seen on his left eye. [32]

The Westminster Abbey effigy became an immediate success and though it did not divert the profitable crowds from visiting Nelson's last resting-place in St Paul's Cathedral, it was an undoubted help in bringing in much needed funds towards the Abbey expenses. Nelson however had a resistance to Westminster Abbey which he believed to stand on insecure foundations - Thorney Island surrounded by the bogs and mudflats of Chelsea and Battersea. He expressed this view on several occasions to Hardy and it was common knowledge that his remains were likely to be laid not in the Abbey, as befitted a great national hero, but in the more modest crypt of St Paul's Cathedral. This curious idiosyncrasy of this extraordinary man can possibly be traced back to the short period between the overland journey home from Naples and the Battle of Copenhagen. Nelson's admiration for Flaxman's sculpture is recorded in a letter to Sir Edmund Berry of 26 January 1801 contributing £200 towards the monument to Sir Ralph Miller, his old comrade of St Vincent and the Nile, and urging Flaxman's claim to be the artist. 'In him we may all trust' answered Berry.[33] Miller's monument was set up in St Paul's in 1801 and, according to the sculptor E. H. Baily, Nelson had said, 'If ever there should be a statue erected of me, I hope Flaxman, you will carve it'.[34] Flaxman's account for £166. 31s was addressed to 'A Davison Esq. St James's Square for Lord Nelson...'[35] The monument was approved of for we next hear that Davison had commissioned Flaxman to make a copy of the Thaller & Ranson bust (107; *p.102*). While work was going ahead on the preparation of the Trafalgar medal for Matthew Boulton, one of the Thaller & Ranson marble busts had been lent from the Royal Collection and was in Küchler's studio for help with the profile. 'Flaxman is making a marble head for Davison; it is a copy from the great bust which stands in Küchler's room...' 'The great bust' does not seem to have been much thought of for Boulton was told that Flaxman's copy 'will consequently be very little like'.[36] It could conceivably have been Mrs Damer's larger than life marble in the

Guildhall, lent by the City of London for the Trafalgar medal, but there is no record of a loan in the Common Council Journals and, moreover, the likeness of the Flaxman busts to the Thaller & Ranson original is so close as to leave no doubt that this was the basis for all the Flaxman busts including the head in the St Paul's monument.

The bust commissioned by Davison is probably that now belonging to the Ministry of Defence (215; *p.174*). A copy was bought by the National Maritime Museum from the third Viscount Bridport who puts forward another of the many claims for various portraits to be the true and only likeness of Nelson:

> ...There is a story in my family that Nelson's niece Charlotte (1787-1874) who married in 1810 Samuel 2nd Baron Bridport, in the presence of her grandson the late Alexander Nelson Hood KCVO (1854-1937), pointed to this bust and said, 'That is the only true likeness that has ever been made of my dear uncle'. This story was told to me by Sir Alexander Hood, my great-uncle. However Charlotte may have been a bit prejudiced; she was only 18 years old in 1805 and at the time of her death her grandson not more than twenty.[37]

As far as is known Nelson never saw a Flaxman bust of himself; certainly no comment from him has come to light. But in due course a Committee of Taste was appointed for the Nelson memorial in St Paul's (219; *opposite*) and it was decided that Flaxman should be the sculptor, with acknowledgement to another competitor, Richard Westmacott.[38] The first payment from the Treasury, £2100 on account of £6300, was received by Flaxman on 14 December 1807, and two other payments in 1815 and 1818.[39] Nollekens told Farington that Flaxman was at work on it in 1808,[40] but the finished monument was not erected in St Paul's till May 1818.[41]

Flaxman's busts differ slightly from the monument. The head in St Paul's, apart from being colossal in scale, is directed to his left; the busts are all facing the spectator. Nelson's empty sleeve, normally fastened across his Bath riband, is concealed beneath the sable pelisse; and the expression and general treatment is patently more idealised. Nelson in St Paul's is the hero and conqueror. In the busts he is seen more intimately and at close quarters.

The busts also differ among themselves, mainly in the positioning of the Stars. Sometimes the Bath is above the Crescent, sometimes below, and the Crescent in the Turkish Star is sometimes inverted. In all versions the socle consists of a circular base surmounted by a rectangular metope

COPENHAGEN   NILE.   TRAFALGAR

Marble statue by John Flaxman, 1807-18, (219)

edged with the capital letter C. The hair is the most distinguishing feature, noticeably more luxuriant than in other busts and especially in the lock covering the Nile scar. The date 1798 on the Nile medal is in Roman numerals. Plaster casts exist and what looks, from a photograph, to have been a plaster cast was used to surmount the chimney-piece in the hall of Trafalgar House.[42]

Another artist to cash in on the aftermath of Trafalgar was the wax modeller and cameo engraver, William Tassie, who assisted his uncle James Tassie and succeeded to the family business in 1799. In 1805 Tassie won £10,000 in the Alderman Boydell lottery and his interest in the firm subsided from then, but not before he was able to contribute to the Nelson industry by turning out quantities of Nelson mementos. As he wrote to his agent, Alexander Wilson:

> ...respecting Lord Nelson's Portrait, we have been so busy making small ones for the Jewellers (the size of rings and brooches) that I had no time to finish a large Portrait before this time. But I have now got one finished nearly the size of Lord Duncan. It is mostly done from De Koster's Print and is thought like. Lady Nelson has had three of the small heads on Cornelian brooches...[43]

Tassie states that the portrait was mostly done from De Koster (164; *p.130*) but there is no doubt that it also owes a great deal to Catherine Andras's wax profile (190; *p.151*) though he allows the hero a more refined nose, a more resolute chin and perhaps a less pained expression. Tassie's medallion was extremely popular and there are versions in most collections (220; *p.153*). Enamels cost twenty-five shillings and waxed plasters sixteen shillings. He bequeathed a large collection of his uncle's and his own casts and medallions to Edinburgh, and over a hundred letters are in the Scottish National Portrait Gallery library.

The large wax *modello* in Monmouth shows several differences, especially in the heavier cast of profile, but if it is by Tassie it may be the 'large Portrait' he wrote about to Alexander Wilson. It certainly bears a closer resemblance to De Koster's print than the final paste enamel medallions and cameos.

NOTES TO CHAPTER 8, AFTER TRAFALGAR

1. Beatty 1807, pp. 61ff. The fatal musket ball, in the Royal Collection, is illustrated in Van der Merwe 1995, p.111.

2. Newspapers 22 November 1805 and Farington 4 December 1805.

3. Charles Mitchell, 'Benjamin West's Death of Nelson', *Essays in the History of Art presented to Rudolph Wittkower* (1967), pp. 265-73. No West portrait of Nelson is known to Professor Helmut von Erffa, an American authority on Benjamin West. The central details are reproduced in Van der Merwe 1995, frontispiece.

4. Pavière 1950, pp.101-11, and reproduced Hibbert 1994, plate 32 (colour).

5. Millar 1969, 762.

6. Captain Edward Williams's account in Joseph Allen, *Life of Lord Nelson* (1852), pp. 295-6.

7. Beatty 1807, p.73.

8. Private letter from Beatty to the Admiralty, HMS *Victory* 15 December 1805 (NMM MS 51/040/2, formerly belonging to Sir Benjamin Outram KCB).

9. Private memo from Beatty to the Rev Alexander Scott, HMS *Victory* 20 December 1805 (ibid).

10. Paper on the back of NMM BHC2270, (see p. 264).

11. Sir George Scharf's Sketchbook 85, p.83 (NPG archive).

12. Letter to Lady Hamilton, 28 January 1801 (Nicolas IV, p.279).

13. The effigy is accompanied by Messrs Lock & Company's account-book showing bills for several of Nelson's hats with green eyeshades 1800-05.

14. Farington 8 July 1806.

15. Ibid. 5 June 1807.

16. Promotions and appointments were announced in the *London Gazette*, 9 November 1805, medal awards on 29 January 1806 (*Naval Chronicle* XV (1806) and Nicolas VII, pp. 304-05).

17. This section is based on letters in the Birmingham Assay Office. I am indebted to J.G. Pollard of the Fitzwilliam Museum for drawing my attention to these invaluable papers and to his article, 'Matthew Boulton and Conrad Küchler' in *The Numismatic Chronicle* X (1970). See also Millet 1995, pp. 98-101.

18. Letter from Beechey to Tuffin, 31 December 1805 (Pollard 1970, p.304).

19. Letter from Tuffin to Boulton, 17 January 1806 (ibid. p. 305).

20. Idem. 26 February 1806 (ibid. pp. 306-7).

21. Idem. p. 307.

22. The Duke of Wellington urged the War Office to alter the regulations about wearing medals on ribbons round the neck, pointing out that army officers on horseback were more likely to be damaged from swinging medals than admirals on their quarterdecks (S.C. Wood in *National Army Report* 1978-79, p.25).

23. Letter from Gill to the Admiralty, HMS *President* 22 November 1837 (PRO Adm. 1/2915 Lieut G.99), published by Captain K.J. Douglas-Morris RN in *Journal of the Orders and Medals Research Society* 138 (1973), p.12.

24. Letter from Tuffin to Boulton, 26 February 1806 (Pollard 1970, pp. 306-7).

25. At the time of writing Davison's medal is shown incorrectly worn, round the neck instead of from the fifth buttonhole.

26. The uniform is described in detail by Tanner & Nevinson 1935.

27. Vere Foster, *The Two Duchesses* (1898), p. 263.

28. Letter from Sir Lawrence Tanner, a descendant by marriage, in *The Times* 8 November 1932 10d.

29. Hill (1836) I, pp. 13-14; Whitley III, p. 99.

30. Modern ophthalmic specialists believe that total blindness need not necessarily have followed (Pugh p.45, Barras II, pp.163-8). In 1800 a German observer at Magdeburg said 'there was nothing noticeable about his eye, and he even seems able to see with it' (Keigwin, p.155).

31. Letter to Lady Hamilton, 28 January 1801 (see p.140).

32. Lambton Este's report, 4 November 1801 (Nicolas VI, p. 257). The right eye is dimmed in Beechey's portrait, the left eye in Hoppner's.

33. Letters from Nelson and Berry, 26 January and 28 March 1801 (Nicolas IV, p. 276).

34. C.R. Leslie, *Autobiographical Recollections* (1860), I, p. 74.

35. Flaxman's Accounts, 27 March 1801 and 9 October 1804. A related drawing is in the Witt Collection and the plaster model over a door in University College (E. Croft Murray, *Walpole Society* XXVIII (1940), p. 71).

36. Letter from Tuffin to Boulton, 26 January 1806 (Pollard 1970, p. 308).

37. Letter from Lord Bridport, 15 December 1947 (NMM archive).

38. Farington 16 and 29 March 1807. Westmacott's relief sculpture, 'The Death of Nelson', originally designed for the Marble Arch, is above the main entrance to Buckingham Palace.

39. Croft Murray op. cit. pp. 78-9. Related drawings are in the BM and V&A.

40. J.T. Smith, *Nollekens and his Times* (ed Whitten 1920) II, p.360.

41. *The Times* 14 May 1818 3d. The monument is illustrated in Margaret Whinney, *Sculpture in Britain 1530-1830* (1964), plates 147-8, and see Fraser 1995, pp.129-30.

42. Photograph in *Country Life* 20 July 1945, pp.112-3. A wax copy (5in. high), by William Cuming, is illustrated in Reilly 1953, p.103.

43. Letter dated 18 December 1805 in the Scottish NPG, partly printed by Dr Duncan Thomson in *Country Life* 27 January 1972.

Polychrome parian bust by Joseph Pitts, 1853, after Whichelo, (238)

Statue by E. H. Baily, 1839-43
London: Trafalgar Square, (233)

EPILOGUE

The years following the funeral in St Paul's led to a profusion of Nelson memorabilia ranging from towering monuments down to the smallest snuff-boxes and intaglio gems.[1] The most popular model seems to have been the portrait by Lemuel Abbott painted after the Santa Cruz action and altered to include the cocked hat and Turkish chelengk (16; *p.31*). Enamel and miniature copies were made by the dozen, with and without the hat, by artists such as Henry Bone, H.P. Bone, Edward Bird, Essex, Grimaldi, George Place and others, and good examples are in the Royal Collection and at Greenwich, Portsmouth, Monmouth and Althorp. Porcelain and faience figures were made based on Abbott's portrait, sometimes with Napoleon as companion, sometimes Wellington. The Rouen-Delft bust in white and vivid blue of about 1850, and the Veuve Perrin bust decorated with flowers and leaves, are specially outstanding examples (234, 235; *below*). The Hoppner and Beechey portraits were copied too but not in such quantity. Occasional variants

Veuve Perrin bust, c.1850, (234)

Rouen-Delft bust, c.1850, (235)

Coloured wax relief by Samuel Percy, c.1810, (229)

184

made up from the De Koster drawing can often be found, and Whichelo's 1805 portrait, itself owing much to De Koster, was used for the polychrome busts by Joseph Pitts dated 1853 (238; *p.181*). The coloured wax figure by Poole, *c.*1810, at Portsmouth (228; *p.271*), is an idealised interpretation deriving from several sources; and Percy's wax high-relief in Brighton (229; *opposite*) is similarly eclectic, probably owing most to Catherine Andras.

Marble busts continued to be produced long after Trafalgar, mostly turned out by the Gahagan family or by imitators (without acknowledgment) of Thaller & Ranson. The Cardosi bust in the National Portrait Gallery is a clear case of this brand of piracy, the sculptor making minute alterations to the Vienna bust, most noticeable especially in the treatment of the hair, then signing his own name on the back as being the author. A copy of the Vienna bust is in the Town Hall, Lewes, signed Turnerelli; and another in a private Hampshire collection is signed Nollekens. A variant by James Bubb, nicknamed 'Tobacconist Bubb' by Gahagan, was exhibited at the Royal Academy in 1810 but is believed by Rupert Gunnis to have been done *ad vivum*, possibly as a student in the Royal Academy Schools. It appears however to owe a great deal to both Gahagan and Thaller & Ranson It was bequeathed by Gunnis to the National Maritime Museum in 1965.[2] A marble bust by Joseph Towne, *c.*1836, is at HMS *Dryad*.

In 1809 when Daniel Alexander was remodelling and adding blocks to the Queen's House at Greenwich, he commissioned the young Francis Chantrey to make colossal plaster busts of Admirals Duncan, Howe, St Vincent and Nelson for the hospital.[3] Three of these (excluding Nelson) were shown at the Royal Academy in 1809. A further set of Admirals, slightly smaller, was commissioned by Samuel Wyatt in 1810 for Trinity House; the plaster model for the Nelson is in the Ashmolean Museum.[4] Chantrey's National Portrait Gallery bust (232; *p.187*), virtually a copy of the Trinity House bust but on a larger scale, was commissioned by William IV and executed in 1835: '1833 Rec[d] an order from his Majesty for a Bust of Admiral Nelson as a companion for that of Wellington to stand in the Palace at Windsor - both to be above the life size'.[5] The cost of making the bust and taking it to Windsor was 250 guineas. It was later moved to the guardroom, where it figures in the 1851 Windsor Castle catalogue, and in 1901 it was presented to the Royal United Service Institute by Edward VII. At the dispersal of the RUSI collection in 1963 the bust was presented (with permission

Marble bust by J G Bubb, c.1810, (226)

186

Marble bust by Sir Francis Chantrey, 1835, (232)

from the Lord Chamberlain's Office) to the National Portrait Gallery together with its pedestal made from the foremast of HMS *Victory*. The pedestal, bound with three iron bands, had been originally presented to the Duke of Clarence (later William IV), kept in a miniature temple at Bushey Park and moved to Windsor at his accession. The hole in it was made by a round shot fired from the French 74-gun *Redoubtable*, and the horseshoe was nailed there by seamen of the *Victory*.[6] A bronze version, given by Lady Chantrey to Greenwich Hospital in 1851, is incised on the back in Chantrey's cursive script: *Admiral Lord Nelson / made by command of / King William the Fourth / in 1834 / by Francis Chantrey*.[7]

Coade Stone bust, attributed to John Bacon, 1807 Hampshire: Portsdown Monument, (227)

One of the most famous monuments in the world, Nelson's column in Trafalgar Square, was not set up until nearly half a century after the Hero's death, but undoubtedly the first monument to be conceived was the tapering square section column with a bust facing the sea from the crest of Portsdown Hill above Porchester. This arose from a meeting of the captains of the squadron and was expressed in a memorandum from Collingwood dated off Trafalgar 2 November 1805.[8] It was agreed that £2000 should be deducted from the prize money for the purpose and the model by J T Grove was exhibited at the Royal Academy in 1807 - 'Cenotaph, erecting on Portsdown Hill, to the Memory of the late Lord Nelson by the Officers, Seamen and Marines of the Fleet under his command at the Battle of Trafalgar' (227; *opposite* and *p.vi*).

The first monument to be set up was a stone pyramid erected near Cork in a few hours by a group of Sea Fencibles overcome with patriotic emotion on hearing the news of Trafalgar and Nelson's death.[9] Thereafter others followed thick and fast. A letter from the editor of the *Norfolk Chronicle* recalls probably the first idea for a column, suggested at a meeting on 17 December 1805 'of the Nobility, Gentry, Clergy and Inhabitants of the County of Norfolk'. Various models were exhibited including designs by Arthur Browne and John Cushing, both of Norwich, but unfortunately insufficient subscriptions were forthcoming and the project had to be dropped, with some local shame, until it was resurrected by the editor of the *Gentleman's Magazine* in 1807. A statue by Thos Milnes was put up in 1847 in the grounds of Norwich Grammar School where the young Horace had been a pupil.[10]

Other monuments were set up in Liverpool by George Bullock (1807), in Dublin by Thomas Kirk (1808 but since demolished), in Great Yarmouth a Coade Stone memorial designed by Wilkins (1811), and in Liverpool Mansion House the apotheosis of a naked Admiral born aloft by a sympathetic 'Victory', designed by Matthew Wyatt but modelled mainly by Westmacott (1813). In Montreal the news arrived during an Assembly Ball in Exchange House and a resolution was immediately proposed to put up a memorial to the Immortal Nelson.[11] The magnificent Coade Stone statue by Joseph Panzetta arrived there in 1809 aboard the famous Canadian trading ship, the *Eweretta*, after its exhibition in Coade & Sealy's Lambeth Gallery where a visiting 'old salt', on being told that the Coade process involved a double firing action, was overwhelmed by nostalgia and flung his arms round the statue exclaiming 'Ah, there was never a British officer who could fire better than his Lordship'.[12] Panzetta was later employed on the Coade Stone pediment at Greenwich, designed in 1810 by the President of the Royal Academy, Benjamin West, and set up in 1813. Here Nelson reclines in the arms of Britannia, surrounded by 'England Scotland and Ireland mourning their irreparable loss', and by Neptune's sea-horses, for the accurate details of which West 'daily attended the King's Mews to study the anatomy of the finest specimens of this animal'. With a subtle touch of verisimilitude the President endowed the King's horses with webbed feet.[13]

Drawing of E. H. Baily in his studio, 1842 with the Trafalgar Square Statue

In the most famous monument of all, Baily's 17 foot statue of Nelson stands on the summit of Railton's corinthian column, 160 feet high, slightly lower than the mainmast of the *Victory* and considerably lower than Wren's Monument to the Great Fire.[14] The Thames Estuary and the North Sea are visible from its summit. Trafalgar Square was not finished till 1830, the column set up in 1839 and the statue placed thereon on 3 November 1843 (233; *p.182*), so all this is well outside the scope of this book, as are the innumerable imaginary reconstructions ranging from the picture by Westall of the young midshipman clubbing a polar bear to the various Victorian idylls - Eastlake's 'Death of Nelson' designed for the House of Lords, Maclise's immense 'Death of Nelson' in the Royal Gallery, Charles Lucy's 'Nelson in his Cabin on the morning of Trafalgar' in the Royal Naval Museum (236; *p274*), G. W. Joy's 'Nelson's Farewell to his Grandmother' exhibited at the Royal Academy in 1883 and now in South Africa, and Andrew Gow's 'Farewell to Nelson' in the Royal Exchange - all these are sincere and evocative portrayals, as indeed are the innumerable inn signs scattered throughout East Anglia needing no further identification than the words 'The Hero'.

NOTES TO THE EPILOGUE

1. The monuments and memorabilia are more fully described in White's *Companion*, chapters 3, 4 and 6.

2. Letters from Rupert Gunnis in NMM archive.

3. Chantrey Ledger (RA library) p.1, and PRO Adm. 80/111. The Ledger is printed in *Walpole Society* LVI (1974).

4. Poole, *Catalogue of Oxford Portraits* (1912), I, p. 215.

5. Chantrey Ledger p.256 and *Walpole Society* op. cit. p. 286.

6. *Official Catalogue* (RUSI 1924) no.2018 where the pedestal is stated to be part of the mainmast; earlier references however, e.g. Nicolas VII p. 348, and a Victorian inventory of the Royal Collection, point to its being the foremast.

7. Sited outside the West Block facing the Old Royal Observatory NMM SCU0084 (*Walpole Society* p. 286).

8. General Memorandum to the Respective Captains of His Majesty's Ships, *Queen* off Cape Trafalgar, 2 November 1805 (Nicolas VII, p. 218).

9. The monument was built in the park of Castle Townsend in five hours, by twelve hundred Sea Fencibles and eight masons, on 10 November 1805 (Nicolas VII, p. 355).

10. *Gentleman's Magazine* 77 (February 1807), pp.125-8.

11. Alison Yarrington, 'Nelson the Citizen Hero', *Art History* VI (1983) pp.315-29, and *The Commemoration of the Hero* (1988).

12. Cit. Elizabeth Collard, *Country Life* 24 July 1969, p. 211.

13. Alison Kelly in *Country Life* 25 January 1959. I am indebted to Miss Kelly for much valuable information on Mrs Coade's products, specially to her article in *The Connoisseur* (January 1978, where the Nelson pediment is illustrated on page 24. Much of this information is in her book, *Mrs Coade's Stone* (1990).

14. The subject of the Naval Monument in Trafalgar Square is treated by my late friend and tutor, T.S.R. Boase, in *The Oxford History of Art 1800-1870* (1959), pp. 300-03, and more recently in J.M. Crook & M.H. Port, *History of the King's Works 1782-1851* (1973), pp.491-4.

GLOSSARY

Aquatint: a form of tone-process engraving which reproduces the transparency of watercolour drawing. Paul Sandby, William Daniell and Gillray, used aquatint with great effect, and the process is still popular.

Basaltes: a black unglazed porcelain produced by Wedgwood in the 1760s and named after the black igneous rock sometimes called 'touchstone' (see.64; *p. 65*).

Cuts: usually woodcuts (or linocuts). These are a form of relief engraving used specially by Thomas Bewick but also, because of ease of reproduction, in publications such as *The Illustrated London News*.

Enamel: enamel miniatures were painted on a primed metal base (copper, silver or occasionally gold), then fired in a high-temperature kiln. The process was laborious and sometimes resulted in failure, but if successful the technique achieved a highly finished glossy surface which insured that the colours did not fade (see 41; *p.209*).

Etching: a form of intaglio engraving in which a copper plate is covered with a resin impervious to acid. The image is then drawn with a needle and the plate immersed in an acid bath which eats away the needle lines. The inked result is then transferred to paper. Rembrandt was the most celebrated exponent of the art, which was also used with great effect by Gillray, Rowlandson, Cruickshank, Sayers and other satirists, in often garishly coloured caricatures (see 67; *p. 216*).

Line engraving: another form of intaglio engraving in which the graving tool (graver) is pushed on to the copper plate leaving a V-section. The plate is then inked and the image transferred to paper. Dürer was its prime exponent but the technique was used later, by William Blake in particular, for illustrations and picture reproduction (see 16; *p.51*).

Lithograph: a form of surface engraving invented in 1798 and named from the Greek lithos, a stone. The drawing is made with a greasy chalk on a slab of stone (latterly zinc), the stone then wetted enabling the colours to grip only on the greasy parts. The medium, still very popular, was used with special effect by early nineteenth century French artists, and in England by Whistler.

Mezzotint: a 17th century Dutch technique perfected by Prince Rupert, and specially popular in 18th century England. The plate is first worked over by a 'rocker' to produce a ground of burred dots. The artist then burnishes or scrapes the plate free of burrs for the highlights, and leaves the darker parts to achieve a deep velvety texture. Reynolds and Gainsborough portraits and Constable landscapes attained a wide significance through mezzotint engravings (see 14; *p.47*).

Parian: a white porcelain named after the island of Paros in the Aegean, famous for its quarries of white marble. Parian ware developed from the Sèvre biscuit porcelain and was taken on by the Derby factory in the 1770s. 'Victorian parian ware, marketed by Minton, Copeland & Garrett, and Worcester, was popular because of its purity of texture and smooth finish (see 218; *p. 267*).

Stipple: another form of intaglio engraving made by dots stippled with an etching needle on a metal plate. The technique was often combined with line engraving to produce a mixed engraving which was a favourite for the reproduction of portrait drawings (see 5; *p.196*).

Vignette: an engraved portrait, usually head and shoulders, with the edges shaded off into the background (see 164; *p. 249*).

Woodbury print: a photographic process invented by Walter Woodbury, 1834-85.

CATALOGUE
OF KNOWN PORTRAITS

NOTE

Measurements are given in both centimetres and inches, height
before width. The terms *right* and *left* refer to the spectator's
right and left except in the case of sculpture.

HS = head and shoulders, HL = half-length,
TQL = three-quarter-length, WL = whole-length.

Abbreviations are amplified on pages 293-9

RIGAUD 1777-81

NELSON BY JOHN FRANCIS RIGAUD 1777-81

1 *Greenwich: National Maritime Museum (BHC 2901)*

Oil on canvas 127 x 101.5cm (50 x 40in). TQL standing to right in captain's full-dress uniform (1774-87), three-cornered hat, white waistcoat and breeches, high white neckcloth, bushy hair powdered grey, grey eyes, pale complexion, his hands resting on hilt of sheathed sword. In left background a seaman standing by the captain's barge, in right background Fort San Juan, Nicaragua, flying the British flag over the Spanish. A later inscription lower right: *Capt. Horatio Nelson / 1781*

COLLECTIONS: commissioned in 1777 by Captain William Locker; Nelson family and exhibited by the third Earl Nelson in 1868; sold by the fifth Earl to the NMM in 1948 (Trafalgar House inventory no.2).

ENGRAVINGS: (1) Small oval stipple, HS only, by R. Shipster (10.5 x 8.5cm) published 14 August 1797 and lettered: *Rigaud pinxt 1786* [sic] */ R. Shipster delt et sculpt / HORATIO NELSON ESQr / now Sir Horatio Nelson, K.B. Rear Admiral / of the Blue Squadron / From an Original Picture in the possession of W. Locker Esq. / Lieut. Govr of Greenwich Hospital.* (see *p.11*)

(2) A later issue, 1799 with the title altered to: *HORATIO NELSON ESQe / now Lord Nelson K.B. Rear Admiral / of the Red Squadron / From an Original painted in the Year 1786.*

The year 1786 in both prints appears to be an engraver's mistake, unless Rigaud painted another version which has disappeared. Certainly it cannot have been *ad vivum,* Nelson serving abroad from 1784 until his return to Portsmouth in July 1787. Shipster borrowed the 1777-81 portrait from Captain Locker who no doubt advised him to add sixteen years to his apparent age and possibly misinformed him about its original date. The right arm, amputated in July 1797, appears of course undamaged.

EXHIBITIONS: National Portraits Exhibition 1868 (9); Guelph Exhibition New Gallery 1891 (133); British Empire Exhibition, Wembly Palace of Art 1925 (N18).

CONDITION: X-ray photography in 1995 revealed a young man in lieutenant's uniform, with a pigtail, a chubby face, and a hat under his arm.

COPIES: a small copy was at Christie's (Sir Henry Sutcliffe-Smith sale) 4 June 1976 (157).

LITERATURE: Nelson's letters to Locker in February 1781 (Nicolas I pp.38-41); Oman 1947, pp.23, 259; Warner 1975, pp.29-30, 131; *Walpole Society* vol. 50, pp.66-7, 120; Pocock 1980, pp.22, 165; Hibbert 1994, p.19.

REPRODUCTIONS: *Magazine of Art* (1898) p.529; Mahan 1897, frontispiece; *Connoisseur* CXXI (1948) p.120; Oman 1947, p.24; Warner *Contemporary Studies* pp.27-30; Naish 1958, pl.1; Warner 1958, frontispiece; Pocock 1980 p.20; Naish 1972, p.1 (colour); Hattersley 1974, p.28; Bennett 1972, p.20; Warner 1975 p.10; Walder 1978, pl. 3b; Pocock 1987, p.28; Hibbert 1994, pl.1 (colour); White's *Companion,* pl. 2 (colour); Van der Merwe cover (colour).

COMMENTS: pages 9-12. ILLUSTRATED: page 18.

COLLINGWOOD

NELSON BY CUTHBERT COLLINGWOOD *c.*1784

2 *Greenwich: National Maritime Museum (PAD 3164)*

Watercolour on off-white paper cut out and mounted on another finer paper watermarked 1812 (torn at the last numeral which is almost certainly 2) and placed on another backing paper 10.6 x 8.1cm (4 3/16 x3 1/5in).
A paper on the back of the wooden panel forming part of the frame is inscribed:

> Portrait of Nelson painted by Collingwood when he and Nelson met at the house of Commissioner Moutray at Antigua about the year 1783. See *The Public & Private Correspondence of Vice Admiral Lord Collingwood* 5th Edition (1837) pages 13 and 14, where this and the fellow portrait are described. Nelson had lost his hair from fever and wore a wig, so Collingwood made this sketch of him and in revenge Nelson made one of Collingwood with his pigtail.
> Purchased at the sale of the effects of Lord Collingwood's daughter. P Fielding [Sir Percy Fielding at Dover *c.*1885]

COLLECTIONS: Mrs Moutray, wife of John Moutray, Commissioner for the Navy Board in Antigua; Collingwood's daughter Sarah (b.1792, m. G.L. Newnham Collingwood); Sir Percy Fielding and bequeathed to the NMM by Major-General Sir Geoffrey Fielding in 1932.

LITERATURE: Collingwood 1837, pp.13-14; Warner, *Admiral Lord Collingwood* (1968), pp.21-2.

REPRODUCTIONS: Warner 1958, p.52; Naish 1958, p.96; Pocock 1968, p.28; Warner *Collingwood*

1968, p.29; Bryant 1970, pp.30-1; Warner 1975, p.40; Walder 1978, fig.3a; White's *Companion*, p.35; van der Merwe 1995, p.71.

COMMENTS: pages 13-14. ILLUSTRATED: page xx.

LEGHORN MINIATURIST 1794

NELSON BY AN UNKNOWN LEGHORN MINIATURIST, 1794

3 | *Greenwich: National Maritime Museum (MNT 0201)*

Miniature in oils on oval card 6.5 x 6.1cm (2¹/₂ x 2³/₈in) including the narrow gold rim; nearly half-length to right in post captain's undress uniform (1787-95), untidy grey hair, pale complexion, grey eyes with a slight cast in his right eye, a small scar below the right eyebrow and another below the left lower eyelid; black neckcloth, white collar and shirt frill; dull blue background; plaited brown hair of three shades set into the back of the case.

COLLECTIONS: commissioned by Nelson himself in Leghorn for his wife and bought from her grand-daughter by the third Earl Nelson; acquired for the NMM from Trafalgar House (TH 97) in 1948.

ENGRAVINGS: (1) Mezzotint by R. Laurie (see *p.16*) with the captain's uniform altered to rear-admiral's and with the riband and star of the Bath added (but no Naval gold medal); dedicated to the Duke of Clarence, published by Laurie & Whittle 13 November 1797 and lettered: *Engraved by Robᵗ Laurie from a Miniature Picture in the Possession of Lady Nelson, Painted at Leghorn;* nearly TQL in rear-admiral's full-dress uniform, riband and star of the Bath, left hand on sword hilt, right sleeve fastened with two ribbons between elbow and shoulder, hair unruly and with a large curly lock over the forehead Battle of Cape St Vincent in the background .
(2) WL version, (see *right*) published by Laurie & Whittle 20 October 1798, showing Nelson standing on a captured French flag on deck, the shore batteries of Aboukir Bay in left background (coloured example in NMM).

LITERATURE: Mahan 1897, pp.451-2; Keate 1939, p.265; Oman 1947, p.259; Naish 1958, pp.191, 263.

REPRODUCTIONS: Naish 1958, pl.IIIb; Pocock 1968, p.45.

COMMENTS: pages 15-17.
ILLUSTRATED: top right and page 19.

3: Miniature by a Leghorn artist, 1794

3: Mezzotint by Laurie & Whittle, 1798

*5: Stipple engraving by William Evans
after the drawing by Henry Edridge, 1798*

6: Stipple engraving by Daniel Orme, after his own drawing, 1798

UNKNOWN ARTIST *c.* 1797

NELSON BY A SHIPMATE, *c.*1797

4 *Monmouth: Nelson Museum*

Watercolour on off-white paper 19 x 15cm (7$\frac{1}{2}$ x 6in), HL profile to right before the loss of his arm, blue coat, hair in queue, writing (but the pen probably added later): *F.A.O. / The First Line to attack - the second will sustain.*

COLLECTIONS: Appleby Brothers *c.*1953, bought Tom Pocock who presented it to the Monmouth Museum in about 1965.

REPRODUCTION: Pocock *1968*, p.52 and 1987, plate 23.

COMMENTS: page 17. ILLUSTRATED: page 8.

EDRIDGE 1797

NELSON BY HENRY EDRIDGE, 1797

5 *Holbrook: Royal Naval School*

Pencil and ink drawing on buff paper, 31.9 x 23.3cm (12$\frac{1}{2}$ x 9$\frac{3}{8}$in). No inscriptions. WL standing on a rocky shore, bare headed, in rear-admiral's undress uniform, riband of the Bath (no star) and one Naval gold medal (St Vincent), left hand on hilt of unsheathed sword, right arm-sleeve with protective ribbons pinned across riband of the Bath and attached to a button on the uniform coat; warships in left background; the right pupil appears slightly enlarged, but no apparent scar on eyebrow or eyelid.

COLLECTIONS: Sir Henry Englefield and, after his death, at Christie's (third day of Englefield sale) 8 March 1823 (36) - 'small whole-length portrait of Lord Nelson, in black lead' - bought by Sir Everard Home, a son of Vice-Admiral Sir George Home, and bequeathed to the Royal Naval School by Sir Everard Home in 1854.

ENGRAVINGS: stipple by William Evans (see *opposite, top*), half-length only in an oval, lettered: *Drawn by H. Edridge / Engraved by Wm Evans/Rear Admiral Sir Horatio Nelson, K.B./Published May 12 1798 by Ant^y Molteno, Printseller to her Royal Highness the Duchess of York, 76 St James's Street.*

EXHIBITION: probably RA 1798 (545)

CONDITION: (April 1977). Faded, bleached, rubbed especially in background, and spotted with small worm-holes filled in during earlier restoration. Repaired by Mrs MacCalum, NMM, Sept. 1967.

LITERATURE: Morrison 1893-4 II p.81; *List of Works, Relics, Plate etc. the Property of Greenwich Hospital...*(1912) p.9; Robinson 1930 pp.314-5

REPRODUCED: W Laird Clowes *The Royal Navy* (1900) V p.144; Warner 1958 p.172

COMMENTS: pages 17-20, 146-8.

ILLUSTRATED: page 21.

ORME 1797-98

NELSON BY DANIEL ORME, 1797-98

6 *Salisbury: private collection*

Brown chalk and black pencil drawing on paper. HS with head turned to left, rear-admiral's full dress uniform, riband and star of the Bath, one Naval gold medal; unruly hair brushed back, black neckcloth, white shirt-frill, empty right sleeve just visible but no sleeve ribbons; heavy features, serious expression.

COLLECTION: offered to the NPG in 1972 by a private collector.

ENGRAVINGS: small oval stipple by Orme himself (see *opposite, bottom*) lettered: *D. Orme Pinx & Sculp. Historical Engraver to his Majesty & the Prince of Wales. / ADMIRAL LORD NELSON, K.B. / Painted by Mr Orme and introduced into his Grand Historical Picture of the Brave Admiral's Victory over / the French Fleet. / Sold & Pub^d Feby 14th 1798 by Mr Orme.* Another print with different lettering, by K Mackenzie, was published for the *British Library* 30 November 1798. Frequent re-issues appeared thereafter including a crudely coloured one in September 1801 and the headpiece on an 1805 broadsheet, *A TRIBUTE to the Memory of HORATIO NELSON etc.* The print appears as a transfer on a commemorative jug issued after Trafalgar to raise money for the Patriotic Fund.

LITERATURE: Naish 1958 p.429; May 1972, pp.98-9, pl.5.

COMMENTS: pages 20-27. ILLUSTRATED: page 25.

NELSON BY J. MILLET AFTER DANIEL ORME

7 | *Portsmouth: Royal Naval Museum*

Watercolour on paper, HS to left in rear-admiral's full-dress uniform, riband and star of the Bath, one Naval gold medal, signed on the outer rim: *J. Millett.*

J. Millett, a little-known miniature painter, exhibited at the Royal Academy in 1837. The watercolour drawing, a straightforward copy of Orme's stipple engraving of 1798, is probably a preliminary study for a miniature portrait.

COLLECTIONS: Lily Lambert McCarthy 40/76.

LITERATURE: McCarthy 1995, no.244.

ILLUSTRATED: right

NELSON AFTER DANIEL ORME

8 | *Sydney, Australia: Paul A. Hopper collection*

Oil on canvas, 35.5 x 30.5cm (14 x 12in), HS to left in rear-admiral's full-dress uniform, star and riband of the Bath, star of the Crescent, two Naval gold medals, sky background.

COLLECTIONS: Mr Frankham, sold Christie's 25 September 1989 (313); Warwick Leadlay Gallery, Greenwich (as 'early 19th century'), reproduced *Country Life*, 9 November 1995, p.52, bt Paul A. Hopper.

The portrait seems to have been worked up from Orme's stipple engraving of 14 February 1798, and from his large oil dated 1799, 'Nelson receiving the surrender of the San José, 14 February 1797', where of course he is shown with his right arm intact. The portrait shows him without his right arm, and with the addition of the Orders and the gold medals for St Vincent and the Nile.

ILLUSTRATED: page 23.

9 | *Portsmouth: Royal Naval Museum*

Miniature on enamel in oval gold frame, signed on back H.H.L. Nelson in full dress uniform, head turned slightly to the left, wearing Bath star and ribbon and one neck medal.

COLLECTIONS: Lily Lambert McCarthy, 242/73.

LITERATURE: McCarthy 1995, No 168.

ILLUSTRATED: page 22.

7: Watercolour by J. Millet after Daniel Orme

SINGLETON 1797

NELSON BY HENRY SINGLETON 1797

10 | *Greenwich: National Maritime Museum (PAF 4391)*

Pencil on off-white paper 39.8 x 26.8cm (15³/₄ x 10¹/₂ in), signed and dated lower left: *H. Singleton 1797*. HL in an oval surrounded by an acanthus leaf to right and a breaking wave to left, supported by a cupid holding a naked sword.

COLLECTION: uncertain before acquisition by the NMM.

ENGRAVINGS: large mezzotint (see *p.28*) by George Keating profile to right with a ship on fire in right background, lettered above: *PALMAM QUI MERUIT FERAT*, and below: *London, Published November 29 1798, by G Keating 18 Warwick Street, Golden Square. / Painted by H. Singleton. Engraved by G. Keating. / The Right Hon Horatio Baron Nelson of the Nile, And of*

11: *Oil attributed to Singleton, c.1797-8*

Burnham Thorpe in the County of Norfolk, Rear Admiral of the Blue, And Knight of the most Honourable & Military Order of the Bath. Coloured copies have the English and French lines of battle in the margins and are lettered *&c &c &c* after *Bath*.

LITERATURE: *The Times* 26 April 1955 14e.

COMMENTS: page 27. ILLUSTRATED: page 26.

11 | *London: Southeby's*

An oil sketch on paper laid down on canvas 33.7 x 27.2 cm (13¼ x 10⅜in) possibly by Singleton but more likely by Keating for his mezzotint, had belonged to the Hood family and was sold Sotheby's 17 December 1981 (120).
A small wax profile was offered to the NPG in 1938.

ILLUSTRATED: above.

ABBOTT 1797

NELSON BY LEMUEL FRANCIS ABBOTT, 1797

12 | *London: private collection (formerly at Kilgraston)*

Oil on canvas 73.5 x 61cm (29 x 24in), uninscribed but with a paper on the stretcher written in ink in Sir Francis Grant's handwriting (of which several examples are in the NPG archive):

The original picture for which Lord Nelson gave Abbot, two sittings. My father the late Francis Grant of Kilgraston, Perthshire, N.B. employed Abbot largely as a portrait painter. Abbot assured Mr Grant that this was the original from which all the other pictures of Nelson painted by him were completed. Mr Grant desired to own this picture and requested Abbot to name his price. Abbot's answer was that no money would induce him to part with the original during his life. After the death of Abbot it was purchased by Mr Grant by private arrangement from his family or executors and the picture has ever since been at Kilgraston.
(signed) Francis Grant P.R.A.[1]

HL to front head turned slightly to left, aged 41, rear admiral's undress uniform, star of the Bath, one Naval gold medal (St Vincent in obverse, i.e., displaying Victory and Britannia) on a white ribbon edged with blue; right sleeve empty and pinned or tied to a button below the medal, the wound opening secured with black ribbons below the epaulette; white waistcoat with two brass buttons and edge of Bath riband; eyes bluish-grey, hair coarse and brushed back, grey or powdered, smiling expression, head longer and leaner than in later versions; sketchy shirt-frill; plain brown background.

COLLECTIONS: the artist and withdrawn from the sale of his effects at Christie's 16 June 1804 (38); Francis Grant of Kilgraston; his son Sir Francis Grant PRA who offered it to the NPG in 1857; his nephew Charles Grant,[2] and sold by him at the dispersal of the Kilgraston collection at Christie's 14 June 1875 (108) when it was bought for 30 guineas by a forebear of Judge Sir Christopher Nicholas Johnston KC (later Lord Sands) who exhibited the portrait at Wembley in 1924; his son Christopher M Johnston who inherited it in 1934 and sold it at Sotheby's 23 March 1977 (91a), bought by a private collector (Peter Morgan).

EXHIBITIONS: British Institution 1857 (149) lent by J Grant Esq; British Empire Exhibition Wembley 1924 (VI6) lent by Lord Sands; possibly New York 1925 lent by Lord Sands.

CONDITION: in 1924, when the portrait was exhibited at Wembley, James Milner (Director of the NPG) noted 'paint badly cracked showing red priming of canvas on his stock above the shirt frill, or it may be repaint which has cracked. The portrait gives an impression of woodenness and not quite the sternness shown in the photograph'.[3] In 1935, according to C. M. Johnston, it was seen at the National Gallery of Scotland by Stanley Cursiter 'who said that it was in perfect condition and required no attention'.[4] In 1941 it was brought by C M Johnston to the NMM where Callender and Spink 'had thought it to be the original sketch but painted over to make it look like a finished portrait'. It was evacuated during the War and returned to the owner in 1947 after being placed on exhibition for a short time in the NMM galleries. In 1976 it was sent to Sotheby's who brought it to the NPG where it was described 'as in terrible condition but in spite of provenance looks like a thoroughly indifferent copy'.[5] It was then subjected to scientific analysis at the NMM where X-ray photography revealed another painting underneath; the canvas was considered to be contemporary with Abbott but the paint much later and the drawing 'very poor giving the effect of a pathetic caricature'.[6] On 23 March 1977 it was sold at Sotheby's and at a preview the present writer considered that, in spite of the damning scientific evidence, the picture contained a good deal of over-painting laid on much later, possibly even by Grant himself or by his nephew, but there was no reason to doubt Grant's written opinion expressed on at least three occasions that this was the original sketch used by Abbott for the production of all his later copies. The question is discussed further on pp. 36-40.

LITERATURE: letters in NPG archive from Sir Francis Grant 1874; letters in NPG and NMM archives between Callender and J D Milner who first noticed the Grant letters; correspondence in *The Times* initiated by Major John Skelton 27 October 1932 and followed up by letters from Callender (29 October), Lord Sands (31 October) and others up to 5 November; full-page spread in *Illustrated London News* 26 November 1932 'A Nelson Enigma: Abbott Portraits which is the Original?' comparing the Kilgraston sketch with three others, NMM GH 151, Mr A W Stanton's version and NPG 394. Further correspondence in NPG and NMM archives brings the subject up to Sotheby's sale 23 March 1977. Richard Walker, *Trafalgar Chronicle* (1994) pp.79-94.

NOTES: (1) The inscription was published by Lord Sands in *The Times* 31 October 1932; there is also a manuscript transcript by James Caw in the NPG archive. (2) Charles Thomas Constantine Grant (1831-91), eldest surviving son of John, Sir Francis Grant's eldest brother (see *Landed Gentry* 1898). (3) Note by J D Milner on the back page of the Wembley Catalogue in NPG library. (4) Letter from C M Johnston to Sir Henry Hake 24 February1935 in NPG archive. (5) Note by Richard Ormond in NPG archive. (6) Report by Miss Gillian Lewis, senior Conservation Officer, NMM.

COMMENTS: pages 36-40. ILLUSTRATED: page 37.

13 | *England: private collection*

DESCRIPTION: Oil on canvas (relined) 76 x 62.5cm (30 x 24¹/₂in). HL to front head turned slightly to left. aged forty-one, in rear-admiral's undress uniform, star of the Bath with the riband just visible beneath the uniform coat, one Naval gold medal (St Vincent in obverse, i.e. Victory crowning Britannia) on a white ribbon with blue borders; epaulettes sketchily painted; right sleeve empty and pinned or tied to a button below the medal; the three black ribbons securing the wound opening in the sleeve, shown in later versions of this picture, do not appear; white waistcoat with two brass buttons and edge of Bath riband; shirt-frill sketchily painted, black neckcloth flat and rubbed. Severe unsmiling expression, eyes slate grey and with no abnormality, hair coarse and brushed back, grey or powdered. Background plain greyish-brown badly rubbed, ships in lower left corner.

INSCRIPTION: (see *opposite*) written in ink on a paper pasted on back of lining canvas:

> *This picture was painted by Abbot at my grandfather's as a present from N to my grandfather. He afterwards sat to Abbot for a similar sized picture for Lady Nelson and though Abbot repeated the picture some forty or more times, Lord Nelson only sat to him twice. I have heard my Aunt Eliza (the little child playing with the dog in the Family Picture) say that this Picture was painted soon after Nelson lost his arm, and she remembers helping N on and off with his uniform coat, in which he sat for the picture, before and after the sittings.*
> *F.L. 1872*

On the original stretcher are Christie's stencils 193 DT and AE 71, Knoedler's stock number (7165) in pencil, and in red paint the numerals 14. 1944. 2.

13: *Stipple engraving by Robert Shipster, after the oil by Abbott, 1798*

13: *Frederick Locker's note on the back of his father's portrait of Nelson by Abbott*

COLLECTIONS: commissioned by Nelson as a present for Captain William Locker and descending in his family to his grandson Frederick Locker-Lampson (the poet) of Rowfant, Sussex; Knoedler 1959; Mrs Samuel P. Rotan of Philadelphia; Christie's 22 June 1979 (133) bought Leggatt on behalf of a private collector.

CONDITION: lined and cleaned probably shortly before 1872 when Frederick Locker pasted his inscription on the new lining canvas; relined and cleaned 1979 (John Hargrave).

ENGRAVINGS:

(1) HL stipple by Robert Shipster (see *above right*) lettered: *Abbot pinxt / Shipster sculp./SIR HORATIO NELSON K.B. / Rear Admiral of the Blue / From an original Painting by Abbott in the Possession / of Willm.*

Locker Esqr Lieut Govr. of Greenwich Hosp.[1] / London Published 1798 by J Brydon at his Print Warehouse Charing Cross. A later issue without the central lettering is lettered: *R. Shipster Sculp. / Published as the Act directs by R. Shipster George Street Woolwich*

(2) HL mezzotint by Valentine Green (see *p.202*) in a 'stone' oval lettered: *Painted by L.F. Abbott / Engraved by V. Green, Mezzotinto Engraver to His Majesty. / THE RIGHT HON: HORATIO BARON NELSON OF THE NILE K.B. REAR ADMIRAL OF THE BLUE / From the Original Picture in the possession of Willm Locker Esqr Lieutenant Governor of Greenwich Hospital. / Published and Sold by V. Green No. 2 New Road, opposite Fitzroy Square, London, Septr 3^{d} 1799, Sold also by R. Green, No. 42 Berners Street, Oxford Street, London.* (Chaloner Smith 89).

(3) Head only, published by V. Green among 'The British Naval Victors', 11 February 1799.

(4) HL mezzotint by Valentine Green in a 'stone' rectangle lettered: *L.F. Abbot Pinx^{t}. / Pub. Nov. 14. 1805 by J. Harris, 30 Conduit Street / V. Green sculp^{t}. / ADMIRAL VISCOUNT NELSON.*

COMMENTS: pages 40-1. ILLUSTRATED: page 39.

13: *Mezzotint by Valentine Green, after the oil by Abbott, 1799*

202

14 *London: National Portrait Gallery (394)*

Oil on canvas 76.5 x 63.5cm (30 x 25in) uninscribed, HL in rear-admiral's uniform and details closely following the Locker portrait described above, but with face and expression slightly softened; hair powdered light grey, eyes clear blue with no trace of abnormality; plain brown background.

COLLECTIONS: Lady Nelson; Rev. Robert Sherson; NPG 1874.

ENGRAVINGS:
(1) WL mezzotint by William Barnard (see *p.47*), left hand holding sword and hat, Santa Cruz in background, lettered: *L.F. Abbott Pinxit. W. Barnard sculpsit / SIR HORATIO NELSON K:B: / Rear Admiral of the Blue. / London Published May 25th 1798, by W. Barnard No. 18 London Street / Fitzroy Square and to be had at Mr Abbott's Pall Mall.* (Chaloner Smith 8; O'D 1).

(2) TQL mezzotint by William Barnard, similar to (1) but without hat, lettered: *Painted by L.F. Abbott. Engraved by W. Barnard. BARON NELSON of the NILE and of BURNHAM THORPE in the COUNTY of NORFOLK, K.B. / From the Original Picture in the Possession of Lady Nelson. / Published 1st Novr 1798 by W. Barnard, No. 18 London Street, Fitzroy Square.* (Chaloner Smith 9; O'D 4).

(3) WL mezzotint by William Barnard, similar to (1) but with Battle of the Nile in background and lettered: *...London, Published 1st June 1799 by W. Barnard, No. 18 London Street, Fitzroy Square. To the Right Honble Lady Nelson / This PORTRAIT of the RIGHT honble / ADMIRAL LORD NELSON, K.B. / Is with permission, humbly dedicated by her Ladyship's most obedient gratefull Servant, W. Barnard / Engrav'd by W. Barnard from an Original Painting by L.F. Abbott Esq. in the possession of Lady Nelson.* (not in Chaloner Smith; O'D 2).

(4) TQL mezzotint by William Barnard, similar to (1) but with older face and no arm-ties, lettered: *L.F. Abbott pinxt. W. Barnard scult. Vice Adml. Lord Viscount Nelson Duke of Bronti &c &c &c Slain in fight, Octr 21st 1805 at the memorable battle of Trafalgar. London Published by Wm. Barnard No.1 Fitzroy Street, Fitzroy Square Jany 1 1806.* (Chaloner Smith 10).

(5) WL mezzotint by William Barnard, similar to (1) but standing on quarterdeck of HMS *Victory*, without arm-ties, wearing two Naval gold medals and three stars, and lettered with arms surrounded by scroll *ENGLAND EXPECTS EVERY MAN TO DO HIS DUTY: L. Abbott Esqr. pinxt /W. Barnard sculpt. / The Most Noble Lord Horatio Nelson* [recitation of titles] *... London Published June 26 1806 by W. Barnard No. 1 Fitzroy Street Fitzroy Square.* (Chaloner Smith 11; O'D 5).

(6) HL mezzotint in colour, by Arthur Hogg, issued by Messrs Frost & Reed Limited, 1923.

EXHIBITIONS: Dublin; a torn label taken from the back, but undated, reads: 'Exhibition of Art, Industries and Manufactures, Exhibition Palace, Dublin'; British Council, Milan 1975, British Painting 1660-1840 .

CONDITION: lined and restored, probably on acquisition in 1874, repairing and retouching a horizontal tear through the top of the head.

LITERATURE: Naish 1958, pp.391, 429-41; Walker 1985/2, pp.358-60.

REPRODUCTIONS: Naish 1958, p.288; Pocock 1968, frontispiece; Hattersley 1974, p.212.

COMMENTS: pages 41-6. A pencil drawing, attributed to Beechey but probably by William Barnard (for or after his mezzotint), was sold at Sotheby's 21 April 1983 (125) and again Wallis & Wallis, 1 Albion Street, Lewes, Sussex, 23 October 1984 (846), signed W.B. 1802 and inscribed later on the back: 'drawing portrait of Lord Nelson by William Beechey, RA 1802. This did formerly belong to my grandfather Captain Hardy, a personal friend of Lord Nelson (signed) Captain Thomas Hardy, Sept. 10th 1887'.

ILLUSTRATED: page 30.

ABBOTT 1798 +

NELSON BY LEMUEL FRANCIS ABBOTT, 1798

15 *Greenwich: National Maritime Museum (BHC2887)*

Oil on canvas *c* 76 x 63.5cm (30 x 25in), HL as in the Kilgraston sketch (12; *p.37*) but with very small variations in the line of the buttons above the Bath star and in the less steep angle of the empty sleeve; ships in left background but the main difference lies in the rounder shape of the head, softer contours, milder expression, fluffier hair, clear blue eyes and generally less warlike aspect; it is probably the first of the 'adonised' variants to which all later versions conform.

COLLECTIONS: given by Nelson to his agent Alexander Davison and bequeathed by his son, Sir William Davison, to Greenwich Hospital in 1873. It hung in the Painted Hall until transferred to the NMM in 1932.

15: *Oil by Lemuel Abbott (Davison's copy)*

ENGRAVINGS: (1) HL mezzotint by Richard Earlom, lettered under motto: *PALMAM QUI MERUIT FERAT / L.F. Abbott Pinx^t. / Publishe'd Decr 19th 1798 by B.B. Evans London / Rich Earlom Sculp / The Right Honorable LORD NELSON K B Rear Admiral of the Blue &c &c &c. / Engraved from the Original Picture in the Possession of Alexander Davison Esq. To whom this Plate is respectfully Inscribed by his obliged & very obedient Servant B. B. Evans.* It was re-issued as a TQL in May 1801. (2) HL mezzotint, (in colour) by R S Syer lettered: *Painted by L.F. Abbott, / Engraved by R.S.Syer. / LORD VISCOUNT NELSON, / Vice Admiral of the White / From the Original Picture in the possession of his Friend Alex^r Davison Esqr St James's Square, / to whom this Print is respectfully dedicated by his obliged humble Serve^t. / Albin R. Burt. / Publish'd by A.R.Burt, 18 St John's Lane, Clerkenwell* (Chaloner Smith 29a). There is no publication date; Commander Robinson says May 1801 but it looks later and moreover Nelson's appointment to Vice-Admiral of the White was 23 April 1804. (3) HL line engraving by J. T. Wedgwood lettered: *THE RIGHT HON. EARL*(sic)*NELSON / Vice Admiral of the White. / Engraved by J.T. Wedgwood from an Original Painting in the possession of Alexander Davison Esqr.*, used to illustrate Campbell's *Lives of the Admirals* (1817) VIII frontispiece.

LITERATURE: NMM 1988, p.63; Walker 1994, pp.88-9.

REPRODUCTIONS: Oman 1947, p.256; Pocock 1987, fig.27; White's *Companion*, p.32; Van der Merwe 1995, p.6.

COMMENTS: pages 46-8.
ILLUSTRATED: page xvi and left.

ABBOTT 1799

NELSON BY LEMUEL FRANCIS ABBOTT, 1799

16 *Greenwich: National Maritime Museum (BHC 2889)*

Oil on canvas 76 x 63.5cm (30 x 25in), no inscription, HL to left in rear admiral's undress uniform, cocked hat, with chelengk, (with six fingers), stars of Bath (lower right), St Ferdinand and Merit (left), Crescent (above right), riband of St Ferdinand (dark blue) over his right shoulder and over the uniform coat, riband of the Bath under the coat and just visible below his empty right sleeve which is fastened under the star of St Ferdinand. Three circular brooches set in seed pearls or brilliants arranged in a triangle below his black neckcloth and white shirt-frill (the upper brooch appears to be a moustachioed man with a sword or spear over his shoulder, the left brooch a Magdalene (or Emma Hamilton), the right a Naval gold medal). Eyes hazel and not clear blue as in NPG and other versions, and his left eye with a noticeable pterygium. The general expression smiling but not specially 'sanctified', the complexion ruddy and weatherbeaten. Bluish-grey background with flames or storm-clouds to left; suggestion of pentimento over his right shoulder.

COLLECTIONS: commissioned by John M'Arthur and at his death presented to Greenwich Hospital by Jasper de St Croix and others in 1849.

ENGRAVINGS: (1) stipple by Piercy Roberts (*opposite*), HL in an oval over Nelson's Arms and lettered: *L F Abbot Esq pinx^t / From a picture in the possession of J McArthur Esq York Place Portman Squ. / P. Roberts sculp^t / THE R^t. HON^ble / LORD NELSON K.B. / REAR ADMIRAL / OF THE RED / DUKE OF BRONTI &c. / Publish'd by Bunney & Gold Shoe Lane April 1 1800.* This print was used as an illustration to the Memoir of Nelson in *The Naval Chronicle* (of which M'Arthur was editor) III (1800) pp 157-91, and described there as 'The portrait ... is taken from the only painting in this country that (and) represents Lord Nelson's additional

The Rt. Honble Lord Nelson K.B.
Rear Admiral of the Red,
Duke of Bronte, &c.

Publish'd by Bunney & Gold Shoe Lane April 1 1800.

16: *Stipple engraving, by Piercy Roberts 1800, after the oil by Abbott*

honours, viz: the plume of triumph and the patent of the Dukedom of Bronti, &c, as worn at Foreign Courts' (p.191). (2) stipple by James Heath HL in a rectangle, lettered: *Engraved by Ja^s, Heath, Historical Engraver to his Majesty, from an original Picture painted by Abbot, in the possession of John McArthur Esq./. THE RIGHT HON^ble LORD NELSON, K.B. VICE ADMIRAL OF THE BLUE, / DUKE OF BRONTI, &c / Published Jany 26 1801, by Ja^s Heath, No.15, Russell Place, Fitzroy Square. Thompson, Newport Street, Colnaghi, Cockspur Street, & Macklin, Fleet Street.* (3) line engraving by J Golding (see *p.51*), HL closely following Abbott's oil and lettered: *Painted by L.F. Abbott / Engraved by J. Golding / LORD VISCOUNT NELSON K.B. VICE ADMIRAL &c &c &c / Aetat 43 / Published Novr 15th 1808 by T. Cadell & W. Davies, Strand.* This print was used as an illustration to Clarke & M'Arthur's *Life* (quarto edition 1809) I frontispiece, described therein as 'From a Painting by the late F. ABBOT in November 1800 ... This Portrait is considered an animated likeness and Mr Golding the engraver, has succeeded in rendering justice to the Painter, after another eminent Artist has failed to give satisfaction in the execution of his plate. Nelson's uniform is decorated with ... together with three Medals suspended from his neck and button holes...' (page xxxvii).

LITERATURE: Clarke & M'Arthur 1809, I xxxvii; Naish 1958, p.552; NMM 1988, p.63.

REPRODUCTIONS: Naish 1972, back cover (colour); Hattersley 1974, p.93 (colour); Hibbert 1994, pl.25 (colour).

COMMENTS: pages 49-52. A pencil and watercolour drawing, probably by James Heath and believed to have belonged to Robert Southey, was exhibited Sotheby's, 'Marine Pictures and Nautical Works of Art', 3 May 1995 (1). (see *opposite*)

ILLUSTRATED: page 31.

Some subsequent versions of the Abbott half-length portrait.

17 | *Edinburgh: Scottish National Portrait Gallery (Collingwood's)*

Oil on canvas 76.2 x 64cm (30 x 25¼in).

COLLECTIONS: said to have been given by Nelson to Collingwood; Baroness Burdett Coutts sale Christie's 4 May 1922 (14) bought Knoedler; presented to the Scottish NPG by Andrew T Reid in 1924.

18 | *Greenwich: National Maritime Museum (Huson Morris)*

Oil on canvas 76 x 62.5cm (30 x 24½in), no ships in left, background.

COLLECTIONS: acquired by Huson Morris c1830 then by descent to his grandchildren who sold it in 1941 as part of their war effort.

COMMENTS: pages 52-3.

19 | *Henley: private collection (Northbrook's)*

Oil on canvas 75 x 62cm (29½ x 24½in), no ships in background.

COLLECTIONS: Countess of Northbrook CBE and sold by her at Christie's 12 October 1945 (1) bought Spink and sold to a private collector. The 1st and 2nd Earls of Northbrook were both First Lords of the Admiralty.

20 | *Portsmouth: Royal Naval Museum*

Oil on canvas 76 x 63.6cm (30 x 25in), Undress rear admiral's uniform, Bath star on left breast, Bath ribbon just visible under uniform coat, one neck medal, plain background. Face much adonised and head repainted. Frill clearly defined, bituminous.

16: *Watercolour drawing attributed to James Heath, c.1801*

COLLECTIONS: Shaftesbury and Arethusa Homes and given by them to the RNM on their closure in 1975.

21 *Portsmouth: Royal Naval Museum*

Enamel miniature by William Grimaldi. Rear admiral's undress uniform, three stars (Bath, St Ferdinand and Crescent), 2 neck medals, Bath ribbon just visible under coat. Hair similar to standard Abbott portrait except that one lock is trained forward to hide the Nile scar. Signed: Grimaldi 1804.

COLLECTIONS: Lily Lambert McCarthy, 41/76.

LITERATURE: Listed in *Catalogue of Paintings by William Grimaldi* 1873; McCarthy 1995, No 173; White's *Companion*, dustcover.

ILLUSTRATED: page 42.

22 *Port Sunlight: Lady Lever Art Gallery*

Oil on canvas 76 x 63.5cm (30 x 25in), a feeble late copy, the shirt-frill left blank.

COLLECTIONS: James Orrock and bought by W. H. Lever (Lord Leverhulme) in 1910.

23 *Stroud: private collection*

Oil on canvas *c.*77.5 x 65cm (30½ x 25½in), probably a very late copy, crudely painted, shirt-frill sketchy.

COLLECTIONS: unknown until the owners, A. W. Stanton, joined *The Times* correspondence 3 November 1932; reproduced *ILN* 26 November 1932 p.859.

24 *USA: private collection (Bridport's)*

Oil on canvas *c.* 76 x 63.5cm (30x 25in), with ships in background.

COLLECTIONS: lst Earl Nelson, his daughter Lady Charlotte Nelson later Lady Bridport and her descendants to the 2nd Viscount Hood (d. 1924); Knoedler No.6786 and sold to America.

25 *USA: private collection, New York*

Oil on canvas *c.* 74 x 62cm (29 x 24½in), probably a very late copy.

COLLECTIONS: formerly with the Navy League, exhibited British Empire, Wembley 1924. Captain Paul Hammond (d c.1976) and in *c.* 1965 given to Melvin A. Conant.

26 *Location unknown since 1804*

Oil on canvas, size unknown but probably the usual half-length, sale of Abbott's effects Christie's 16 June 1804 (89), 'Lord Nelson, framed, bt. Winstanley £4.16.0'.

27 *Location unknown since 1840*

Oil on canvas, size unknown but probably the usual half-length, belonging to Sir Jeffrey Wyatville and known from an enamel copy in NPG, exh. RA 1840 (907) by H.P. Bone, '...from the original by Abbott in the possession of the late Sir Jeffrey Wyatville, RA &c'.

28 *Location unknown since 1868*

Oil on canvas *c.* 76 x 63.5cm (30 x 25in).

COLLECTION: Norman Wilkinson and lent by him to the National Portraits Exhibition 1868 (27).

29 *Location unknown since 1891*

Oil on canvas, probably the usual half-length, lent to the Guelph Exhibition 1891 (307) by W.S. Green and possibly bought at Puttick & Simpson 9 June 1891.

30 *Location unknown since 1927*

Chalk on paper size unknown, reproduced in Admiral Sir Mark Kerr's *Land Sea and Air* (1927) p.248.

31 *Location unknown since 1931* (Deuchar's)

Oil on canvas *c.* 76 x 63.5cm (30 x 25in).

COLLECTIONS: Miss Deuchar of Trafalgar Lodge, Edinburgh in 1920 (Miss Deuchar's ancestor fought at Trafalgar and was possibly a son of David Deuchar, an Edinburgh engraver and Raeburn's art master); Barbizon House 1922-3; Howard Young Gallery 1931; Knoedler no. LC 450.

Several whole-length and three-quarter length portraits are known, with the heads probably painted by Abbott, the remainder added by William Barnard or others. The Northcote version (36) is specially interesting.

32 *London: Lloyd's Nelson Room*

Oil on canvas *c.* 236 x 145cm (93 x 57in), WL standing in rear-admiral's full-dress uniform but with vice-admiral's shoulder-straps (two crowns), Santa Cruz in background.

COLLECTIONS: Duke of Westminster and Christie's 3 February 1961 (42), bt Leggatt Bros and from them by the Lloyd's Patriotic Fund to mark the opening of the new Lloyd's Building in 1961. The Lloyd's Patriotic Fund was formed in 1803. From it grants were paid to the next of kin of sailors killed in action, and presentations of silver plate were made to officers who had distinguished themselves in battle. Nelson received two grants of £500 to be laid out in plate after the battles of the Nile and Copenhagen, and it is some of that silver, the kernel of the collection, from which the Nelson Room derives its name.

A copy of the head, possibly by Barnard, is in a Hampshire private collection.

LITERATURE: B.E. Parker, 'Lloyd's of London' in *Connoisseur Year Book* (1960), pp.83-8; Clifford Musgrave, 'The Treasures of Lloyd's' in *Connoisseur* (June 1970), p.94.

33 | *London: Wimbledon Town Hall*

Oil on canvas *c.* 250 x 140cm (97 x 64in), WL standing on shore, one Naval gold medal, Star of Garter (sic), ships and rock background.

COLLECTIONS: Sir Robert Hadfield who bequeathed it to the NPG in 1940; it was declined by the Trustees, returned to Lady Hadfield, and sold Hampton & Sons, November 1942 (710), there catalogued as 'Admiral Lord Nelson by W. Barnard after L.F. Abott (sic)' but withdrawn before the sale. Purchased by the Urban District of Merton and Morden in 1943.

34 | *London: Crown Estate Commissioners, Pall Mall*

Oil on canvas, *c.* 250 x 183cm (98 x 72in), WL as above without Santa Cruz background, the head by John Jackson, remainder by J.E.H. Robinson.

COLLECTIONS: bought by subscription for the United Service Club 1831, transferred to the Crown Estate Commissioners in 1975, now on loan to the Institute of Directors, Pall Mall.

35 | *Greenwich: National Maritime Museum*

Oil on canvas, *c.* 201 x 122cm (79 x 48in), WL with arm tie-ribbons, two Naval gold medals, three stars, Santa Cruz background, probably by William Barnard.

COLLECTIONS: Pierpont Morgan sale, Christie's 31 March 1944 (112), bt Spink for the NMM from the Caird Fund (BHC2891); loan to the Ministry of Defence since 1944.

ILLUSTRATED: page 45.

36 | *Herefordshire: Clive Richards' Collection*

Oil on canvas, *c.* 76 x 63 cm (30 x 25 in), HL as above (NMM 2891) but holding a letter to Rear Admiral Thomas Graves, his second-in-command at Copenhagen, painted by James Northcote RA, in whose Account Book it appears in 1813 (*Walpole Society* 58 (1996), p.96, no.582 and fig.35).

ILLUSTRATED: page 43.

37 | *London: Army and Navy Club, Piccadilly*

Oil on canvas, TQL but folded to HL in 1963 to fit the new premises.

COLLECTIONS: bought for the Club in 1852.

38 | *London: private collection, Lincolns Inn*

Oil on canvas (relined), *c.* 76 x 63.5cm (30 x 25in), standard HL copy, possibly early but unfinished.

COLLECTIONS: 'from an old house in Tynemouth', possibly Collingwood's; bt by the present owner in Northumberland in 1984.

39 | *Cumbria: Muncaster Castle*

Oil on canvas, 140 x 110cm (55 x 43¼in), TQL with star of KCB only, Copenhagen background. The hair falls forward in an unusual way, perhaps by Barnard.

40 | *Location unknown since 1804*

Sale of Abbott's effects, Christie's 16 June 1804 (89), bt Winstanley £4.16.0

41 | *Location unknown since 1840*

Sir Jeffrey Wyatville's, known from an enamel copy by H.P. Bone, dated 1840, now in the NPG (see *27*). A smaller enamel copy, also by H.P. Bone and dated 1845, is in the Royal Collection (Buckingham Palace), given by Queen Mary to George V, Christmas 1935 (KGV 414).

42 | *Location unknown since 1858*

Oil on canvas, *c.* 209 x 151cm (82½ x 59½ in), WL standard standing type, Santa Cruz in background.

COLLECTIONS: T. Bryant, 30 St James's Street, and offered by him to the NPG, 8 June 1858 (Scharf TSB.I.34 in NPG archive).

43 *Location unknown since 1860*

Oil on canvas, less than life size, WL standing as above.

COLLECTIONS: 'Barnard of Gravesend from Ly Hamilton's sale / seen with the Honble Fred: Byng in the basement of the House of Lords / GS March 26 1860'
(note and sketch by Scharf in TSB.IV.12, NPG archive).

44 *Location unknown since 1954*

Oil on canvas, *c.* 76 x 63.5cm (30 x 25in), standard HL copy.

COLLECTIONS: Robinson & Foster sale, 17 June 1954 (95).

45 *Location unknown since 1960 (Haslewood's)*

Oil on canvas, *c.* 76 x 63.5cm (30 x 25in), standard HL copy.

COLLECTIONS: given by the Nelson family to William Haslewood, Nelson's lawyer, and by descent to his great-great nephew whose widow sold it at Sotheby's, 19 April 1944 (88), bt Everard; Sir (Percy) Malcolm Stewart Bt. and sold by his Trustees at Knight Frank & Rutley, 18 October 1960 (13).

41: *Enamel by Henry Pierce Bone, 1840, copied from the Abbott owned by Sir Jeffrey Wyatville.*

46 *Location unknown since 1969*

Oil on canvas, 50 x 37 cm (19 x 14$\frac{1}{2}$in), small WL with star of KCB and one Naval gold medal.

COLLECTION: Mason's Yard Gallery, St James's, London, in 1969.

47 *London: Buckingham Palace*

Enamel, oval miniature set in pearls and inscribed in red paint on the plain white counter-enamel: *Nelson / London April 1845 / Painted by Henry / Pierce Bone / Enamel Painter to Her Majesty / & Prince Albert / &c From the Original / by Abbott.*

COLLECTION: given to George V by HM Queen Mary, Christmas 1935 (KGV 414).

GAHAGAN 1798

NELSON BY LAWRENCE GAHAGAN, 1798

48 *Portsmouth: Royal Naval Museum*

Marble bust 51cm (20in) high, incised on the front: *NELSON*, and on the back: *1798*. Head and neck only, the hair disorderly, without queue, and hanging over his forehead to conceal the Nile scar; faintly smiling expression, curved breastline, the nose damaged and repaired.

COLLECTIONS: given to the Royal Naval Museum in 1996 by Bryan Hall.

EXHIBITIONS: probably RA 1798 (1050) as 'Bust of Lord Nelson'. This is mentioned in a letter from Lady Nelson, 6th May 1798: ' Tomorrow we go a strong party to the Exhibition...The bust is there...but too old for you' (Naish p.429). Sotheby's loan exhibition, 'Rule Britannia', January 1986 (135).

COMMENTS: pages 61-5. Gahagan seems to have listened to Lady Nelson's remarks, or perhaps the public disapproved of the smiling expression. Later productions presented a grimmer, more formidable aspect.

ILLUSTRATED: page 59.

49 *Rev Alfred Gatty DD (olim)*

Plaster bust painted as bronze, about 30cm (12in) high, the head only about 12.5cm (5in). *Inscribed on the back: L. Gahagan fecit Jan^{ry}. 1st. 1801. From Life.* Head and neck, the hair long and wavy with queue.

COLLECTIONS: Rev Dr Alexander Scott, Nelson's foreign secretary and chaplain on the *Victory*; Rev Alfred Gatty in 1890.

LITERATURE: letter from Gatty in which he says that Dr Scott always said the likeness was excellent, as was also the wax figure in the little chamber over the Islip Chapel in Westminster Abbey (*Notes and Queries* 8 February 1890 p.107).

50 *Bath: Victoria Art Gallery*

Plaster bust painted as bronze, 54.5 cm (21¹/₂ in) high, incised front *NELSON* and back: *L. Gahagan Fecit 1804*. HS, head turned slightly to right, bare shoulders, disorderly hair without queue, straight breast line curved at the corners.

COLLECTIONS: Mr and Mrs Frank Keevil in 1933. The Keevils are an old Bath family of moulders, woodcarvers and cabinet-makers. In 1923 Charles Drage wrote to Callender about Mr Keevil's bust of Nelson and said 'he has just made me a very good copy for the sum of only £3' (letter in NMM archive), but this may be an original by Gahagan.

ILLUSTRATED: right.

51 *Greenwich: National Maritime Museum (SCU 0099)*

Plaster bust painted brown, 54.5cm (21¹/₂in) high, incised on the back: *Nelson by Gahagan 1804 / F. Keevil and Sons, Moulders, Bath*. HS, head turned slightly to right, bare shoulders, disorderly hair with queue on his right shoulder, straight breast line.

COLLECTIONS: unknown before acquisition by the NMM but possibly made by the Keevils *c.*1923.

52 *Greenwich: National Maritime Museum (SCU 0097)*

Terracotta bust 38cm (15in) high, incised on the back (nearly illegible):... *Gahagan ... London* HS, head turned to his left, bare shoulders, disorderly hair without queue, straight breast line.

COLLECTIONS: bought for the NMM, through Spink from Sotheby's (various properties) 30 May 1933 (33).

ILLUSTRATED: opposite.

53 *Greenwich: National Maritime Museum (SCU 0096)*

Bronze bust 38cm (15in) high, incised on the back: *Nelson / born 1758 / died 1805*. This relates closely to

50: *Plaster bust by Lawrence Gahagan, 1804*

the NMM terracotta bust (52) and may be a published cast from it.

COLLECTIONS: John F Walter of Drayton Hall, Ipswich (died 1927); bought from his son Colonel Francis Walter of Great Yarmouth by the Caird Fund 1953 having been on loan to the NMM since 1935.

54 *Anglesey: Plas Newydd*

Bronze bust 54.5cm (21¹/₂in) high, incised roughly: *NELSON 1805.*

52: *Terracotta bust by Lucius Gahagan*

57: *Marble bust by Lawrence Gahagan, 1805*

212

55 *Greenwich: National Maritime Museum (SCU 0098)*

White plaster bust 54.5cm (21¹/₂ in) high, incised on the back: *Published by L. Gahagan Dec'. 1ˢᵗ. 1839 / Lord Nelson sat to L. Gahagan in 1798.* HS, head turned to his right, bare shoulders, disorderly hair without queue, curved breast line. Nose broken off and replaced.

COLLECTIONS: unknown before acquisition by the NMM in 1948. A version with a similar inscription was offered to the NPG in 1928.

56 *Norwich: Castle Museum*

Plaster bust painted as bronze, 54.5cm (21¹/₂ in) high, incised as NMM 48/733 above and with a tattered label on the back written presumably in the sculptor's hand: *I had seven sittings from Admiral Nelson when he resided in Old Bond Street, London ...*

COLLECTION: given to the Castle Museum in 1842 by Richard Ward (not apparently a son of Horatia).

ILLUSTRATED: page 60.

57 *New York: Homan Potterton collection*

Marble bust 29cm (11¹/₂ in) high, incised on the back: *L.Gahagan Fecit MDCCCV.* Head and bare shoulders turned to his right, hair brushed forwards and with queue on his right shoulder, with smiling expression and a different cast of features to the usual Gahagan type; curved breast line.

COLLECTIONS: provenance uncertain.

ENGRAVING: stipple published in London by J. Parry 4 June 1806, the head looking slightly more upward and with a severer expression.

ILLUSTRATED: opposite, left.

58 *Newcastle-upon-Tyne: Newcastle University*

Lead alloy head 37cm (14¹/₂in) high including socle; no inscription; head turned slightly to his left, unsmiling.

COLLECTIONS: Thomas Edward Hodgkin (d 1921); his nephew Dr Charles Bosanquet who gave it to the University in 1968. A similar head was with Captain D. Cooper RN of Windlesham in 1958 (letter from O. Warner to Captain Cooper 24 January 1958 in NMM archive).

ILLUSTRATED: right.

59 *Rudding Park (olim)*

Marble bust 48.6cm (19¹/₈in) high, no inscription, head and draped shoulders, head turned slightly to his left, no queue, smiling expression.

COLLECTIONS: Rudding Park, Yorkshire (Sir Everard Radcliffe) and sold by his executors Christie's 17 October 1972 (448) bought Mullen.

ILLUSTRATED: page 214.

58: *Lead alloy bust by Lucius Gahagan*

59: *Marble bust by Lucius Gahagan*

60 *London: Mrs Marion Cox, 48 Knightsbridge (in 1936)*

Bust (material unspecified) incised: *L. Gahagan / Fecit .../ MDCCCVI 19 Suffolk (?) Street, Middlesex Hospital.*

COLLECTIONS: seen and admired by Robert Nicholls and offered to the NPG by Mrs Marion Cox, owner of a Knightsbridge antique shop, in December 1936 (letter in NPG archive).

61 *London, Highgate: private collection*

Plaster bust painted black, 38cm (15in) high, incised on the back: *Pub^d. by L. Bruchany April lst 1814 / By Authority of the Mod^r. W.P.C. / London.* Head and bare shoulders turned slightly to his left, no queue, straight breast line.

COLLECTIONS: uncertain.

62 *Germany: private collection (in 1926)*

Wooden bust about 25cm (10in) high, no inscription.

COLLECTIONS: Carl von den Osten-Fabeck (Korvettenkapitan a. D. Rittergutbesitzer) 'bought long ago from an antique dealer in Berlin' (letters dated July-August 1926 in NPG archive).

63 *Hampshire: private collection*

Copeland & Garrett felspar porcelain busts of Nelson and Wellington of 1858-1882, 25cm high, Nelson craggy and romanticised to a hardened sea-dog.

LITERATURE: Charles & Dozzie Shin, *Victorian Parian China* (1971) pp. 72,3.

SHOUT 1798

NELSON BY ROBERT SHOUT, 1798

64 *Portsmouth: Royal Naval Museum*

Wedgwood black basalt bust, 28.5cm (11^1/$_4$in) high, impressed on the back: *NELSON / Wedgwood E* and incised in cursive: *Pub^d July 22nd / 1798 / R. Shout sc^t / Holborn.* HS in rear-admiral's full-dress uniform, one Naval gold medal incised: *NILE*; riband and star of the Bath, head turned to his right, empty sleeve pinned across the riband, neckcloth, frilled shirt, very bland hair style knotted at end of queue, severe expression.

COLLECTIONS: Lily Lambert McCarthy 276/77.

LITERATURE: Grant 1910, pp. 170-4 and plates XXXIX-2; Warner, *Connoisseur* CXLII (1958), p.32; Reilly 1989, II p.460, plate 733; McCarthy 1995, no.188.

COMMENTS: pages 61-6. Versions of Shout's bust are plentiful, for example at Barlaston, Greenwich (2), Monmouth, North Walsham and Castle Museum, Norwich.

ILLUSTRATED: page 65.

NELSON attributed to ROBERT SHOUT

65 *Greenwich: National Maritime Museum (SCU 0083) (loan from Lord Cottesloe since 1980)*

Gilt bronze bust, 35.5cm (14in) high including the square base, uninscribed. HS in rear-admiral's full-dress uniform, head turned to his right, one Naval

65: *Bronze bust by (or after) R. Shout*

gold medal with the obverse displayed (St Vincent), riband of the Bath, star of the Garter *(sic)*, empty sleeve pinned across the riband which is secured at the waist by a large free-standing naval button, neckcloth, frilled shirt, meticulously carved epaulettes, neat and orderly hair with unknotted pigtail, faintly smiling expression. The rear-admiral's star on the shoulder-strap is misinterpreted in the shape of a flower.

COLLECTIONS: early history unknown until Henry Willet's sale of effects in Brighton in about 1945, then catalogued as 'reputed to have been presented to Lady Hamilton by the people of Naples', bought by Harold Davies of Brighton and sold to Lord Cottesloe who gave it to his son, Commander the Hon John Fremantle, as a wedding present.

ENGRAVING: a related mezzotint by Barnard (see *p.64*), is lettered: *Gahagon Model* Barnard sculp / To His*

excellency the Marquis of Circello / His Sicilian Majesty's Envoy Extraordinary & Minister Plenipotentiary to His Britanic Majesty / This Portrait of ADMIRAL LORD NELSON, BARON NELSON of the NILE, and of / BURNHAM THORPE in the County of NORFOLK, & K.B. / is by Permission Dedicated. / London, Publish'd as the Act directs 21 Oct' 1805 being the day for commemorating his LORDSHIP'S / ever memorable & Glorious Victory over the French &c &c &c.

Barnard has apparently used Shout's Wedgwood bust from the shoulders downwards, but for the head has substituted an adaptation of his own mezzotint of the Abbott portrait (see *p.47*), with its disorderly hair and more rugged features. It bears no resemblance to the Gahagan busts. The print is recorded in Russell (11a) but not by Chaloner Smith.

REPRODUCTION: Warner *Trafalgar*, p.17.

COMMENTS: page 65. ILLUSTRATED: left.

NELSON, HERCULANEUM BUST, c.1805

66 *Portsmouth: Royal Naval Museum*

Buff stoneware bust impressed: *HERCULANEUM*, 21.6cm (8½ in) high, head turned slightly to his right, vice-admiral's full dress uniform, riband of the Bath, star of the Garter, one Naval gold medal; trophy of crossed cannons, flags and fouled anchor on the flared plinth.

The Herculaneum pottery was founded in Liverpool in 1796, its years of prosperity being 1800 to 1820.

About eighteen portrait busts have been traced including, Nelson, Washington, Admirals St Vincent, Duncan and De Winter, and General Abercromby. None of them are dated but the Nelson bust in the Williamson Art Gallery, Birkenhead, is estimated at 1805 on the evidence of the Herculaneum mark being impressed twice, once in Roman capitals and once in Gothic, as a mark of respect for public mourning. However the bust clearly derives from Robert Shout's bronze (see 65, *left*), the significant features being the neat hair brushed back in the pre-Nile style, the presence of only one Naval gold medal (St Vincent), and the star wrongly shown as the Garter. The Herculaneum busts of St Vincent and Duncan appear to originate with engravings.

COLLECTIONS: Lily Lambert McCarthy 37/74.

LITERATURE: Alan Smith, *The Illustrated Guide to Liverpool Herculaneum Pottery* (1970) p.44 and plate 114; McCarthy 1995, no.185.

ILLUSTRATED: page 65.

67: *James Gillray, 'Extirpation of the Plagues of Egypt', 1798*

69: *James Gillray, 'John Bull taking a Luncheon', 1798*

216

GILLRAY 1798-1805

NELSON BY JAMES GILLRAY, 1798

67 *Portsmouth: Royal Naval Museum*

Etching (coloured impression) on paper, 24.5 x 36cm (9⅝ x 14⅛in), lettered: *Pubᵈ Octʳ 6ᵗʰ 1798 by H. Humphrey 27 St James's Street / Jˢ Gʸ inv & fecᵗ / Extirpation of the Plagues of Egypt; - Destruction of Revolutionary Crocodiles; - or - The British Hero cleansing ye Mouth of ye Nile.*

A ferocious Nelson wades through the waters of Aboukir Bay brandishing a club marked *British Oak* and scattering crocodiles right and left; from a hook protruding from his right sleeve he drags ashore a fleet of tri-coloured crocodiles transfixed by hooks through their jaws; one crocodile (*L'Orient*) explodes in the background. The Nile wound is represented by a bloody cross over his *left* eye. A print of a day later, *The Gallant Nelson*, shows the scar correctly over his right eye (McCarthy, 1995, no.20).

LITERATURE: George 1942, 9250.

REPRODUCTIONS: Naish 1958, pl. XIV; Hattersley 1974, p.88; Warner 1975, pp.92-3 (double-page spread); Hibbert 1995, fig.19; McCarthy 1995, nos. 19-20.

ILLUSTRATED: page 216 and detail page 62.

68 *Portsmouth: Royal Naval Museum*

Etching (coloured impression) on paper, 24.5 x 18.7cm (9¾x 7⅜in), lettered: *Jˢ Gillray del. & fecᵗ / Pubᵈ Decʳ 1ˢᵗ 1798 by H. Humphrey No 27, S James's Street / The HERO of the NILE.* WL standing on deck in uniform over which he wears the Sultan's scarlet sable-lined pelisse; below is a burlesque of his coat of arms with money-bags instead of the cross patonce.

LITERATURE: George 1942, 9269.

REPRODUCTIONS: Pocock 1968, p.73; Walder 1978, pl.11; Hibbert 1994, fig.23.

COMMENTS: pages 6, 57. ILLUSTRATED: page 63.

69 *Portsmouth: Royal Naval Museum*

Etching (coloured impression) on paper 24.5 x 36 cm (9 5/8 x 14 1/8 in) lettered *Gillray invi & fect / Published Octr 24 th 1798 by H Humphrey St James's Street / JOHN BULL taking a Luncheon: or British Cooks cramming Old Grumble-Gizzard with Bonne Chere.* A grossly fat and florid John Bull sits at a table

loaded with dishes of ships and cannon, exclaiming *What! More Frigasees? - why you sons o'bitches you, where do ye think I shall find room to stow all you bring in?* He is stuffing himself with captured warships which are being presented to him on dishes by various British admirals: (from l to r) Warren, Howe, Bridport, St Vincent and Duncan. Nelson stands right foreground, presenting a dish marked *Fricasee a la Nelson* and with a piece of paper hanging from his pocket marked *List of French Ships Taken Burnt & Destroyed.* He is shown left profile, with the Nile wound (wrongly) over his left eye and a hook protrudes from his right sleeve. He wears a rear admiral's undress uniform, with the star of the Bath.

COLLECTIONS: Lily Lambert McCarthy, 275/73(15). Examples exist in most of the other main collections.

ILLUSTRATED: page 216.

NELSON BY JAMES GILLRAY, 1801

70 *Portsmouth: Royal Naval Museum*

Etching (hand-coloured impression) on paper 25.4 x 20cm (10 x 7⅞in), lettered: *London Published May 8ᵗʰ 1801. by H. Humphrey No.27 St James's Street / From Sir Willᵐ Hamilton's Collection* - and on the socle

70: *James Gillray, 'From Sir William Hamilton's Collection', 1801*

the Death of ADMIRAL·LORD·NELSON — in the moment of Victory!

71: _James Gillray, 'The Death of Admiral Lord Nelson', 1805_

below his feet: *DAM . N . QV . I . Σ . Σ . Ω . N .* 'Until fairly recently this print was assumed to be of Sir William Hamilton himself, but in 1985 Dyfri Williams suggested that it portrays Nelson in the shape of the Meidias Hydria, probably the best-known vase from Hamilton's collection in the British Museum. Certainly if Sir William was to be portrayed as one of his vases it would have been a tall thin one. This seems to be a very reasonable idea, especially as Gillray had already satirised the other two members of the *Tria Juncta In Uno*, Hamilton as 'Connoisseur' and Emma as 'Dido in Despair'. The letters on the base are obscure but probably mean either 'Damn Nelson' or 'Admiral Nelson'.

LITERATURE: George 1942, 9754; Jenkins & Sloan, *Vases and Volcanoes* (British Museum exhibition catalogue, 1996) p.302.

ILLUSTRATED: page 217.

NELSON BY JAMES GILLRAY, 1805

71 *Portsmouth: Royal Naval Museum*

Etching (coloured impression) on paper 24.5 x 18.7 cm (9 3/4 x 7 3/8 in) lettered, *Gillray invt & fect / Published Decr 23d 1805 by H Humphrey 27 St James's / this Design for the Memorial intended by the City of London to commemorate the Glorious Death of the immortal / Nelson, is with every sentiment of respect, humbly submitted to the Right honbl the Lord Mayor & the Court of Aldermen.* Nelson, wearing a full dress vice admiral's uniform with the Bath star and ribbon and one neck medal, sits wounded on a cannon on the deck of the *Victory*. He is supported by a weeping Britannia (a caricature of Emma Hamilton); while Captain Hardy (a caricature, of King George IV) staunches his wound with a handkerchief and a sailor (a caricature of the Duke of Clarence) presents him with a captured French flag. In the background, Royal Marines can be seen firing at Frenchmen in the fighting top of the *Redoutable*, while above them Fame blows a trumpet and writes the word *Immortality* on the clouds.

COLLECTIONS: Lily Lambert McCarthy, 120/73. Examples exist in most of the other main collections.

ILLUSTRATED: opposite.

DE VAERE 1798

NELSON BY JOHN DE VAERE, 1798

72 *Portsmouth: Royal Naval Museum*

White profile medallion on light blue background in rear-admiral's full-dress uniform, St, Vincent gold medal, riband and star of the Bath, hair neat, and in queue. Jasper ware versions are in most collections and in black basalt, black on white, and various shades of green, blue and lilac dip. Produced by Wedgwood

The original wax model is in the Wedgwood Museum accompanied by De Vaere's receipt: 'Rec^d Novr 9th 1798 of Messrs Josiah Wedgwood of Byesley two pounds 12/6 for modelling the Lord Nelson & 2/6 for his Print - £2-15-0 (signed) J. De Vaere'. A version is applied to the side of a buff-coloured caneware jug decorated with anchors and the legends *NELSON / AND / VICTORY* and along the top: *THE WOODEN WALLS OF OLD ENGLAND* (see p. 67)

COLLECTIONS: Lily Lambert McCarthy 272/73, 178/73.

LITERATURE: Harry Barnard, 'The Etruria Museum', *The Connoisseur* 85 (1930), p.295; Reilly & Savage 1973, p.256; Reilly 1989, II fig.854, p.725; McCarthy 1995, no. 200 and 233.

COMMENTS: pages 66-69. ILLUSTRATED: page 75.

BOULTON AND KÜCHLER 1798

NELSON: DAVISON'S NILE MEDAL, 1798

73 *Portsmouth: Royal Naval Museum*

Gold medal 4.75cm 1³/₈in) diameter.
Obverse: Peace standing on a rock by the sea, olive branch in her right hand, her left supporting an oval shield with profile bust of Nelson in rear-admiral's full-dress uniform, riband and star of the Bath, hair brushed back, incised: *EUROPE'S HOPE AND BRITAIN'S GLORY,* and around: REAR-ADMIRAL LORD NELSON OF THE NILE. Signed on the rock with Küchler's initials C.H.K.

Reverse: View of Aboukir Bay with the English and French Fleets at sunset, around: *ALMIGHTY GOD HAS BLESSED HIS MAJESTY'S ARMS.* Exergue (in small capitals): *VICTORY OF THE, NILE / AUGUST 1. 1798.* Signed on exergual line (in small capitals): *M. B SOHO C. H. KUCHLER. FEC. JOIESIS*

73: *Davison's Nile medal, 1798*

Edge: (sunk in small capitals): FROM ALEX^r. DAVISON ESQ^r. ST. JAMES'S SQUARE = A TRIBUTE OF REGARD

COLLECTIONS: The medal was issued in Gold, Silver, Silver Gilt and Bronze, according to rank, and most of the main collections contain examples of all four types. The RNM gold medal is part of the Douglas-Morris Collection. There are two gold examples at the NMM: one presented to Nelson by Davison and given to Greenwich Hospital by the widow of Jasper le Croix and the other presented to Captain Thomas Troubridge and loaned, to the Museum by his descendant. A number of the known examples of silver, silver-gilt and bonzed medals have been named by their recipients but this was only done unofficially.

LITERATURE: NMM Medal Catalogue (in progress) LL19; Mayo 1897, pp.178-82; Milford Haven 492; Gordon pp. 16-17; Pollard 1970, pp.284-6; Brown 1980, 447; McCarthy 1995, no.29.

REPRODUCTIONS: Hattersley 1974, p.84 (colour); Warner 1975, p.145.

COMMENTS: pages 68-70. A copy, containing copper from HMS *Victory*, was presented to the Kaiser, *c.*1910.

ILLUSTRATED: above and detail page 66.

DAMER 1798-9

NELSON by the Hon ANNE SEYMOUR DAMER

74 *London: Guildhall*

Colossal marble bust 76cm (30in) high, incised in Greek capitals on the back: *ANNA SEIMORIS DAMER / EMOIEI*. Head facing forwards and directed slightly downwards, hair brushed forwards covering the Nile scar, lips turned down distinctively, nose turned up at end, hair in queue; riband of Bath, stars of Bath, St Ferdinand, Turkish Crescent (C open to right), two Naval gold medals (St Vincent above, Nile below incised: *NELSON AUG MDCCXCVIII*); shirt-frill a noticeable feature.

COLLECTIONS: offered by Mrs Damer to the City Corporation in 1799 and presented in 1803.

EXHIBITION: RA 1804 (937) - 'Bust of Lord Nelson in Cimra Marble' (probably a misprint for Carrara Marble).

ENGRAVINGS:
(1) large mixed stipple, profile to left lettered: *Engraved from the Bust / THE IMMORTAL NELSON / Published & Sold Octr 2nd 1805 by Edwd Orme 59 Bond Street, London.* A single experimental proof in

PALMAM QUI MERUIT FERAT

THIS BUST of LORD NELSON EXECUTED IN MARBLE BY THE HON^{BLE} ANNE SEYMOUR DAMER

ON HIS RETURN TO ENGLAND AFTER THE BATTLE of THE NILE 1801 WAS PRESENTED BY HER

TO THE CITY of LONDON AND IS NOW PLACED IN THE COUNCIL CHAMBER GUILDHALL

74: *Stipple engraving by Charles Knight, 1806*

221

mixed etching, stipple, roulette and aquatint, extensively hand-touched with grey and white wash especially round the profile outline, is in the NMM print room.

(2) large stipple by C. Knight (see *p.221*), full-face in niche, lettered *PALMAM QUI MERUIT FERAT / THIS BUST of LORD NELSON executed in marble by the HON^ble ANNE SEYMOUR DAMER / on his return to England after the BATTLE of the NILE 1801 was presented by her / to the CITY of LONDON and is now placed in the COUNCIL CHAMBER GUILDHALL / Dedicated by permission to the Right Hon. the LORD MAYOR, the Worshipful COURT of ALDERMEN, and the COMMON COUNCIL of the CITY of LONDON / by their obedient Humble Servant / C. Knight / Drawn, Engraved & Published June 1st 1806, by C. Knight, Webb Lane, Hammersmith.*

REPRODUCTION: McCarthy 1995, p.129.

(3) stipple by James Godby, HS to right in profile lettered: *HORATIO LORD VISCOUNT NELSON / The original Bust was executed in Marble from the Life & presented to the City of London by the Honble Anne Seymour Damer / and is now placed in the Council Chamber of Guildhall / Published July 10th 1806 by Edwd Orme, Bond Street London.* This was used as frontispiece to *Orme's Graphic History of Nelson* (1806). A copy of this print in the NMM is annotated in pencil: 'Done by Mrs Damer at Naples in Oct 1798. Lord Nelson sat in the coat he had worn in the battle of the Nile, which he gave to Mrs D.'

COPIES: a bronze cast in the Royal Collection (Windsor Castle) was made in 1827 for the Duke of Clarence and inscribed on the plinth: TO - / HIS ROYAL HIGHNESS THE DUKE OF CLARENCE / *Lord High Admiral of England / this bust executed by herself / is respectfully presented / by / The Honourable Anne Seymour Damer / -MDCCCXXVII* - Another bronze copy was made for the King of Tanjore, and a copy, containing copper from HMS *Victory*, was presented to the Kaiser, *c.*1910.

LITERATURE: Nicolas VII, pp.347-8; Noble 1908, pp.156-61

COMMENTS: pages 73-8. ILLUSTRATED: page 79.

NELSON BY B PAPERA, *c.*1802

75 *Barlaston: Wedgwood Museum*

Plaster bust painted black about 25cm (10in) high, unmarked except for *Nelson* scratched into reverse of socle. HS in rear-admiral's uniform, neckcloth and shirt-frill, two small Naval gold medals resting on edge of riband of the Bath, stars of Bath (above), St Ferdinand (left), Crescent (right), hair brushed forward and parted in centre, severe unsmiling expression; unincised metope socle on circular pedestals.

COLLECTIONS: uncertain; the bust derives from Mrs Damer's 1798 bust and is attributed by the Wedgwood authorities to Papera though it does not appear to have become part of their published stock.

LITERATURE: Robin Reilly, *Wedgwood* (1989), II p.457.

COMMENTS: pages 73-4. ILLUSTRATED: page 77.

NELSON BY WILLIAM JOHN COFFEE 1806

76 *Greenwich: National Maritime Museum (SCU 0095)*

White plaster bust 29.2cm (11¹/₂ in) high, incised *John Coffee 1806.* Head turned slightly to his right, in a loose-fitting toga-like garment with a button on his left shoulder, hair brushed forward, parted in the centre and thick at the back but not in queue, corners of the mouth turned down, cheeks sunken and generally drawn expression as though in pain.

COLLECTIONS: Sotheby's 19 September 1980 (137) bought NMM.

COMMENTS: page 74. The bust derives from Mrs Damer's 1798 bust. An unsigned version was at the Covent Garden Gallery in 1980.

GUZZARDI 1799

NELSON BY LEONARDO GUZZARDI, 1799

77 | *London: Admiralty Boardroom*

Oil on canvas *c.* 262 x 176cm (103 x 70in) enlarged at edges, signed and dated on the rim of the targe lower left: '*LEONARDUS GUZZARDI PINX. PANOR^mi. 1799.* WL standing in rear-admiral's full-dress uniform, cocked hat worn high on forehead, chelengk, riband and star of the Bath, one Naval gold medal (St Vincent); he stands on deck in front of a carronade beside a chair draped with the scarlet sable-lined pelisse given by the Sultan with the chelengk; in the bottom left corner a helmet, some round shot and a targe signed and dated as above; his right sleeve is fastened below the Bath riband; his left hand points to the Battle of the Nile raging in the right background, blue draperies to left. His complexion a suffused pink, the eyes greyish-blue. 'The right eyebrow is deficient in hair and there is a vertical scar arising from about the mid-point of the eyebrow and extending upwards over the right frontal boss. The eyes are essentially straight with bright corneae, equal pupils and with a suggestion of bilateral pterygium as the only external abnormality' (*Pugh* p. 46).

COLLECTIONS: commissioned by Sir William Hamilton who gave it to his nephew Charles Greville; inherited by his nephew Robert Fulke Greville who presented it to the Admiralty in 1848.

ENGRAVINGS:

(1) a HL stipple vignette by J Skelton was used as frontispiece in Pettigrew's *Life of Nelson* (1849) lettered: *...from the Original picture in the Board Room of the Admiralty ...*

(2) A mezzotint by John Young of Keymer's copy of this portrait (see *p.224*), was published by M H Keymer in 1800 lettered: *Painted by M H Keymer Yarmouth, from a portrait by a Celebrated Artist at Palermo, Portrait Painter to the King* (Chaloner Smith 57).

ILLUSTRATED: pages 4 and 82.

This picture is the only known signed full-sized version of Guzzardi's portrait and is discussed on pages 78-91 It is probably the original from which a number of small copies were made, either by Guzzardi himself or by later copyists, all measuring about 86 x 52cm (33 x 20in). The following list covers the known replicas and copies.

78 | *Naples: Museo di San Martino*

Oil on canvas 86.1 x 52.1cm (34 x 20¹/₂in), WL signed and dated *LEONARDUS GUZZARDI Pin. 1799*, riband and star of the Bath and one Naval gold medal.

COLLECTIONS: probably the first copy and made for the Neapolitan royal family; before being transferred to the Museo di San Martino it hung in the Palazzo Reale, Caserta, one of King Ferdinand's country palaces.

EXHIBITIONS: 'Portrait' Florence 1911 (Thieme-Becker XV 372); Naples 1944 in honour of a visit from HM King George VI (information from Edward Croft Murray); 'Lady Hamilton' GLC Kenwood 1972 (85).

REPRODUCTION in colour in Doria, Bologna, Pannai *Settecento Napolitano* (Turin 1962) plate XII.

79 | *Greenwich: National Maritime Museum (BHC 2895)*

Oil on canvas 84 x 58cm (33 x 20in), WL signed and dated *LEONARDUS GUZZARDI PIN 1799*, riband and star of the Bath and one Naval gold medal; inscribed on back of canvas: *For our Master the King.*

COLLECTIONS: probably the second copy and made for Nelson himself; it descended in the family and was bought from Earl Nelson in 1948 (TH 3).

REPRODUCTIONS: Naish 1958 p 304; Pocock 1968 p 102; Warner 1975, frontispiece (colour).

ILLUSTRATED: page 81.

80 | *London: private collection*

Oil on canvas 82.5 x 49.5cm (32¹/₂ x 19¹/₂in), WL signed and dated *LEONARDO GUZZARDI 1799*, riband and star of the Bath and one Naval gold medal.

COLLECTIONS: probably the third copy and painted for one of the Nile captains; possibly the copy offered to the NPG by Joseph Franklin 14 July 1859 (Scharf TSB II 12); Sotheby's (various properties) 21 June 1967 (77) bt Rosenthal; Christie's (property of a nobleman) 2 April 1971 (69) bt Appleby.

81: *Mezzotint by John Young after Keymer's copy of Sir William Hamilton's Guzzardi*

83: *Oil by Leonardo Guzzardi presented by Nelson to the Sultan of Turkey, 1799.*

ENGRAVING: mezzotint by John Young (*opposite*) lettered: *ADMIRAL LORD NELSON OF THE NILE / Painted by M. H. Keymer, Yarmouth, from a Portrait by a Celebrated Artist at Palermo, Portrait Painter to the King. / Engraved by Jno Young Engraver to His Rl Highs the Prince of Wales. / London, Publish'd decr 8th 1800, by M.H. Keymer.*

COMMENTS: pages 84. ILLUSTRATED: page 85.

82 | *London: Government Art Collection (GAC 15080)*

Oil on canvas 60.3 x 48.9cm (23¼ x 19¼in), HS copy of Guzzardi's WL, riband and star of Bath, one Naval gold medal and chelengk with eight feathers. The Nile scar is prominent above his right eyebrow, eyes are greenish-grey without abnormality, purplish-pink complexion.

COLLECTIONS: bought *c.*1930 in Portsmouth by Mrs Crawley and Miss Violet Woodhouse; bequeathed to Mrs Crawley's nephew Esme Strachey who sold it at Christie's 24 July 1980 (123), bt GAC.

CONDITION: cleaned and restored by GAC on acquisition in 1980 when X-ray photography revealed another portrait underneath.

83 | *Istanbul: Dolmabahce Palace*

Oil on canvas *c.* 84 x 51cm (33 x 20in), WL unsigned. star of the Crescent and Davison's gold medal both worn on his right breast, riband and star of the Bath and two Naval gold medals.

COLLECTIONS: painted for the Sultan and sent to the Ottoman Court in exchange for the Turkish gifts which had arrived in Naples in December 1798. This and remaining copies show Nelson wearing the Turkish Order of the Crescent, received in November 1799 but not gazetted in London until March 1802.

ILLUSTRATED: top left.

84 | *Portsmouth: HMS Nelson*

Oil on canvas 84 x 51cm (33 x 20in), WL unsigned. Star of the Crescent on his right breast, riband and star of the Bath and two Naval gold medals.

COLLECTIONS: provenance uncertain until sold by Lady Brownrigg at Sotheby's 2 June 1943 (109) bt Leggatt; later at Michelman Priory and now HMS *Nelson.*

81 | *London: private collection*

Oil on canvas 76.2 x 62.2cm (30 x 24¼in), HS only in a painted oval, riband and star of the Bath and one Naval gold medal.

COLLECTIONS: probably Matthew Keymer's copy made in Yarmouth in November 1800 and acquired by Captain Sir Richard Pearson (commander of the *Serapis* 1779); his descendant Admiral Sir Hugh Evan-Thomas (d.1928); his brother Owen Evan-Thomas, a picture dealer of Dover Street, London, and bought from him by Captain Paul Hammond USN; his niece Beatrice Lady Wright.

85 *Greenwich: National Maritime Museum (BHC 2896)*

Oil on canvas 213.5 x 117cm (84 x 46in), unsigned WL wearing riband of the Bath and on his left breast stars of the Crescent (above) and Bath (below) and two Naval gold medals. Considerably overpainted and might benefit from cleaning, possibly revealing an inscription.

COLLECTIONS: Nelson family; Nelson-Ward collection and acquired in 1946.

86 *Location unknown since 1863 (Ball)*

Oil on canvas, probably the usual HL.

COLLECTIONS: given by Nelson to Alexander Ball (captain of the *Alexander* at the Nile) and offered by his son Sir William Keith Ball to the NPG in 1863.

87 *Location unknown since 1897 (Morrison)*

Oil on canvas sight size 68.5 x 54.5cm (27 x 21¹/₂in), unsigned HS only with stars of the Bath and Crescent on his left breast, two Naval gold medals and Davison's gold medal.

COLLECTIONS: offered to the NPG by Thomas Gullick in May 1882 (TSB XXIX 72); Alfred Morrison and reproduced in Beresford & Wilson *Nelson and his Times* (1897) p 107.

88 *Location unknown since 1952*

Oil on canvas, size uncertain.

COLLECTIONS: Colonel D.M. Reid, 41 Ashburnham Mansions, London SW10 in August 1952 (NMM archive).

89 *London: private collection 1983*

Oil on canvas 46.5 x 33cm (18¹/₄ x 13in), WL signed and dated 1799 with inscription altered slightly to read: *LEONARDUS GUZZADI PINZ - PANOR - 1799.*

COLLECTIONS: Bonham's 22 July 1982 (172) and again 2 September 1982 (40); brought in to NPG for inspection, 2 February 1983, by F.B. Cockett, FRCS; and Bonham's again 5 August 1983 (99).

90 *Dartmouth: Britannia Royal Naval College*

Oil on canvas 218.5 x 127cm (86 x 50in) inscribed on targe: *LEONARDUS GUZZARDI PNIX. PANOR^m. 1799.* WL standing in rear-admiral's full-dress uniform as in the Admiralty Boardroom original but without the additional strips round the edges.

COLLECTIONS: (See Appendix III)

CONDITION: the picture suffered severely when the College was bombed in 1942 and was restored by Frost & Reed in 1963.

LITERATURE: letter from Callender to Rear-Admiral Ruck-Keene (Captain of the College) 31 August 1918 (NMM archive); William Winter 'The History of the Dartmouth Version', *Britannia* (Dartmouth College Magazine, July 1967).

COMMENTS: page 89 and Appendix III pp.285-7.

91 *London: National Portrait Gallery (785)*

Oil on canvas 86.3 x 51.6cm (34 x 20³/₈in), inscribed on the back of the chair; *L. Acquarone da un ritratto di Nelson*

COLLECTIONS: this is a late 19th century copy, of the Dolmabahce Palace portrait, (83; *p.225*), presented by His Imperial Majesty the Sultan Abd-ul-Hamid II to the NPG in 1888. The original in the Turkish Treasury had been noticed by Sir Charles Dilke in about 1887 during his tour of Greece, Turkey and India following the divorce proceedings in 1886. His attempts to acquire the original were met, very properly, by the Sultan's refusal and compromise with the copy by Acquarone. This copy is set in a heavily decorated frame surmounted by a trophy of swords, spears, two crescent-headed flagstaffs and two books in a weighing-scale, the whole crowned with a sunburst containing the Imperial emblem of the Sultan Abdul Hamid II (full-page cut in *The Graphic* 16 June 1888 p. 637).

LITERATURE: Various letters from Nelson dated December 1798, November 1799 and January 1802, mainly about the Turkish Orders (Nicolas III, IV and V); Harrison 1806 II p.391; *Naval Chronicle* XX (1808) p.111; Admiralty Memorandum by Admiral W A Baillie Hamilton, 15 April 1875 NMM archive);*Notes and Queries* 7th series IV (1887) p.367; letter from Scharf to *The Times* 24 March 1888 about the NPG copy; Admiralty Memorandum by Sir Eric Geddes, January 1918 (copy in NMM archive); letter from Callender to Rear-Admiral Ruck-Keene (Captain of RN College, Dartmouth) 31 August 1918 (copy in NMM archive); letter from Callender to *The Times* 21 October 1930, about Keymer's portrait; correspondence between Callender and David Bonner Smith (Admiralty librarian) July 1939, referring to the Admiralty Boardroom version (Callender Papers in NMM archive); Gino Doria, F. Bologna & Guido Pannai *Settecento Napolitano* (Turin 1962) refers briefly to Leonardo Guzzardi; William Winter 'The History of the Dartmouth Version'

Britannia (Dartmouth College Magazine, July 1967, pp.15-17); Walker 1985/2, p.361, 1985/1, p.186-8

ILLUSTRATED: page 90.

NELSON AFTER GUZZARDI

92 | *Herefordshire: Clive Richards' Collection*

Miniature, oval 80mm (3¹/₈in) high in a rectangle ormolu frame. HS copy of Guzzardi's Dolmabahce version but without Davison's Nile medal on his right breast.

COLLECTION: Duke of Sussex; sold by Bonhams 21 November 1995 (136).

ILLUSTRATED: page 83.

HEAD 1798-1800

NELSON ATTRIBUTED TO GUY HEAD, 1798-1800

93 | *Greenwich:National Maritime Museum (BHC 2903)*

Oil on canvas 84 x 65cm (33 x 25¹/₂in), uninscribed. HL to left in a white bloodstained shirt open at the neck, white bloodstained bandage over his brown hair; his left hand to his breast partly concealing the white and blue ribbon and medal of St Vincent; blue eye; Battle of the Nile in left background, rigging to right.

COLLECTIONS: probably painted in about 1800, then given by Nelson to Lady Parker, wife of Admiral Sir Peter Parker, and bequeathed by her daughter, Mrs Ellis, to the Greenwich Hospital collection in 1869; transferred to the NMM in 1934. A smaller version was in the collection of another branch of the Parker family in Suffolk (NMM 648/2/38 and 11/38 Book 11).

CONDITION: canvas lined and restored in about 1900.

EXHIBITION: 'Lady Hamilton', Kenwood 1972 (72).

LITERATURE: Greenwich Painted Hall Catalogue (1922), 162; NMM 1988, p.483.

REPRODUCTIONS: Walder 1978, p.59 and dust jacket in colour.

COMMENTS: pages 58 and 91.

ILLUSTRATED: page 56.

NELSON BY GUY HEAD, 1798-99

94 | *London: National Portrait Gallery (5101)*

Oil on canvas 223.5 x 169cm (87³/₄ x 66¹/₂in), WL standing on the deck of HMS *Vanguard* with a midshipman. Nelson stands facing his head turned to the left, rear-admiral's undress uniform, white waistcoat and breeches, black neckcloth, white shirt-frill, black shoes with gold buckles, two gold seals on a gold chain, riband and star of the Bath, one Naval gold medal (St Vincent) on a white ribbon with blue borders; his left hand holds sword blade and rests on the breech of a carronade, his right sleeve empty and pinned across the Bath riband; florid complexion, blue eyes, grey hair in queue.

The midshipman to left in blue coat, buff trousers, white waistcoat, black sword band with gold anchor badge over his right shoulder, holds the French admiral's sword partly wrapped in a captured French ensign.

Aboukir Bay in the background with two battle-scarred ships flying white ensigns hoisted over French tricolours; a pilot cutter in the harbour flies a tricolour.

FRAME: probably contemporary, 8 inch carved wood with shield, ball, bead and oakleaf decoration. The tablet inscribed:*NELSON Receiving the French Colours at the Battle of the Nile. Painted from Life by HEAD. PRESENTED TO LADY HAMILTON BY LORD NELSON.* This is possibly the frame mentioned by the Right Hon George Rose to Lady Hamilton 17 November 1805 - '...a picture by Mr Head being framed at Brydons'.

COLLECTIONS: commissioned probably by the King of Naples, given by Nelson to Lady Hamilton and in her house at Merton or Blackheath; Alderman Joshua Smith whose widow's estate was disposed of in about 1858 when it was offered to the NPG by Richard Phillips, an upholsterer of 5 Marylebone Street, Golden Square - 'this picture together with portraits of Lady Hamilton, the King and Queen of Naples and Sir William Hamilton came from Merton and passed through the hands of a Mrs Smith' (NPG archive). The picture was declined by the Trustees and Phillips put it up for sale at Christie's with three others (including Füger's portraits of Lady Hamilton and the Queen of Naples) all 'from Lady Hamilton's house, Blackheath' (Christie's 13 July 1860 lots 238-41), where it was bought by Edward Adolphus Radclyffe for 40 guineas and sold to John Finlay of Moss Park (? near Glasgow); Scharf saw it again at Radclyffe's, 123 Pall Mall, on 14 June 1866, price £150 attributed to Head (*Scharf TSB* II 96); it was presumably unsold and returned to Moss Park and in possession of Finlay's grandson, Robert Munro; his daughter Mrs Maria Maclaren who said that family tradition believed it to have been painted 'from life by command of the King after the Battle of the Nile and presented to Nelson by the King... Nelson doubtless thought he would leave it to the nation but he left it with many other things to Emma Lady Hamilton from whose Trustees it was purchased by my husband's grandfather' (*letters in NPG archive*); on loan from Mr Robert Maclaren of Airth Castle to Glasgow Corporation 1916-20; with Mrs Maclaren at the Craigs, Linlithgow, where it formed the subject of some correspondence with Callender in April and May 1939 (*NMM archive*); seen in May 1948 by Sir Henry Hake at Allan House, Fearn, where Mrs Maclaren was living with her daughter Mrs Munro; considered for purchase by the NMM in 1948; Sotheby's 14 July 1976 (104) from the collection of Mr I G Maclaren. DFC TD, and bought by Leggatt on behalf of the NPG.

CONDITION: cleaned and retouched by Mrs Sophie Plender in November 1976.

LITERATURE: Walker 1977, pp.393-4, 1985/2, pp.360.

COMMENTS: pages 91-3. ILLUSTRATED: page 87.

GRIGNION 1799

NELSON BY CHARLES GRIGNION 1799

95 *Greenwich: National Maritime Museum*
Pencil drawing on white paper 22 x 17.7cm (8⁵/₈ x 7 in), inscribed and dated in very neat script lower left: *C. Grignion Naples 1797* (not in the artist's hand); HL seated to left, aged 41, left arm dangling over back of chair, bare-headed, in rear-admiral's undress uniform, riband of the Bath, his left hand concealing the star, right sleeve pinned across the riband.

COLLECTIONS: Grignion's brother Thomas Grignion; Commander James Bremer RN, and presented by him to the Royal United Services Institution; transferred to the NMM in 1962.

ENGRAVING: lithograph by Miss H. S. Turner (*c.* 1835-40) lettered: *EARL NELSON from a drawing in the United Services Museum - taken from life by Charles Grignion in Naples 1797 / Printed by Graf & Soret*, plate in H S Turner's *Sixty Portraits from Unedited Originals* (nd). Lithograph by C. Couzens, printed by M & N Hanhart.

EXHIBITION: Nelson Exhibition, Admiralty, February 1895.

CONDITION: several large bleached circular patches (1979).

LITERATURE: Cumberland in *Monthly Magazine*, January and November 1809; RUSI *Official Catalogue* (1924), no.646; Whitley II, pp.224-5; Warner 1958, p.361; Warner 1975, reproduced p.113.

COMMENTS: pages 93-94. ILLUSTRATED: page 95.

PALERMO MINIATURIST 1799

NELSON BY A PALERMO ARTIST, 1799

96 *Norfolk: private collection*
Red and black chalk and watercolour on creamy paper 23.5 x 18.4cm (9¹/₄ x 7¹/₄in), the oval section 16.5 x 13.8cm inscribed in Lady Hamilton's handwriting: *Admiral Lord Nelson Duke of Bronte painted from the Duke of Bronte at Palermo 1799 from Lady Hamilton to her friend Mrs Nelson;* HS in profile to left in rear-admiral's full dress uniform, star of Crescent above star of the Bath, two Naval gold medals and Davison's gold medal; bareheaded, hair tidy and in queue tied with black ribbon, flat top of head, slightly sneering expression.

COLLECTIONS: Lady Hamilton and given by her to Nelson's sister-in-law Sarah, later first Countess Nelson (d 1828); bequeathed by the first Earl's second wife Hilare to her nephew Captain Robert Hilaro Barlow and sold by his grand-daughter Constance Menton (née Barlow) Sotheby's 28 November 1923 (66) bt Walter Spencer and sold by him to Sir Harold Mackintosh later Lord Mackintosh of Halifax.

LITERATURE: Warner 'Two Drawings of Nelson' in *Country Life* 2nd August 1956 p. 244

COMMENTS: pages 94-9. Several versions of this miniature exist, more finished and in some cases wearing the cocked hat with chelengk.

ILLUSTRATED: page 96.

97: *Miniature attributed to the Palermo artist*

97 | *Portsmouth: Royal Naval Museum*

Miniature on ivory 7.9 x 6.7cm (3¹/₈ x 2⁵/₈in), profile to left in rear-admiral's undress uniform, star of the Bath, two Naval gold medals on regulation blue and white ribbons, Davison's Nile on blue and white ribbon from third buttonhole; bareheaded with untidy sandy hair in queue tied with black ribbon, flat top to head, slightly jutting lower lip and double chin; sea and white cliffs through a window right.

COLLECTIONS: Originally Emma Hamilton's and from her descended via Horatia to Nelson's great-grandson, Maurice Suckling Ward. Presented by his widow to the Victory Museum in 1957.

LITERATURE: Warner 'Relics of Nelson and the Hamilton Family' in *Country Life* 8 May 1958 p.995.

ILLUSTRATED: above.

98 *Dorset: private collection*

Red chalk drawing, profile to left in rear-admiral's undress uniform, stars of Crescent (above), Bath, two Naval gold medals, Davison's Nile medal, cocked hat with chelengk (with seven fingers set in a circular base), hair in queue.

COLLECTIONS: Admiral Sir Thomas Masterman Hardy and by family descent to the present owner.

ENGRAVING: (of a similar drawing): stipple by Thomas Burke (see *p.231*) lettered: *Engraved by Burke from an original Drawing taken at Palermo / in Possession of Captn J.B. Savage of Marines / BARON NELSON of the NILE / Published by John Brydon No 7 Charing Cross, London 1st of August 1800.*

LITERATURE: letter from Hardy in A. M. Broadley & R.G.Bartelot *The Three Dorset Captains at Trafalgar* (1906).

ILLUSTRATED: page 97.

99 *Private Collection*

Miniature with stars of Crescent (above), Bath and St Ferdinand, battle scene in left background, generally more rugged, and signed and dated *E. Nash 1800*.

COLLECTIONS: R. L. Bayne-Powell Christie's 12 May 1954 (19) and lent to British Portrait Miniatures Exhibition, Edinburgh 1965 (340), then Sotheby's 11 October 1994 (54).

ILLUSTRATED: page 231.

100 *Monmouth: Nelson Museum*

Oval miniature on ivory described as above.

COLLECTIONS: uncertain, probably bought by Lady Llangattock in about 1900.

ILLUSTRATED: right.

101 *Greenwich: National Maritime Museum*

Pencil drawing touched with red on off-white paper (discoloured) watermarked *TW 1796*, 27.5 x 21.5cm (10³/₄, x 8¹/₂in), inscribed in ink: *Horatia* (sic) *Lord Nelson &c &c &c by* (monogram) *1802 the writing underneath his own with his left hand*, and in pencil: *Bisogna una carta biangha, de dietro al Ritratto;* profile to left wearing, hat and chelengk, probably a copy done in England from the Dorset Hardy drawing above; the monogram has not yet been deciphered but could be *J^o D.*

REPRODUCTION: Pocock 1987, fig.34.

100: *Miniature attributed to the Palermo artist*

FÜGER 1800

NELSON BY HEINRICH FRIEDRICH FÜGER

102 *London: National Portrait Gallery (73)*

Oil on canvas 67.8 x 50.2cm (26³/₄ x 19³/₄in), HS to left aged 42, in a dark blue coat and neckcloth and light blue jersey; rather long and untidy grey hair, grey eyes equally bright and apparently normal, slightly aquiline nose, thin unsmiling lips; greyish-yellow sky background, no inscription.

COLLECTIONS: painted in Vienna and in the artist's studio till his death in 1818; the artist's son till 1823; Moritz von Tschoffen till 1859; Ewer Gallery, Oxford Street, London, from whom purchased by the NPG in 1859.

ENGRAVINGS: no contemporary engraving appears to exist until an oval cut was published in. *The Illustrated London News* Supplement 30 September 1871, p.309.

EXHIBITIONS: Österreichisches Museum für Angewandte Kunst, Vienna 1968-9 (illustrated 181); 'Angelica Kauffmann und ihre Zeitgenossen',

98: *Stipple engraving by Thomas Burke, 1800*

99: *Miniature by Edward Nash, 1800*

Vorarleberger Landesmuseum, Bergenz, 1969; 'Faces as Art' Carlton House Terrace (NPG) 1976; 'The Golden age of Naples', Detroit and Chicago 1981-2 (59); 'Joseph Haydn', Eisenstadt 1982 (780).

VERSION: an oval miniature copy belonged to Sir Edmund Gosse in 1887.

CONDITION: still on the original canvas and stretcher; cleaned and restored 1976 (Freeman).

LITERATURE: documents in the NPG archive, (see Appendix II p. 283); Warner 1971, pp.13-15; Walder 1978, p.351; Walker 1985/2, p.362.

REPRODUCTIONS: W.A.P. Phillips, 'Chance in History: Nelson's Pursuit of Bonaparte', *History Today* XV (1965), p.177; Geoffrey Bennett, 'Admiral Ushakov: Nelson's Russian Ally', *History Today* XXI (1971), p.725; Bennett 1972, p.180; Warner 1975, p.123.

COMMENTS: page 105.

ILLUSTRATED: frontispiece

103 *Portsmouth: Royal Naval Museum*

Oil on canvas 68.5 x 54cm (27 x 21^1/$_4$in), HS to left aged 42, in rear-admiral's full dress uniform, two Naval gold medals (St Vincent and the Nile) suspended from a blue ribbon round his neck, and Davison's Nile medal on his right breast, and over the riband of St Ferdinand (blue in a red border) and the Bath (red); stars of the Crescent (above), St Ferdinand and Merit (left) and the Bath (below); rather long and untidy grey hair, hazel eyes both equally bright and apparently normal, slightly aquiline nose, thin unsmiling lips; bluish-yellow sky background, no inscription.

COLLECTIONS: painted in Vienna in 1800 but history unknown until its purchase by Gerard B. Lambert later in the 1920's from a dealer who 'stated that it was from a private collection formerly in Hampstead' (Warner *Nelson's Last Diary*); presented by his daughter Mrs Lily Lambert McCarthy to the RN Museum in 1972.

VERSION: a modern miniature copy by D Oliver of Edinburgh 1905 is in Buckler's Hard Museum, Beaulieu River.

LITERATURE: Warner *Nelson's Last Diary* (1971) pp.13-15; McCarthy 1995, no. 176.

REPRODUCTIONS: RN Museum colour postcard; White's *Companion*, colour pl.5.

COMMENTS: pages 104-5.

ILLUSTRATED: page 111.

LIFE MASKS

LIFE MASK OF NELSON, 1800

104 *Greenwich: National Maritime Museum (SCU 0106)*

Plaster mask 21.6 x 12.2cm (8^1/$_2$ x 4^3/$_4$in), eyes open; the mask is accompanied by the matrix in two sections.

COLLECTIONS: early provenance uncertain but traditionally made for Mrs Matcham though more likely to have been made in Vienna as a guide for the marble bust by Thaller & Ranson. Charles Tasker, his son and grand-daughter Miss Frances T Tasker who offered it to the NPG in 1926 but sold it to the Rev Hugh Nelson-Ward who gave it to the NMM in June 1939.

EXHIBITIONS: RN Exhibition Chelsea 1891 (3164) lent by J G Tasker; Naval and Fisheries Exhibition 1905; 'Save the Victory Fund' at Spink's 1928 (86).

ILLUSTRATED: opposite. and page 108.

105 *Portsmouth: Royal Naval Museum*

Plaster mask 21.6 x 12.2cm (8^1/$_2$ x 4^3/$_4$in), eyes closed.

COLLECTIONS: early provenance equally uncertain and similar to the NMM version. Bought from an antique shop in the Isle of Wight in 1924 by HM Queen Mary and presented by her to the *Victory* Museum, Portsmouth.

EXHIBITIONS: 'Save the *Victory* Fund' at Spink's 1928 (86a); 'Nelson and his Surgeons' RN Hospital, Haslar 1967.

ILLUSTRATED: page 109.

106 *Portsmouth: Royal Naval Museum* (on loan)

Plaster mould, eyes open and without hair the mask being cut across the top of forehead; noticeably broader in shape than the other two and with no seam lines.

COLLECTIONS: Nelson Ward (reproduced Beresford & Wilson p.222); Mrs M E Weekes (reproduced *Pugh* p 40).

EXHIBITION: 'Nelson and his Surgeons' RN Hospital, Haslar 1967.

LITERATURE: Callender 1928; Wilkinson 1931, appendix II; Pugh 1968, pp.39-42; Walker 1980; Nash 1993.

COMMENTS: pages 107-112.

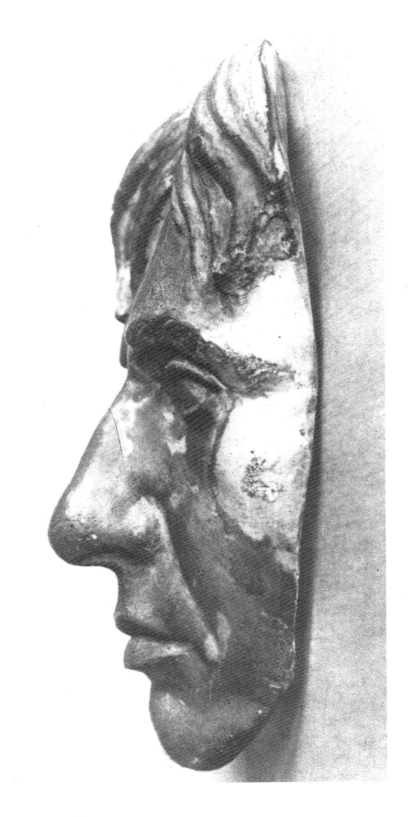

104: *Life mask (profile)*

233

119: *Plaster copy of the Cardosi version of the Thaller & Ransom bust*

THALLER & RANSON 1801

NELSON BY THALLER & RANSON, 1800-01

107 *Greenwich:National Maritime Museum (SCU 0088)*

Marble bust 69cm (27in) high, incised on reverse: *FRANZ THALLER / ET / MATTHIAS RANSON / VIENNAE AUSTR.. / MDCCCI.* HS turned slightly to his left in rear-admiral's full-dress uniform, ribands of the Bath and the Crescent, stars of the Crescent (above), St Ferdinand (left), Bath (right), two Naval gold medals in front (St Vincent and the Nile, the Nile in reverse incised NILE / FIRST AUGUST / 1798), below the stars another gold medal fastened with a bow of ribbon displaying the *Victory* and *Britannia* but probably intended to represent Davison's Nile medal; the empty right sleeve fastened straight across, the two naval gold buttons at the cuff worn horizontally.

COLLECTIONS: 'Made in Vienna; subsequently stood in the drawing room at Merton, given by Lady Hamilton to Alderman Smith; purchased from Miss Pettigrew whose father, Thomas Pettigrew (Nelson's biographer), had it from Smith's widow in payment of his fee; purchased by Herbert Agar and given to the 3rd Earl Nelson' (*Trafalgar House Inventory*); acquired by the NMM with other Nelson relics from Trafalgar House in 1948.

EXHIBITION: Guelph 1891 (1614) lent by the 3rd Earl Nelson.

LITERATURE: Walker 1980, pp.319-27, 1985/2, p.362.

COMMENTS: pages 107-112. The Thaller & Ranson bust was shipped to England probably in 1801. It proved to be immediately popular, especially after Copenhagen, and copies were made by a variety of sculptors, though none made any acknowledgements to the original Viennese artists. There are often small anomalies in the treatment of the hair and Orders.

ILLUSTRATED: page 102.

108 *Bournemouth: Russell Cotes Art Gallery*

Marble bust 69cm (27in) high, no inscription but a softened variation of the Vienna original.

COLLECTIONS: uncertain but formerly attributed to Flaxman.

109 *British Columbia: Esquimault Naval College*

Marble bust 69cm (27in) high, no inscription.

COLLECTIONS: Nelson collection, acquired from Trafalgar House by the NMM in 1948 (48-720/5), lent to Esquimault in 1952 and later presented at the suggestion of HRH the Duke of Edinburgh.

110 *Dorking: private collection*

Marble bust 69cm (27in) high, no inscription but similar to the NPG version by Cardosi.

COLLECTIONS: uncertain.

111 *Greenwich: National Maritime Museum (SCU 0091)*

Marble bust 69cm (27in) high, no inscription but a softened variation of the Vienna original and with the crescent in the Turkish star reversed.

COLLECTIONS: Thomas Hope of Deepdene; Captain Spink; Sir Bruce Ingram who presented it to the NMM in 1932 in memory of his son.

112 *Portsmouth: Royal Navy*

Plaster bust 69cm (27in) high, incised *F Baldacie* and probably a commercial cast from the original though the Nile scar appears to have been altered to lie horizontally above the eyebrow.

COLLECTIONS: Parker Gallery; Sir Leicester Harmsworth and given by him to the RN College, Keyham in 1933.

113 *King's Lynn: private collection*

Marble bust 69cm (27in) high, no inscription and a remote copy of the Vienna original with a less severe expression and several interesting variations in the decorations, viz: (1) the star of the Turkish Order (top right) has no crescent in the centre. (2) the star of St Ferdinand (middle left) appears to have a Naval gold medal in the centre instead of the standing figure of St Ferdinand. (3) the star of the Bath is correct but there is an unknown medal below it bearing apparently the head of Britannia or Minerva (presumably intended to represent Davison's Nile medal). (4) the two Naval gold medals at the neck, usually St Vincent and the Nile, are certainly not as normally represented; one appears to contain a pyramid, the other some sort of naval trophy or rostral column.

COLLECTION: Christie's (various properties) 30 October 1969 (2).

114 *Lewes: Town Hall*

Plaster bust 69cm (27½in) high, incised on reverse: *Turnerelli*. A copy by Peter Turnerelli of the Vienna bust.

COLLECTION: presented to the town of Lewes by the Rev Richard Rideout 1808.

115 *London: Admiralty House, Whitehall*

Marble bust 69cm (27in) high, no inscription but a softened copy of the Vienna original.

COLLECTION: presented by Sir Philip Sassoon in 1938.

116 *London: Lloyd's Nelson Collection*

Plaster bust painted as bronze 69cm (27in) high, no inscription and probably a cast.

COLLECTIONS: presented to Lloyd's by D. B. Robertson *c.* 1947 and said to have come from a bombed house in South Kensington.

117 *London: National Portrait Gallery (2668)*

Plaster bust painted as bronze 69cm (27in) high, incised on the back: *D. Cardosi* and pirated from the Thaller & Ranson original though the hair style is slightly different.

COLLECTION: Miss Jane Scott Bell and bought from her 1934.

118 *London: Royal College of Defence Studies, Belgrave Square*

Marble bust 69cm (27in) high, no inscription and a weak copy of the Vienna original.

COLLECTION: presented by Gerald Kerin in 1958.

119 *Portsmouth: Royal Naval Museum*

Plaster bust painted black 69cm (27in) high, no inscription but similar to the NPG bust by Cardosi.

COLLECTION: Lily Lambert McCarthy 336/73.

ILLUSTRATED: page 234.

120 *Norwich: Castle Museum*

Marble bust attributed to Cardosi or Turnerelli, no inscription.

121 *Beccles: Leman House*

Marble bust after Thaller & Ranson, no inscription.

122 *Private collection*

Marble bust 69cm (27in) high, incised on the back: *NOLLEKINS Sculp*ᵗ. a close copy by Nollekens (the more usual spelling).

COLLECTIONS: offered to the NPG in 1944 then sold 12 October 1944 (99), (page 9 of unidentified catalogue in NMM archive). Mottisfont Abbey, Hampshire (Mrs Maud Russell) then Sotheby's 16 June 1983 (200) bt Tristram Jellinek.

123 *Location unknown since 1912*

Marble bust, no inscription but said to be by Nollekens.

COLLECTIONS: Sir John George Tollemache Sinclair (d 1912). Sir John commissioned Leverotti, an assistant sculptor in Brucciani's workshop, to make a small bronze copy, perhaps that in NMM, on a marble base.

124 *Location unknown since 1933*

Marble bust.

COLLECTION: letter from 'Collector' in *The Field* 25 March 1933.

127: *Plaster mask painted as terracotta*

125 *Location unknown since 1971*

Marble bust 69cm (27in) high, no inscription but a good firm copy of the Vienna original.

COLLECTION: Parker Gallery, London, in 1971.

126 *Location unknown since 1977*

Marble bust 69cm (27in) high.

COLLECTIONS: Colin Denny, Nautical Picture Shop, 18 Cale Street, London, sold in 1977.

127 *London: National Portrait Gallery (2767)*

Plaster mask painted as terracotta, probably a squeeze of the Thaller & Ranson marble bust.

ILLUSTRATED: opposite.

SCHMIDT 1800

NELSON BY JOHANN HEINRICH SCHMIDT 1800

128 *Greenwich: National Maritime Museum (PR 55-303)*

Pastel on octagonal paper 30 x 24cm (11³/₄ x 9¹/₂in), signed and dated above his right head: *Schmidt. / F. 1800*. Inscribed in ink on a paper stuck to reverse of frame: *This original portrait of Ld / Nelson was executed at Dresden / for Hugh Elliot H.M. Minister to the Court of Saxony, - was given / by him to his daughter Emma, Lady / Hislop, & by her to her daughter: / Emma Countess of Minto.*

HS in rear-admiral's undress uniform, riband and star of the Bath, stars of St Ferdinand (left) and the Crescent (above, crescent in reverse), two Naval gold medals at the neck, St Vincent above (obverse) and the Nile below (reverse) both on white ribbons with blue borders, Davison's Nile medal (obverse) fastened with a blue bow above the St Ferdinand star; black neckcloth, his right sleeve pinned horizontally across the chest partly covering the star of the Bath; hair light grey, powdered, fairly tidy and growing thickly at the back. 'There is a patch of powder above the right eyebrow to conceal the Nile scar and the right eye is shown perhaps slightly divergent and with a pale indistinct blue iris, compared with the bright blue of the other eye, and with no discernible pupillary aperture' (*Pugh* 1968, p 46).

COLLECTIONS: commissioned by the Hon Hugh Elliot, (British Minister in Dresden) and by descent in the family until purchased from Lord Minto by the NMM in 1955.

LITERATURE: Callender 1943, p.314; Oman 1947, p.402; Walder 1978, p.344.

REPRODUCTIONS: ILN 12 November 1955, full page spread; Warner 1958, p.173; Hattersley 1974, p.97; Hibbert 1994, pl.27; White's *Companion*, p.49.

COMMENTS: pages 112-4. ILLUSTRATED: page 116.

Three other versions are known

129 *Greenwich: National Maritime Museum*

Pastel on paper on copper 30 x 24cm (11³/₄ x 9¹/₂in), inscribed lower left above the shoulder: *Schmidt fec.à Dresde 1801*, and on the back in another hand: *Nelson Admiral anglois peint d'après nature 1801 par H. Schmidt peintre du Roi.*

COLLECTIONS: the artist's family until in the collection of his grandson, Fritz Arndt-Oberwald (reproduced R R Holme *Horatio Nelson: England's Sailor Hero* (1905) frontispiece); C G Boerner auction rooms Leipzig 4-6 December 1911 (375); J F Walter of Drayton Hall, lent to the NMM in 1938 and purchased with the Walter Collection in 1960.

130 *Whereabouts unknown since 1905*

Probably pastel and similar to above, dated 1808.

COLLECTION: Fritz Arndt-Oberwald (reproduced Holme *op cit* p.43), possibly the pastel version in a private collection, Berkshire, descended in the family from Letitia Hublon who married Baron von Seilitzsch and lived in Dresden till 1805. A similar portrait of Suvarov is in the same collection.

131 *St Peter Port, Guernsey (Lord Glendevon)*

Oil on steel 95 x 75mm signed on the back: A miniature copy of Schmidt's pastel portrait done in Dresden in October 1800.

COLLECTIONS: presumably the miniature appearing at auction in Vienna, Gilhofer & Rauschburg 28 April 1911 (73). Declined by the NMM 'at the end of the war' (c.1945), then bought by Lord John Hope (Lord Glendevon) 'from a little gallery off St James's Street for £40' (see letter in NPG, archive).

The earliest date for this miniature seems to be the Vienna sale in 1911. Lord Glendevon told me that it is signed by Schmidt on the back but I have not seen the miniature and, in view of the unusual steel vehicle and the fact that Schmidt is not known to have painted many miniatures, I wonder if this could be a copy painted with an eye to the centenary celebrations in 1905.

BEECHEY 1800 - 1801

NELSON BY SIR WILLIAM BEECHEY, 1800

132 *London: National Portrait Gallery (5798)*

Oil on canvas 62.3 x 48.3cm (24$\frac{1}{2}$ x 19in), inscribed on reverse of the original canvas: *WB. pinx^t. / Presented to his / beloved son / Cap^{tn}. Beechey. / 1830.* (see p.124) HS in rear-admiral's full-dress uniform, the silver stars on the epaulettes not shown (Nelson was promoted Vice-Admiral of the Blue on 1 January 1801); ribands of the Bath and St Ferdinand, stars of the Bath (above), St Ferdinand and the Crescent; two Naval gold medals (St Vincent and the Nile) on blue ribbons against a white shirt, dark blue neck-cloth; grey hair altered from an earlier position on the head to coincide with the revised and finished version at Norwich. *Brown* eyes and the Nile scar over his right eye which is noticeably less lustrous than the left though there is no sign of pterygia.

COLLECTIONS: five other 'preliminary' sketches are recorded. NPG 5798 could conceivably have belonged to the Earl of St Vincent, engraved in 1815, sold at St Vincent's death in 1823 and bought back by Beechey himself. Thereafter it remained in the Beechey family, given by the artist to his son in 1830, by descent to G.B. Dixon and on his death in 1856 to his widow Margaret Dixon; sold at Bonham's 21 July 1966 (241) bought by Hugh Leggatt and placed on loan to the Trustees of the NPG; bought by the NPG in 1985.

ENGRAVINGS: stipple vignette ('From the original Picture by Sir William Beechey, R.A. in the Possession of the Earl of St Vincent...') by R. Cooper for Cadell & Davies's *Contemporary Portraits* (1815) (see *p.118*); mezzotint by Lawrence Josset 1968.

EXHIBITION: 'Lady Hamilton' Kenwood 1972 (96).

CONDITION: cleaned and lined 1966 (Leggatt); earlier restorations and darkened paint in the sky removed in 1972 (Clifford Ellison).

LITERATURE: NPG Annual Report 1966-67, pp.43-4; Walker 1985/2, p.363.

REPRODUCTIONS: Oman 1947, p.144; Pocock 1968, dust cover (colour); Howarth 1969, p.63; Winifred Gérin, *Horatia Nelson* (1970), p.32; *Reader's Digest* (Jan 1971), p.145; Robin Gibson & Keith Roberts, *British Portrait Painters* (1971), p.32; Naish

1972, pl.4 (colour); Warner 1975 p.155 (colour); Fraser 1987, p.119; Hibbert 1994, pl. 24 (colour); White's *Companion*, pl. 4 (colour).

COMMENTS: page 124. ILLUSTRATED: page 122.

Oil sketches related to Beechey's original study for the WL commissioned by the Corporation of Norwich in 1800.

133 *Greenwich: National Maritime Museum (BHC 2892)*

Oil on canvas 39.5 x 35.5cm (15$\frac{1}{2}$ x 14in), head only to right, his left eye mid-brown, his right eye blue-grey.

COLLECTIONS: bequeathed to the NMM by John C. McGrath in 1893 as 'a sketch for the Norwich whole length'. Reproduced in Pocock 1968, p.88.

ILLUSTRATED: opposite.

134 *Norfolk: Heydon Hall*

Oil on canvas 47 x 39.5cm (18$\frac{1}{2}$ x 15$\frac{1}{2}$in), HS oil sketch.

COLLECTIONS: the artist's family and given by Canon Beechey, his great-nephew, to Colonel W.E.G.L. Bulwer of Quebec House (Duleep, Singh, *Portraits in Norfolk Houses* (1927) II p.141). It was described unreliably by Roberts as 'the original finished sketch in oils (canvas 17$\frac{1}{2}$ x 15$\frac{3}{4}$in) of the head and shoulders of this great picture; this sketch is of very fine quality, full of vigour and life' (Roberts 1907, p.75).

135 *Location unknown since 1823 (St Vincent's)*

Oil on canvas probably 62.3 x 48.3cm (24$\frac{1}{2}$ x 19in), i.e. same size as NPG (5798) above.

COLLECTIONS: Earl Saint Vincent and probably sold at his death in 1823. It is known from an engraving by Robert Cooper from a drawing by W. Evans, *From the original Picture by SIR WILLIAM BEECHEY, R.A. in the Possession of the / Earl of St Vincent / Drawn by W. Evans. Engraved by R. Cooper / Published June 21. 1815, by T. Cadell & W. Davies, Strand London.*

136 *Location unknown since 1968*

Oil on canvas, HS wearing one Naval gold medal, size unknown.

COLLECTIONS: Captain D.H.C. Cooper of Windelsham (d.1968). Oliver Warner thought 'it might be a preliminary study for the full length'

133: *Oil sketch by Sir William Beechey, 1800*

('Unfamiliar Portraits of Nelson' in *Connoisseur* CXLII (August 1958) p.33). This may be identical with the Heydon Hall version above.

NELSON BY SIR WILLIAM BEECHEY, 1800-01

137 *Norwich: St Andrew's Hall*

Oil on canvas 261.4 x 182.6cm (103 x 72in), WL standing on deck in rear-admiral's full-dress uniform, ribands of the Bath and St Ferdinand, stars of the Bath (above), St Ferdinand and the Crescent; badge of St Ferdinand fastened at the waist, two Naval gold medals (St Vincent and the Nile); full-dress cocked hat with the chelengk on the sable-lined pelisse to right, sword leaning against a carronade draped with a Spanish standard to left, rigging in background.

FRAME: a sumptuous gilt rectangle supported by corinthian columns festooned with oak and laurel leaves, a fleur-de-lys and viscount's coronet on the top corners, the whole surmounted by Nelson's armorial shield supported by trophies and oak and laurel branches.

COLLECTION: commissioned by the Corporation of Norwich in 1800 and in St Andrew's Hall since 1801.

ENGRAVINGS: large mezzotint by Edward Bell (*opposite*) lettered: *Painted by Sir Wm Beechey R.A. / Engraved by Edward Bell / HORATIO LORD VISCOUNT NELSON, DUKE OF BRONTE K.B. / Vice Admiral of the White &c &c &c / Engraved from the Original Picture in St Andrew's Hall Norwich painted at the particular Request of the Corporation of that City / to whom this plate is most respectfully dedicated by their much obliged fellow Citizen and humble Servt / Jeremiah Freeman / Published May 1 1806 as the Act directs by J Freeman and E Bell No 2 London Lane Norwich.*
Similar prints with variations were made by H R Cook (for Harrison's *Life* 1806), R Earlom (from the Guildhall London version), W Say 1806, R Cooper 1815, W Holl 1819, W Maddocks 1820 and T Hodgetts 1840.

EXHIBITIONS: RA 1801 (125); *Rule Britannia 1986* (107).

LITERATURE: A.D. Bayne, *History of Norwich* (1869), p.289; Roberts 1907, pp.18, 74-6.

REPRODUCTION: *Rule Britannia 1986*, cover (colour).

COMMENTS: pages 120-4. ILLUSTRATED: page 123.

Some recorded versions of the Beechey portrait

138 *London: Admiralty*

Oil on canvas *c.* 76 x 63cm (30 x 25in), HS, a modern copy given by Lord Bruntisfield in 1943.

139 *London: Apsley House*

Oil on canvas 136 x 111cm (53½ x 43½in), TQL probably by Beechey.

COLLECTIONS: bought by the 1st Duke of Wellington and possibly a copy commissioned by him from Beechey.

ENGRAVING: line engraving by Thomas Hodgetts 1840.

LITERATURE: *The Athenaeum* 8 January 1853; *Quarterly Review* XCII (1853) p.468; C. M. Kauffmann *Catalogue of Paintings in the Wellington Museum* (1982) p. 31.

140 *London: Drapers' Company*

Oil on canvas *c.*261 x 182cm (103 x 72in), WL copy by Beechey 1807.

COLLECTIONS: commissioned by the company after Trafalgar; it was left to the discretion of the Court whether the work should be entrusted to Beechey, Hoppner or Opie. This is the 'large picture of Lord Nelson 200 guineas' noted in Beechey's Account Book for 13 June 1807.

LITERATURE: Roberts 1907 p.225; Rev. A.H. Johnson *History of the Worshipful Company of Drapers of London* (1912) III pp. 370-1.

141 *London: Guildhall*

Oil on canvas 140 x 117cm (55 x 46in), TQL copy by Beechey.

COLLECTIONS: commissioned and presented by Alderman John Boydell, *c.*1805, but not mentioned in Beechey's Account Books (Roberts pp. 220 ff) which are missing for the years 1792-1806.

ENGRAVING: mezzotint by Richard Earlom 1806.

142 *London: Ministry of Defence*

Oil on canvas TQL copy.

COLLECTIONS: bought from Commander Evelyn Culme-Seymour in 1970.

Reproduced in Hattersley 1974 p.150.

137: *Mezzotint by Edward Bell, 1806, after Beechey*

143 *Portsmouth: HMS* Victory

Oil sketch on paper mounted on board 70 x 53.5cm (27¹/₂ x 21in), inscribed on the back in Beechey's hand: *Orig^l. Picture WB* (monogram).

COLLECTIONS: lent in 1966 by H. Morton Lee who believed it to have been a preliminary study for the Norwich WL and to have been handed down in the artist's family; this is possible but it has the appearance of being a sketch made from Bell's mezzotint. It was bought for HMS *Victory* by the Society for Nautical Research 1967 (AGM in *Mariner's Mirror* LIII (1967) p.304).

HOPPNER 1800

NELSON BY JOHN HOPPNER, 1800

144 *Greenwich: National Maritime Museum (BHC 2897)*

Oil sketch on canvas 68.5 x 56cm (27 x 22in). HS slightly to left in rear-admiral's full-dress uniform, riband of the Bath, uniform and background only sketched.

144: *Oil sketch by John Hoppner, 1800*

COLLECTIONS: Bishop of Ely sold 1864; Earl of Leven and Melville; Caird Collection and presented by Sir James Caird in 1935.

Presumably this is the sketch used later in 1801 and onwards for the Prince of Wales's whole-length portrait (see 146, *p.127*). There appears to be only one star on the shoulder strap indicating a date before Nelson's promotion to vice-admiral on 1 January 1801. Therefore the only opportunity Hoppner would have had for a sitting would be in November and December after Nelson's arrival from Yarmouth in London, at the time when he was giving sittings to Beechey and probably Simon De Koster and Mrs Damer.

LITERATURE: NMM 1988, p.215.

COMMENTS: page 125. ILLUSTRATED: bottom, left.

145 *Portsmouth: Royal Naval Museum*

Oil sketch on canvas, 76 x 63cm (30 x 25in), HL to left in rear-admiral's full-dress uniform, riband of the Order of the Bath, two naval gold medals (St Vincent, the Nile), three stars (Bath, Ferdinand, Crescent), stormy background to left. Brown eyes, his left slightly darkened.

COLLECTIONS: J.W. Biddulph of Burton Park, Petworth; Christie's 24 April 1897 (100) as by Beechey; acquired by Dr William S. Bigelow and given by him to Boston Museum of Fine Arts, sold to Historical Portraits Limited, 30 Old Bond Street; bt by the RNM in 1992.

REPRODUCTIONS: Hibbert 1994, cover of paperback edition 1995 (colour); White's *Companion*, colour plate 3.

COMMENTS: pages 125-8. As with No.144 Nelson wears rear-admiral's uniform, indicating a date for the sitting before his promotion to vice-admiral on 1 January 1801. The head is posed four-square on the neck. In the finished picture (see 146; *p.127*) the head is tilted sideways, suggesting a change of mind, either by the artist or Nelson himself who may have been suffering from a slipped disc or some arthritic condition due to one of his many wounds. The absence of the highlight in his left eye seems to have been noticed by Lord Palmerston in December 1800: 'the worst is that his only eye is so weak as sometimes to give great alarm' (see p.128), and by January 1801 he complained to Emma that 'the film is so extended that I only see from the corner farthest from my nose'. In November 1801 a naval medical report noted a thick opaque membrane on his left eye (see p.175), and this was confirmed by Catherine Andras in her Westminster Abbey effigy (see 214; *p.171*).

ILLUSTRATED: page 126.

146: *Stipple engraving by Henry Meyer, 1805, after Hoppner*

146: *Mezzotint by Charles Turner, 1806*

NELSON BY JOHN HOPPNER, 1800-01

146 *London: Royal Collection, St James's Palace*

Oil on canvas 238.8 x 147.9cm (94 x 58¼in), WL standing on a rocky shore in rear-admiral's full-dress uniform, ribands of the Bath and St Ferdinand, stars of the Bath, St Ferdinand and the Crescent, badge of St Ferdinand by the sword-hilt, two Naval gold medals (St Vincent and the Nile); in the background is a view of the Battle of Copenhagen. His left eye appears without the corneal highlight.

COLLECTIONS: painted for the Prince of Wales and received at Carlton House in 1810. For details of movements within the Royal Collection see Millar p.54.

ENGRAVINGS:
(1) stipple by Henry Meyer (see *p.243*) lettered: *Hoppner Pinxt R.A. / Engraved by H. Meyer / THE RIGHT HONble LORD NELSON K.B. VICE ADMIRAL OF THE BLUE, DUKE OF BRONTI &c. / London Published by Colnaghi, Cockspur Street, Novr 4th 1805.*

(2) mezzotint by Charles Turner (see *left* and *p.169*) lettered: *Painted by J. Hoppner Esq R.A. Portrait Painter to H.R.H. the Prince of Wales / Engraved by C. Turner ADMIRAL LORD NELSON / From a Picture in the Possession of His Royal Highness the Prince of Wales. To whom by Permission, this Print is most humbly dedicated by His Royal Highness's very grateful and devoted Servant / J. Hoppner. / London: Pub. Jan. 9. 1806, by Colnaghi & Co &c &c &c No 23 Cockspur Street opposite Suffolk Street, Charing Cross.* In this very popular engraving Turner altered the background to show the Battle of Trafalgar instead of Copenhagen. A coloured impression in the Monmouth Museum has the ribands of the Bath and St Ferdinand blue instead of red and pink.

(3) Later prints: stipple by Cochran 1820, HL plate in Jerdan's *National Portrait Gallery*. Mezzotint anon. published by Colnaghi 1828. Line engraving by Finden published by Harding 1829. Stipple by Robinson, TQL, published by Fisher Son & Co. Stipple by Woolnoth, plate to Knight's *Portrait Gallery* (1833).

LITERATURE: Farington 25 March 1802; McKay & Roberts, p.182; Millar 1969, no.849.

REPRODUCTIONS: Oman 1947, p.496; Millar 1969, pl.180; Warner 1975, pl.VIII; Hattersley 1974, front (colour); Hibbert 1994, pl.26 (colour).

COMMENTS: pages 125-8. ILLUSTRATED: page 127.

Some recorded versions of the Hoppner portrait

147 *Dartmouth: Britannia Royal Naval College*

Oil on canvas, TQL copy by W.A. Menzies *c.* 1910 presented probably before 1914 by Lord Leith of Fyvie.

148 *Catania, Sicily: Lord Bridport*

Oil on canvas *c.* 240 x 150cm (95 x 59in), WL copy probably by Hoppner himself.

COLLECTIONS: probably painted either expressly for Admiral Alexander Hood, lst Viscount Bridport, or it may have been inherited by Nelson's niece Charlotte Mary, *suo jure* Duchess of Bronte, who married the 2nd Lord Bridport in 1810, and then at Cricket St Thomas, Somerset, till the house was sold in 1897.

149 *Aberdeenshire: Fyvie Castle*

Oil on canvas *c.* 240 x 150cm (95 x 59in), WL copy probably by Hoppner himself.

COLLECTIONS: Nelson family, traditionally presented to Lady Nelson by a grateful nation and bequeathed by her to Lord Bridport; Christie's (Bridport sale) 13 July 1895 (35) bt Agnew, sold to Lord Leith and the property of the National Trust for Scotland since 1984.

150 *Greenwich: National Maritime Museum (BHC 2898)*

Oil on canvas 239 x 147.5cm (94 x 58in), WL copy by Matthew Shepperson presented to Greenwich Hospital in 1824.

151 *Holkham Hall, Norfolk*

Oil on canvas *c.* 127 x 102cm (50 x 40in), TQL copy with uniform altered to vice-admiral's, Trafalgar in left background instead of Copenhagen, and therefore probably based on Turner's mezzotint.

152 *King's Lynn: Town Hall*

Oil on canvas 231 x 142cm (91 x 56in), WL copy by Samuel Lane.

COLLECTION: the copy marked the beginning of Samuel Lane's association with Hoppner and his long and successful career as a portrait painter. The commission is recorded in Farington's *Diary* 2 March 1806: '...Lane & his brother called being just arrived from Lynn - The Corporation of that town have voted that a copy from a picture of Lord Nelson be painted by *Lane* and put up in the Town Hall. Mr Lane wrote a letter to Hoppner to desire his son might copy a portrait of Lord Nelson painted by him for the Prince of Wales. This letter was sent to me for my opinion & I expressed a doubt abt sending it to Hoppner, who now has the picture from the Prince to make copies from it & might not choose to admit others to do it. It seemed to me best, if application was to be made it should be by Mr Coke to the Prince of Wales...' In September Lane called on Farington again 'to inform me that Hoppner had consented to allow him to copy his Portrait of Lord Nelson for the Corporation of Lynn'. By November the copy was well under way and seen by Farington at Lane's lodgings. The commission meant much to Lane, then aged twenty-five, and on 17 January 1807 he delightedly visited Farington to tell him 'he had just called on Philips who told him Hoppner was much pleased with his Copy of Lord Nelson's portrait, & wd be glad to

employ him in copying Mr Pitt's portrait, & Philips added wd probably farther employ him'. The copy was delivered to King's Lynn in February 1807 and the Corporation 'Resolved - that the Mayor be requested to express to Mr Lane the peculiar gratification this Corporation feels in possessing such a masterly portrait of that Illustrious Hero from the hand of an Artist so nearly connected with this town. And at the same time to present Mr Lane with the Sum of Two Hundred Guineas in the name of this Corporation'. Apart from the two hundred guineas King's Lynn approved of Lane's copy to the extent of providing an elaborate frame surmounted by a viscount's coronet, no doubt set on its mettle by the sumptuous frame supplied for Beechey's portrait by the Corporation of Norwich.

LITERATURE: Farington 2 March, 10 September and 18 November 1806, and 17 January 1807; King's Lynn Hall Book No.13, 14 February 1807 (MS c/o the town clerk); William Richards *The History of King's Lynn* (1812) p 1178.

153 *King's Lynn: the Lynn Museum*

Oil on canvas 22.2 x 18.5cm (8¾ x 7¼in), HS believed to be a preparatory sketch by Samuel Lane.

154 *Knowsley Hall (Earl of Derby)*

Small watercolour copy by William Derby, probably from Finden's engraving and probably before 1842.

155 *London: National Maritime Club*

Oil on canvas, copy by Miss Belle Cornelius made from Shepperton's copy in the NMM in 1912 (*The Times* 23 January 1912).

156 *London: Ten Downing Street*

Oil on canvas 233 x 147cm (92 x 58in), WL copy of the Royal Collection original made by W. A. Menzies (1910) and presented by William Lockett Agnew in 1910.

157 *Portsmouth: Royal Naval Museum*

Oil on canvas *c.*240 x 150cm (95 x 59in), WL copy by G.F. Clarke, with Trafalgar in background, commissioned by a group of Flag Officers and presented to Admiralty House, Portsmouth, in 1875.

158 *Versailles: Château de Versailles*

Oil on canvas 72 x 56cm (28½ x 22in), HL copy made by an American artist, G.P.A. Healy, in about 1835.

159 *Windsor Castle: Royal Collection*

Enamel copy by Henry Bone exhibited RA 1805 (429); a pencil drawing for this (see *right*) is in the NPG library (Bone Drawings II 40) inscribed: *Lord Nelson after Hoppner / Aug^st 27-2 / for HRH the Prince of Wales, Augst 1804* (erased) / *1805*. Another Bone enamel, signed and dated 1808 was at Christie's 22 May 1973 (83) bt Woollett.

160 *Portsmouth: Royal Naval Museum*

Enamel copy of the Bone miniature made for the Nelson Ward family by Falls. Half length, rear admiral's full dress uniform, two neck medals, stars of Bath, St Ferdinand and Crescent, ribbons of Bath and St Ferdinand.

COLLECTIONS: Nelson Ward family. Presented to the Victory Museum by Mrs Maurice Suckling Ward, in memory of her husband, in 1957, 49/57

ILLUSTRATED: opposite.

161 *America: private collection*

Oil on canvas, WL sold Mr Bryant of St James's Street at Christie's, 23 June 1865 (43), bt Cox for £100. Then probably 3rd Earl Nelson, Trafalgar House, sold 1947; Woolley & Wallis, Normanswood, Tilford, Surrey, 14 March 1951 (323); H. & R.L. Cobb, Sevenoaks, The Hermitage, West Malling, Kent, 18 November 1964 (87), bt John Munday; Peter Johnson, Lowndes Lodge, November 1987, and said to be by J. Morton after Hoppner, with Copenhagen in background.

162 *Location unknown since 1904*

Oil sketch on canvas 58.5 x 39.5cm (23 x 15$\frac{1}{2}$in), sold H.F. Huth of Sevenoaks at Christie's, 19 March 1904 (60), 'a small whole-length study for the large picture'.

163 *England: private collection, Hampshire*

Collage, TQL set in a blue curtain background, built up in card and dressed in rear-admiral's uniform.

159: *Drawing for an enamel by Henry Bone, 1805*

160: *Enamel copy by Falls of Bone's miniature after Hoppner*

DE KOSTER 1800

NELSON BY SIMON DE KOSTER, 1800

164 *Greenwich: National Maritime Museum (PAE 5386)*

Pencil on oval buff paper 14.7 x 12.1cm (5³/₄ x 4⁷/₈in). Head in profile to left, uniform collar; paper very brittle and slightly torn at the top. The drawing is accompanied by a sheet of paper written in ink:

The original likeness of
Lord Nelson
taken at Merton, by Simon de Koster, in 1800 a few days before he sailed for Denmark, when on the 30th of March 1801: he fought the battle of Copenhagen.

This likeness was taken for Lady Hamilton, who afterwards had a second done, that she might choose the one she thought the most perfect. She preferred the second, though everyone else thought this, the first, the more exact resemblance, & Mr de Koster kept this for himself.

Upon the death of Lord Nelson, a few small prints were taken from this drawing, & sold most rapidly, & from them, all the subsequent Paintings & Prints have been copied.

This account was written by & pasted on the back of the frame by Mr de Koster himself - & was carefully torn off & lost, when, upon his death, it came into my possession, & was sent to be re-gilt, - Eliz. Maudsley.

COLLECTIONS: the artist; Elizabeth Maudsley; Earl Nelson and acquired from Trafalgar House in 1948.

ENGRAVINGS:
(1) Small line and stipple vignette lettered faintly: *Drawn & published by S. De Koster, 15 Suffolk St Charing + 1800.*

(2) Small line vignette by J Stow (*opposite*) lettered: *BARON NELSON OF THE NILE / Drawn from Life by S. De Koster Decᵣ 8th 1800 / Engraved by Jaˢ Stow / London, Published Janᵞ 1 1801 by J. Brydon Nº 7 Charing Cross.* A copy of this print in a private collection in Devonshire has the following letter from Nelson fixed to the back (see *below*):

Merton Febᵞ 2nd 1802
Sir - There are so many prints of me that it is not in my power to say which is the most like the original, for no one of them is like the other, but I rather think a little outline of the head sold at Brydon's Charing + is the most like me. With many thanks for your good wishes I am Sir
Your most obedient servant
Nelson & Bronte
Thomas Forsyth Esqʳᵉ

The present owner, an admiral's widow, is a descendant of Thomas Forsyth and both print and letter have been in her family possession since that date. They were both cleaned and repaired at the NMM in 1978-79. A similar tradition has come down

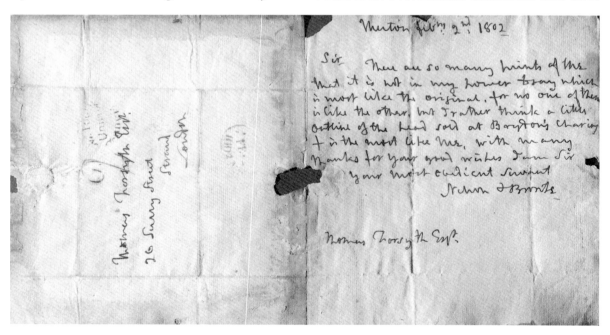

164: *Letter fixed to back of print by J. Stow of De Koster portrait*

Drawn from Life by S. De Koster Dec.r 8 1800.

Engraved by Jd Stow.

BARON NELSON of the NILE.

London, Published Jan.y 1 1801 by J. Bryden, N.o 7 Charing Cross.

164: *Vignette by J Stow after the drawing by De Koster*

in the Fyers family, and another copy was given by Nelson in 1804 to C. Anker, later (1814) Norwegian ambassador in London (photograph in NPG library given by R. Anker).

(3) Same picture used as a medallion in a plan of the Battle of Copenhagen, published by Brydon 1802

(4) Same picture, a vignette by S.I. Neele with views of the 26 captured ships, after S. De Koster and Mrs Inherheny; another as a medallion with the 26 ships, by T. Butterworth, engr, and pub. by P. Roberts 16 March 1802, without acknowledgement to De Koster.

(5) Same picture, etched vignette by Forsmann, pub. Brydon 11 January 1806, lettered: *Died in the Moment of Victory Oct. 21, 1805, aged 47 Years.* A copy in the RNM (McCarthy Collection) has in facsimile of his writing: *Lord Nelson of the Nile Kt. Bt. Duke of Bronte in Sicily - Knight of the Imperial Order of the Crescent and of the Great Cross of St Ferdinand and of Merit, a Vice Admiral of the Blue Squadron of His Majesty's Fleet - January 11th 1801.* (see *opposite*)

(6) Same picture, mezzotint in a figured oval lettered: *Baron Nelson of the Nile / Drawn from Life by S. De Koster, London / Engraved by J.G. Huck, Hanover 1806* - a variant with white uniform collar and vice-admiral's shoulder straps.

(7) Same picture, large stipple vignette by T. Burke lettered: *Drawn from the Life the 11th Decr 1800 by S. De Koster / Engraved from the original Drawing in his Possession by T. Burke. / London Published as the Act directs by S. De Koster 15 Suffolk Street, Charing Cross Jany 1st 1807.*

(8) Etching by George Cruikshank published in Southey's *Life of Nelson* (1813), vol I.

(9) Re-published frequently throughout the nineteenth century.

COMMENTS: pages 128-132. ILLUSTRATED: page 130.

165 *Portsmouth: Royal Naval Museum (72/57)*

Pencil and watercolour on oval paper, 7 x 3.1cm (2¾ x 1¼ in), framed in a gold locket with, in front, an oval blue enamelled brilliant set with initial N surrounded by pearls, a viscount's coronet above, oakleaves below, and Nelson's hair laid on cream silk behind. Inside on the left, opposite the drawing is inscribed: *Some of the late Admiral Lord Nelson's Hair - cut off from the back part of his head, by his desire, about an hour before he died after the Battle of Trafalgar To be given to Lady Hamilton who gave it to me. J.H.*

Presumably De Koster's second version, framed in the gold locket she drew from her bosom when the Trafalgar medal was under discussion, saying 'it was the best likeness ever taken from him' (see pp. 129, 167).

COLLECTIONS: Lady Hamilton; probably James Harrison, and descending through Suckling/Ward family until presented in 1957, to the Victory Museum by Maurice Suckling Ward's widow, in memory of her husband.

LITERATURE: Warner 'Relics of Nelson', *Country Life* 8 May 1958, p.995.

ILLUSTRATED: page 164.

166 *Edinburgh: Scottish National Portrait Gallery (863)*

Pastel on paper 48.3 x 37.8cm (19 x 14⅞ in), HS in profile to left in rear-admiral's undress uniform, stars of Crescent (above), St Ferdinand (left) and the Bath (right), two Naval gold medals below shirt-frill, Davison's gold medal at third buttonhole; cocked hat with chelengk with 13 fingers set on top of circular diamond base with bow. The drawing basically derives from De Koster but owes something to the Palermo miniature of 1799 (100; *p.230*) and may have been concocted from Burke's engraving also published by Brydon in August 1800.

COLLECTIONS: bought by the Scottish NPG in 1917.

167 *Greenwich: National Maritime Museum (BHC 2900)*

Oil sketch (unfinished) on canvas 61 x 50cm (24 x 19¾in), HS to left in vice-admiral's undress uniform, riband of the Bath, grey hair in queue, grey eye, leathery weather-beaten skin, cloudy background.

COLLECTIONS: Nelson's elder sister Susan; Lady Bolton and her grand-daughter Miss Frances Girdlestone; bought from her by Sir James Caird and given to the NMM in 1935. An oil copy was made for Miss Girdlestone in 1935.

ILLUSTRATED: page 131.

168 *Greenwich: National Maritime Museum (PAE 5388)*

Pencil drawing, head only, accompanied by an ink note: 'Done by my Dear Father & Sir Thomas Hardy had the fellow one to it & said it was 'the best likeness of Nelson he had ever possessed'- Ann Alldridge'.

COLLECTIONS: O'Byrne; Lieutenant George Manley Alldridge 1844.

*Lord Nelson of the Nile K.^t B.th
Duke of Bronte In Sicily – Knight of
the Imperial order of the Crescent
and of the Great Cross of St Ferdinand
and of Merit, a Vice admiral of the
Blue Squadron of His Majestys Fleet –
January 11.th 1801 –*

Died in the Moment of Victory Octr 21 1805 . Aged 47 Years

164: *Vignette by Forsmann, after the drawing by De Koster*

169 *Greenwich: National Maritime Museum (PAE 4145)*

Pencil drawing, oval paper sight size 12 x 9.2cm (4³/₄ x 3¹/₂in), head only in profile, based on De Koster but signed *HN* and inscribed on the back: 'Sketch of Horace done by his sister at Hilborough, given by Katherine Knyvet Nelson to F.K.S.'

COLLECTIONS: one of Nelson's sisters, either Catherine or Susan; Katherine Knyvet Nelson; Rev F. Keeling Scott R.D. (Vicar of Swaffham and later St Mark's Brighton) and sold by him Sotheby's 27 July 1843 (522) bt Colnaghi.

170 *Greenwich: National Maritime Museum (MNT 0036)*

Circular miniature, fair hair, coarse features square face, blue uniform with red shoulder straps, deriving from De Koster but with affinity with Burke's print of Palermo miniature (98; *p.231*).

COLLECTIONS: Mrs C. B. Hooper; Worcester Public Library.

171 *Monmouth: Nelson Museum*

Oil on copper 27 x 22cm (10³/₄ x 8³/₄in), rather crude early 19th century copy, probably acquired by Lady Llangattock c 1900.

172 *Norwich: Castle Museum (1.550.973)*

Oval watercolour miniature 6.9 x 5.8cm (2³/₄ x 2¹/₄in), HS profile to left in rear-admiral's full-dress uniform, riband and star of the Bath, hair ruffled in front, smooth at back and tied in queue. Backing paper inscribed in a modern hand: 'Nelson. By Simon / de Koster / Purchased Sotheby's / 9.11.44 from Admiral / St Clair Thomson's / Collⁿ Lot No. 41 / ? LSS Jamaica / 12.11.52', and in another hand 'Painted 8.12.1800'.

COLLECTIONS: Admiral St Clair Thomson's sale Sotheby's 9 November 1944 (41); L Stuart Stanley; Sotheby's 5 February 1973 (184a) bt Lavender £390; Leo Pratt & Son and bought by Norwich Castle Museum.

173 *Portsmouth: Royal Naval Museum*

Oil on canvas, oval shaped in a gilded frame, c. 60 x 51cm (23 x 20in), very similar to 167 and, like it, rather sketchy. HS to left in vice admiral's undress uniform, riband of the Bath (no star visible), grey hair in a queue, grey eye.

COLLECTIONS: Believed to have belonged originally to a cousin of Sir William Hamilton and eventually became part of the Suckling Ward Collection. Presented to the Victory Museum by Mrs Maurice Suckling Ward in memory of her husband in 1957.

ILLUSTRATED: page 139.

174 *Portsmouth: Royal Naval Museum*

Enamel oval miniature in a blue and gold enamel frame Artist unknown, probably late C19th. Full dress uniform, black neck cloth, shirt-frill, grey hair. Bath star, gold neck medal on red ribbon. Sketchy battle-scene in background.

COLLECTIONS: Lily Lambert McCarthy 243/73.

LITERATURE: McCarthy 1995, No.172.

ILLUSTRATED: page 139.

BOWYER 1800-1805

NELSON BY ROBERT BOWYER, 1800

175 *Windsor Castle: Royal Collection*

Miniature, watercolour on ivory, 7.8 x 6.2cm (3¹/₈ x 2⁷/₁₆in), HS to right in rear-admiral's undress uniform, riband and star of the Bath, one Naval gold medal (St Vincent), blue eyes (the right slightly enlarged), hair powdered and straggling, weatherbeaten face.
COLLECTIONS: bought from the artist by the Prince Regent in 1812.

LITERATURE: Walker 1992, p.316.

ENGRAVINGS:
(1) line engraving by Worthington at the top centre of Smirke's Plate 2 of the 'Four Great Naval Victories' lettered: *COMMEMORATION of the XIVth FEBRUARY MDCCXCVII ... Pub^d by R. Bowyer, Historic Gallery Pall Mall, June 1. 1803.*

(2) line and stipple engraving by Worthington (*opposite* and detail *p.133*), HS to right as in (1) above, in a rectangular frame partly concealed by a tablet *NELSON* supported by tritons, lettered: *R. Bowyer del / W.H. Worthington sculp.* This was also published by Bowyer himself and used as frontispiece to Churchill's *Life of Lord Viscount Nelson* (1808).

(3) line and stipple engraving by Scriven (see *p.135*), oval set amid etched storm-clouds, a battle scene

NELSON.

175: *Line engraving by W. H. Worthington, after the miniature by Bowyer*

below, the name *NELSON* above in an uroboros (a snake devouring its tail as a symbol of eternity) against a sunrise, and lettered below: *Engraved by E Scriven from a miniature for which Lord Nelson sat to Mr Bowyer / Published 9th Decr 1805, by R. Bowyer, Pall Mall.* Probably intended for use as a frontispiece but apparently never used as such. An early 19th century oil copy, canvas 99 x 68.5 cm (39 x 27in), is in the Nelson Museum, Monmouth.

An oval miniature copy probably made from one of the engravings above, signed and dated *T.A.C. 1818* (the last numeral indistinct but either 5 or 8) was stolen from a private collection in Highgate in 1979.

COMMENTS: pages 132-4. ILLUSTRATED: page 138.

NELSON BY ROBERT BOWYER, 1805

176 *Whereabouts unknown*

Drawing, possibly watercolour, nearly HL to right in vice-admiral's full-dress uniform, ribands of the Bath and St Ferdinand, stars of the Bath (above), St Ferdinand and Crescent, one Naval gold medal; bare-headed, the hair brushed downwards, a lock concealing the Nile scar, both eyes apparently normal.

COLLECTIONS: the drawing is at present only known from a brief mention in the *Monthly Magazine* for January 1806, and two engravings:

ENGRAVINGS:
(1) Line engraving by W. Bromley, WL standing by the sea, left hand on a rock, in uniform and Orders as above, published 21 October 1809, the fourth anniversary of Trafalgar. An oil painting of this subject, canvas 89 x 67cm (35 x 26½in) sight size, unsigned and probably made from Bromley's engraving, is in the Monmouth Museum. This is a crude affair, not at all worthy of Bowyer's meticulous miniaturist style, but the copy is exact except for the addition of an unidentifiable star and the omission of the Naval gold medal.

(2) Mezzotint by Charles Turner (see *p.152*), HL to right, lettered: *ADMIRAL LORD NELSON / Engraved by Turner from a drawing by R. Bowyer Esqre / For Capt Brenton's Naval History. / London Published Feby 1. 1823 by C. Turner, 50 Warren Street, Fitzroy Square.* This appeared as the frontispiece in Brenton, *Naval History of Great Britain,* vol II (1823).

COMMENTS: page 148-50.

STONE SCULPTURE

NELSON IN COADE STONE, 1800

177 *Dorking: private collection*

Coade stone bust 66cm (26in) high, incised along base of socle: *Coade & Sealy. Lambeth / 1800.* Full dress uniform as rear-admiral, ribands of the Bath and St Ferdinand, stars of the Crescent (above), St Ferdinand and the Bath, two Naval gold medals in front (St Vincent and the Nile), below the stars a third medal fastened with a bow of ribbon and displaying Victory crowning Britannia but presumably intended to represent Davison's Nile medal (73; *p.220*). The two gold buttons at the cuff are worn horizontally as in the Thaller & Ranson bust (107; *p.102*).

COLLECTIONS: Rear-Admiral Armar Lowry-Corry (1793-1855), his son Rear-Admiral Alvin Corry (1849-1907), his widow (who had a thick layer of black paint removed by Albert Amor Limited, St James's, in 1935), and their daughter, Mrs Kathleen Lutyens-Humpfrey.

LITERATURE: Kelly pp.139-40, 234-5, 297.

COMMENTS: pages 136-7. ILLUSTRATED: opposite.

178 *Bicton Park, Devonshire (Orangery)*

A copy dated 1806 (reproduced Kelly p.140).

179 *Haiti*

A copy, incised *Coade & Sealy Lambeth* and ordered by the Emperor Henri Christophe in 1816, was found on an altar in the Acul Mountains, used as a Fetish of the Mountain Streams (*The Times* 6 November 1860, 12a-b).

180 *Greenwich: National Maritime Museum*

A copy unincised, Christie's 10 November 1980 (25), bt NMM.

KEYMER 1801

NELSON BY MATTHEW H KEYMER, 1801

181 *Great Yarmouth: Town Hall*

Oil on canvas 64 x 52cm (25 x 21in), HL head slightly to right, vice-admiral's full-dress uniform, bare-headed, ribands of Bath and St Ferdinand, stars of Bath

177: *Coade Stone bust, 1800*

(above), St Ferdinand and Crescent (in reverse). The hair is carefully arranged to conceal the Nile scar; the eyes appear to be normal.

TABLET INSCRIPTION: 'This Original Portrait of the late Lord Nelson by Keymer, a Member of the Society of Friends, was presented to them by that Artist to perpetuate the Memory of that ever to be lamented Hero, who fell, Crowned with Victory, in the Battle of Trafalgar on the 21 October 1805'.

FRAME: rope and ball frame surmounted by a trophy of four flags, two cannon, three wreaths of bay and oak leaves, and a cartouche ribbon inscribed: 'England Expects Every Man to do his Duty'.

LITERATURE: Charles J. Palmer *Perlustration of Great Yarmouth* (1872); Prince Frederick Duleep Singh, *Portraits in Norfolk Houses* (1927) II pp. 405-6 from 'notes taken on 1 December 1910'; Sir Geoffrey Callender's letter in *The Times* 21 October 1930 reproducing Keymer's portrait for the first time and

citing Palmer's *Perlustration* and Oswald Driver's MS *History of the Society of Friends*, a notebook written in pencil, not dated but about 1879. Reproduced on frontispiece in Williamson's *Nelson* (1931)

COMMENTS: pages 84, 137-140

ILLUSTRATED: page 86.

HAYTER AFTER KEYMER

NELSON BY CHARLES HAYTER

182 *London: Victoria & Albert Museum*

Ink and wash on tracing paper, *c.*100 x 75cm (4 x 3in), surmounted by a tablet of fame inscribed by a recording angel and supported by a cherub.

HS to right, rugged features, short unruly hair, lock over Nile wound, eyes identical, right eyebrow slightly tilted, heavy turned-up nose. Two ribands over right shoulder (Bath and Ferdinand), two Naval gold medals, three stars (Bath, Ferdinand, Crescent).

COLLECTIONS: Angelo G.K. Hayter (the artist's great-grandson); V & A Museum E.152-1920.

The drawing is a copy, presumably intended for a miniature, of Matthew Keymer's portrait of 1801, in the Town Hall, Great Yarmouth. A note by the artist's great-grandson, Angelo Hayter, accompanies the drawing: *Similarly* [referring to two portraits of Dr Johnson above] *the portrait (coloured) of Ld Nelson, though there is not the same time limit, looks to have been copied from another portrait.* It comes from an album of sketches for miniatures with, inside the cover, an explanation in Charles Hayter's handwriting: *Let it not be supposed that the following Sketches were preserved thro any View to perpetuate the Character of the person who did them, as they are merely a sort of Measure taken of the picture intended, and placed behind the Ivory, which being transparent gave the artist the aid in making his Outline on the ivory which he desired - and as many pictures require Copies, this Same Sketch (by preserving) answers the Original intention. He is so fully conscious of the necessity of this remark that he has wrote the names on mo[st] on account of the entire want of* Minute *resemblance & drawing.*

The whereabouts of Hayter's finished miniature is not known at present (see p.141).

183: *The Copenhagen badge, 1801* (enlarged)

THE COPENHAGEN BADGE 1801

183 *Portsmouth: Royal Naval Museum*

Oval silver-gilt medallion, 4.0 x 2.7cm (1⁵/₈ x 1in), bust of Nelson in profile to left, vice-admiral's full-dress uniform, riband and star of the Bath, one Naval gold medal, hair in queue, around: *ADMˡ LORD NELSON OF THE NILE / Aprˡ 2 1801*. The oval is supported by a trophy consisting of an anchor and cable, cannon and shot, shell ornament below, ribbon loop above, total measurement 4.8 x 4.8cm (1⁷/₈ x 1⁷/₈in).

COLLECTIONS: McCarthy, 39/74. Most of the other main collections have either bronze or silver-gilt examples. Milford Haven describes a gold specimen in Dr Payne's collection, which may have been presented to Nelson by Alexander Davison though there is no evidence for this assertion. This particular example has *DONEGAL 74* engraved on the back and the example at the NMM bears the engraved inscription, *CAPT GEO. MURRAY H.M.S EDGAR*.

LITERATURE: Milford Haven 492; McCarthy 1995, No 40; Hattersley 1974 pp 118-9; Warner 1958 p.143.

COMMENTS: page 70. ILLUSTRATED: opposite.

RISING 1801

NELSON BY JOHN RISING, 1801

184 *Greenwich: National Maritime Museum (BHC 2902)*

Oil on canvas 91.5 x 71cm (36 x 28in), signed and dated on the rock to right: *J.C. Rising 1801*. WL standing on shore in vice-admiral's undress uniform, sword in his left hand pointing to a naval action in the left background; riband of the Bath nearly concealed beneath his coat, stars of the Bath (above), St Ferdinand and the Crescent; two Naval gold medals (St Vincent and the Nile).

COLLECTIONS: early history unknown; Christie's 14 March 1927 (71); Major Cyril Walter and lent by him to the NMM in 1936; bought from the Caird Fund in 1960.

ENGRAVINGS: mezzotint by John Young lettered: *Engraved by Jnᵒ Young from the Original Picture by John Rising. / London, Novr. 2d 1801, Published by Jno Young, No. 58 Upper Charlotte Street, Fitzroy Square /*

To His Royal Highness the Prince of Wales, this Plate of / VICE ADMIRAL LORD VISCOUNT NELSON, DUKE OF BRONTI, &c. &c. &c. / is by permission most humbly dedicated by His Highness's devoted Servant and Engraver / John Young. Stipple with variations by Thomas Tegg was published 1 January 1807 (coloured copy in NMM).

EXHIBITION: RA 1802 (764).

COPY: a small oil copy from the late Sir Henry Sutcliffe Smith's collection was at Christie's 4 June 1976 (152).

COMMENTS: page 145. ILLUSTRATED: page 144.

CAULFIELD 1802

NELSON BY JAMES CAULFIELD, 1802

185 *London: Christie's*

Pen and ink on off-white paper, c.25.5 x 23cm (10 x 9in), two WL figures walking up the steps at Blenheim Palace, inscribed: *He was very Brown in the Face (Tanned greatly) His Countenance had a Firm expression, but was not repulsive. / He held himself well, erect: - like a Man accustomed to Command - and who would be first every where. He was dressed in a Cocked Hat - Blue Coat and yellow Buttons - Pantaloons and Hessian Boots - Not Uniform - / As seen by Mr Caulfield, going up Blenheim Steps.*

In spite of the inscription, Nelson seems to be wearing uniform, sword, and shoes (not Hessian boots).

COLLECTION: Christie's manuscript sale, 20 June 1990 (184), bt Christie's.

LITERATURE (for the visit to Blenheim only): Oman 1947, pp.502-3; Walder 1978, p.433; Pocock 1987, pp.278-9; Howarth 1988, p.279; Hibbert 1994, p.303.

COMMENTS: the visit took place on 23 July 1802 at the beginning of the tour to the West Country, when Nelson and the Hamiltons were snubbed by the Duke of Marlborough. Caulfield also produced another drawing, pencil, square c.18 x 18cm (7 x 7in), showing Nelson's head only, in profile to left, with craggy face and straight hair in queue (Christie's 20 June 1990, 184).

ILLUSTRATED: page 258.

He was very Brown in the
Face. (Tanned greatly)
His Countenance had
a Firm expression, but was
not repulsive.
He held himself well, erect.
— like a Man accustomed
to Command — and who
would be first wrong where
He was dressed in a Cocked
Hat — Blue Coat and gilt
Buttons — Pantaloons and
Hessian Boots — not in
Uniform —
As seen by Mrs
Caulfield, going up
Blenheim Steps.

185: *Drawing by James Caulfield, 1802*

DOWNMAN 1802

NELSON BY JOHN DOWNMAN, 1802

186 *Leicestershire: private collection*

Black chalk and watercolour, on off-white paper 31 x 24 cm (12 x 9¹/₂in) inscribed on the back: *HORATIO NELSON, 1802 / Admiral Lord Nelson of the Nile, / who conquered foes with wondrous spoil.* Half length, head in profile to left, vice-admiral's uniform, cocked hat to right, riband and star of the Bath, two Naval gold medals and Davison's Nile medal, two ribbons fastening the right sleeve aperture below the shoulder, right sleeve loosely folded at the cuff. Hair and features romanticised.

COLLECTIONS: Downman family album IV vol 5, sold by Miss Downman to the Rev George Neville Grenville, Dean of Windsor and of Butleigh Court, Glastonbury; Butleigh House (Mrs Maitland); the Hon Mrs Ralph Neville and her sale Sotheby's 9 December 1931 (110) bought Agnew who offered it to the NMM and NPG when the album was broken up in 1958.

LITERATURE: Ralph Neville Grenville *Downman Albums at Butleigh Court* (1865); G C Williamson *John Downman A.R.A.* (1907); *Illustrated London News* 20 March 1954 p.433 (whole page photograph); Warner, 'Unfamiliar Portraits of Nelson', *Connoisseur* (August 1958), p.33.

COMMENTS: pages 145-6. ILLUSTRATED: page 147.

EDRIDGE 1802

NELSON BY HENRY EDRIDGE, 1802

187 *London: National Portrait Gallery (879)*

Watercolour and pencil on paper 32.1 x 22.2cm (12 x 8³/₄in), signed dated lower left: *H. Edridge 1802.* WL standing by a cannon mounted on a trunion, its muzzle resting on a defence wall and covering a harbour possibly intended to represent Bastia or Calvi; vice-admiral's full-dress uniform, riband and stars of Bath (above), St Ferdinand, the Crescent, and St Joachim received in June 1802; no Naval gold medals. The head is more closely finished than the remainder, the hair rather wiry in texture.

COLLECTIONS: the artist probably for use as a master-copy, then by family descent to a great-niece ('Edridge was my Grandfather's uncle') Mrs Isabelle Mitchell (née Wilkinson) who sold it to the NPG in 1891.

ENGRAVINGS: stipple by Anthony Cardon published in 1802 and again in half-length as frontispiece to Clarke & M'Arthur's *Life of Nelson* (octavo edition 1810).

LITERATURE: Nicolas VII p.19; Farington 6 August 1802; Morrison II p.181. Oliver Warner 'Nelson and his biographer' in *Country Life* 8 Nov. 1956 p.1063.

COMMENTS: pages 17-20, 146-8.

ILLUSTRATED: page 149.

Copies made from the master copy are:

188 *Portsmouth: Royal Naval Museum*

Watercolour and pencil on paper 32.1 x 22.5cm (12⁵/₈ x 8⁷/₈in), signed and dated lower left *Edridge 1802*, otherwise identical with NPG 879 (see 187).

REPRODUCTION: *Pugh* 1968, p.22.

189 *Hampshire: private collection*

Watercolour and pencil on smooth buff paper sight size 30 x 20cm (11³/₄ x 8in), inscribed on reverse: *from life H. Edridge*, unfinished but clearly intended to be a close copy of NPG 879 (see 187).

COLLECTIONS: Charles Sackville Bale and his sale Christie's 13 May 1881 (359); Hogarth & Sons, bought from them by E A Drummond and still in the family collection.

ENGRAVING: lithographic facsimile printed in Paris and published by Colnaghi 5 December 1881, the face and hands coloured.

EXHIBITIONS: Royal Naval Exhibition, Chelsea 1891 (924) lent by E A Drummond; *Rule Britannia* 1986 (108) in colour.

ANDRAS 1805

NELSON BY CATHERINE ANDRAS, 1805

190 *Greenwich: National Maritime Museum
(OBJ 0575)*

Pink wax relief profile 7.5cm (3in) high, incised under the shoulder: *C. Andras 1805.* HS in vice-admiral's full-dress uniform, riband and star of the Bath, one Naval gold medal, thick hair brushed forwards and tied in queue, mounted on oval amber glass with a gilt border set in a white mount and wooden frame. The cravat and forelock slightly damaged.

COLLECTIONS: H M Queen Mary and presented by her in 1935.

REPRODUCTION: Van der Merwe 1995, p.82.

ILLUSTRATED: page 151.

191 *London: Victoria & Albert Museum*
Wax relief profile, dated 1806.

LITERATURE: Warner, *Unfamiliar Portraits* 1988 p.32.

192 *Greenwich: National Maritime Museum
(OBJ 0576)*

Pink wax relief profile as above, mounted on brown glass background; on reverse is an old blue handwritten label imitating prints: *Portrait of Lord Nelson for which His Lordship sat to Miss Andras, modeller in wax to Her Majesty. 87 Pall-Mall.*

COLLECTIONS: Sir Henry Sutcliffe-Smith and lent by him to the NMM in 1946; sold to the Museum in 1974 by E A Sutcliff-Smith.

193 *Greenwich: National Maritime Museum
(OBJ 0577)*

White vitreous paste profile as above, incised under the shoulder: *C. Andras June 1812.*

COLLECTIONS: probably Horatia Nelson then Nelson-Ward collection and presented to the NMM in June 1939 by the Rev Hugh Nelson-Ward and his brother the late Admiral Philip Nelson-Ward in memory of their grandmother Horatia, daughter of Lord Nelson and Lady Hamilton.

194 *Greenwich National Maritime Museum*
Wax relief profile as above, without incision under shoulder; inscribed in ink on reverse: *Portrait of*

Lord Nelson for which his Lordship sat to Miss Andras 87 Pall Mall.

COLLECTIONS: probably Nelson's elder sister Susan; Lady Bolton and her grand-daughter Miss Frances Girdlestone; bought from her by Sir James Caird and given by him to the NMM in 1935.

LITERATURE: *Illustrated London News* 22 October 1938 (full page enlargement).

The waxes were turned out in quantity from a mould, some dated 1805, 1807, and 1812, others undated. In general the earlier ones are of finer quality, sometimes hand-finished and often carefully mounted on a variety of backgrounds. Several were bought by Sir Bruce Ingram in 1937 from Miss Dorothy Andras of Toronto, a great-niece. A specially good one, in a London private collection, is framed in ebony topped with a viscount's coronet.

COMMENTS: pages 134, 150-3.

WHICHELO 1805

NELSON BY JOHN WHICHELO, 1805

195 *Lincolnshire: private collection*
Chalk drawing on off-white paper 55.9 x 43.2cm (22 x 17in), laid on canvas. HS in profile to left, in vice-admiral's undress uniform, star of the Bath, black neckcloth, white shirt-frill, grey hair, grey eye, leathery and weather-beaten complexion. A paper on reverse is inscribed in ink in the artist's handwriting:

THE ILLUSTRIOUS NELSON
The Glory of his Country! The terror of his Enemies! and a luminous Example to Posterity!!! - Crowned with Victory this Illustrious Hero fell in the service of his Country, in the memorable Engagement with the combined Fleets of France and Spain off Cape Trafalgar Oct[r] 21st 1805.

This Head was sketched from the Hero, during his short stay at Merton the beginning of September 1805 by me
John Whichelo.

COLLECTIONS: given by the artist to Rear-Admiral Sir William Parker in 1838 and in the family possession ever since.

LITERATURE: reproduced photographically in Mahan 1879, II p.364.

COMMENTS: pages 153-6. ILLUSTRATED: page 155.

CRAIG 1805

NELSON EXPLAINING HIS PLAN OF ATTACK FOR TRAFALGAR, 1805

196 *London, Sotheby's*

Watercolour on paper, 16.5 x 26cm (6^1/$_2$ x 10^1/$_4$in), Nelson in cocked hat seated at a table in his state cabin, surrounded by the captains who are numbered up to 25.

COLLECTIONS: Montague Guest; John Mitchell of New York; Sotheby's 5 April 1973 (102), bt Pike Ltd, £300.

ENGRAVING: by J. Godby, pubd Edward Orme, 9 January 1806, with a key giving the 'Names of the GALLANT HEROES who Commanded on the 21st Octr 1805'. Reproduced Hibbert 1995, colour plate 29; van der Merwe 1995, p.106.

COMMENTS: page 156. ILLUSTRATED: below.

196: Watercolour drawing by William Marshall Craig, c.1805

DEVIS 1805

NELSON BY ARTHUR WILLIAM DEVIS, 1805

197 *Greenwich: National Maritime Museum (BHC 2423)*

Oil on canvas 35.5 x 30.5cm (14 x 12in), uninscribed but with a MS letter on the back from Nelson to Captain Page, HM Ship *Caroline*, dated 4 March 1803 (printed in *Nicolas* V p.46); HL to left in vice-admiral's undress uniform, cocked hat with black silk cockade and green eyeshade; stars of the Bath (above), St Ferdinand and the Crescent (in reverse); black neckcloth, white shirt-frill, no Naval gold medals.

COLLECTIONS: believed to have belonged to Admiral Benjamin William Page and given by him to the Rev W. S. Halliday, Vicar of Glenthorne, Lynton, North Devon (1840-46); lent by his descendant, Dr A. M. Halliday in 1967 to NMM.

ENGRAVING: Woodbury print reproduced in Beresford & Wilson p.193.

EXHIBITION: RA 1807 (43); National Portraits Exhibition 1868 (5), lent by the Rev W S Halliday.

COMMENTS: pages 159-66. Admiral Page's picture was one of many copies made by Devis from the original commissioned by Dr Beatty and used as a frontispiece to his *Authentic Narrative*.

ILLUSTRATED: page 163.

198 *Location Unknown*

Oil on canvas, the original commissioned by Dr. Beatty.

COLLECTIONS: Dr Beatty, then uncertain.

ENGRAVING: stipple by Scriven (see *opposite*) lettered: *A W Devis pinx^t / E Scriven sculp. / LORD VISCOUNT NELSON / Duke of Bronte &c &c &c / In the Dress he wore when he received his Mortal Wound / 21st Octr 1805 - / Published by Cadell & Davies Novr 17 1806* and used as frontispiece to Dr William Beatty's *Authentic Narrative of the Death of Nelson* (1807).

199 *Hampshire: private collection*

Sepia wash on paper 10.9 x 8.7cm (4^1/$_4$ x 3^1/$_2$cm), finely drawn and probably the copy made by Scriven for the stipple engraving above, which is identical in size.

COLLECTIONS: uncertain; a torn and nearly illegible paper on the back is inscribed in ink: 'To... Honble E. Mar... to Mrs Wa... th... 15th January ...' and a sale label 10B. Acquired by the present owner's father *c.* 1925.

ILLUSTRATED: below.

199: *Sepia drawing for Scriven's engraving after Devis*

200 *Location unknown (Capel's)*

Oil on canvas, unfinished sketch.

COLLECTIONS: Admiral Sir Thomas Bladen Capel, Nelson's flag officer at the Nile and captain of the *Phoebe* at Trafalgar.

ENGRAVING: stipple and line by Skelton lettered: *A W Devis del (1805) / J Skelton sculp / LORD VISCOUNT NELSON, K.B. / &c. &c. &c. / from the original sketch in the possession of / Admiral the Honble Sir T. Bladen Capel, K.C.B.* and used as frontispiece to Pettigrew's *Life of Nelson* (1849) vol II.

LITERATURE: Pettigrew describes this as 'being the last taken of the Immortal Hero - it is unfinished and was executed just before his departure for Trafalgar, the last therefore ever painted from life' (Vol I p.xiv). Pettigrew was probably confusing this with the Whichelo portrait (195; *p.155*), Devis just before Trafalgar being firmly confined in the King's Bench prison.

201 *Location unknown (Lady Hamilton's)*

Oil on canvas possibly signed and dated 1806 (Pettigrew I xiv).

COLLECTIONS: according to the 3rd Earl Nelson this was admired by Lady Hamilton who persuaded Dr Beatty to lend it to her, then lost it overboard en route to Calais in a box containing Nelson relics. This may not be true as later on a number of Lady Hamilton's Nelson relics were acquired by Alderman Smith (Nicolas VII p.395); Mrs Smith owned a Devis portrait in 1849 (Pettigrew), inherited by her daughter Princess Gonzago in whose house, 9 Lower Seymour Street, it was seen by Sir George Scharf in 1871. Scharf did not note the date - merely that it was inscribed *A Devis* in the lower left corner, and on the strainer: *A W Devis No 7 Newman Street* where Devis lived from 1807 to 1810. Devis exhibited a portrait of Nelson at the RA 1807 (43) - possibly this one.

202 *Dalmeny: Earl of Rosebery*

Miniature *c.* 15 x 11.5cm (6 x 4^1/$_4$in), inscribed on reverse *Painted for Capt Page in 1805 by A.W. Devis* and similar to the usual Devis versions except for pearls sewn into his silk cockade.

COLLECTIONS: uncertain but probably bought by the 5th Earl of Rosebery *c* 1905.

198: *Engraving by Edward Scriven after Devis*

203 *Greenwich: National Maritime Museum (BHC 2270)*

Oil on canvas 34.5 x 29.5cm (13$^{1}/_{2}$ x 11$^{1}/_{2}$in), inscribed in ink on reverse of canvas: *The Earl Nelson / 1852 Trafalgar,* and in smaller lettering: *Lynmouth 1845.*

COLLECTIONS: probably a mid-19th century copy of Captain Page's version (NMM L67-36) above; on the reverse is a paper written in ink by the 3rd Earl Nelson: 'This picture was presented to me by the Rev. R.S. Halliday of Glenthorne, Linton, N. Devon, being a copy of the *last picture* ever taken of my great uncle - // The original was painted by A. Devis 1805 for Captain (now Admiral) Page and he presented it to Mr Halliday.//
A. Devis was Assistant Surgeon on board the *Victory* [presumably a reference to the help he gave Dr Beatty at the autopsy], and afterwards a painter of some note. Sir Wm Beattie (sic) who attended Lord Nelson in his last moments was anxious to have a good likeness of the Admiral and employed Devis to make him one for which he assisted him by hints and by allowing him to see the dead body. The likeness, Sir Wm told me was the only true one he ever saw, and Lady Hamilton was so pleased with it that, though Sir Wm refused to give, he was as yet induced to lend it to her.// On her passage from England to France the box containing it and many other relics fell overboard. Fortunately the artist broke his promise to Sir Wm and painted a second picture (at the same time as he was at the first) for Admiral Page ... painted by an amateur artist ... Nelson.' Acquired by the NMM from Trafalgar House in 1948.

COMMENTS: page 162.

204 *Essex: private collection*

Oil on canvas 35.5 x 30.5cm (14 x 12in).

COLLECTIONS: unknown before 1961 when it was bought at Meyer's curiosity shop off St Martin's Lane, London. The frame matches that on the Rev Halliday's copy (NMM BHC 2270) above. It could conceivably be one of the versions listed 'location unknown' above.

205 *Portsmouth: Royal Naval Museum*

Oil on canvas *c.* 86 x 71cm (34 x 28in), a considerably enlarged copy by the Hon H Cadogan.

COLLECTIONS: Presented to HMS *Victory* in the late 19th century and transferred to the Victory Museum when it opened in 1938.

206 *London: private collection*

Pastel on paper fixed to cardboard 36.2 x 31.9cm (14$^{1}/_{4}$ x 12$^{1}/_{2}$in), a rather crude but vigorously worked copy with burning ships in background.

COLLECTIONS: Fleet Surgeon E. Weightman and inherited from him by the present owner.

207 *Location unknown since 1969*

Private collection, Long Melford, and a photograph shown to NPG in 1969.

208 *Location unknown since 1971*

Oil on canvas, private collection Wilmslow and shown to NPG in 1971.

209 *Location unknown since 1975*

Oil on canvas 36 x 30cm (14$^{1}/_{2}$ x 11$^{3}/_{4}$in), sold Sotheby's (various properties) 26 November 1975 (70), possibly a version offered to the NPG in 1974.

210 *London: National Portrait Gallery*

Pencil drawing on paper 13.3 x 10.3cm (5$^{3}/_{4}$ x 4in) squared up drawing by Henry Bone inscribed *1812 Lord Nelson for the Honble Cap^{n} Capel,* intended for an oval enamel (NPG Bone Drawings III 18).

THE DEATH OF NELSON, 1805 1807

211 *Greenwich: National Maritime Museum (BHC 2894)*

Oil on canvas 193.5 x 261.5cm (77 x 103in), Nelson lies, mortally wounded, in the cockpit of HMS *Victory.* A key exists identifying the accompanying figures.

COLLECTIONS: given by Lord Bexley to Greenwich Hospital in 1825 (loan GH91).

EXHIBITIONS: British Institution 1809 (70).

LITERATURE: *ILN* 24 April 1937 (repr); Oman 1947, p.632; Pavière 1950, pp.132-3; Nelson Dispatch II (1987), part 9; NMM 1988, p.150.

COMMENTS: pages 159-166. ILLUSTRATED: page 265 and details pages 158, 161.

212 *Portsmouth: HMS* Victory

Oil on canvas, possibly a preparatory sketch for the Greenwich version.

COLLECTIONS: Presented to the ship by Admiral Sir George Hope.

BOULTON AND KUCHLER 1805

NELSON: TRAFALGAR MEDAL by Küchler

213 *Portsmouth: Royal Naval Museum*

Gold medal 4.8cm (1⁷/₈in) diameter.

Obverse: HS in profile to left in vice-admiral's full-dress uniform, riband and star of the Bath, one Naval gold medal, badge of the Bath showing below; around: *HORATIO VISCOUNT NELSON. K.B. DUKE OF BRONTE. &c.* Signed on truncation: *C.H.K.*

Reverse: View of the Battle of Trafalgar; around on a scroll: *ENGLAND EXPECTS EVERY MAN WILL DO HIS DUTY. Exergue: TRAFALGAR / Oct⁰. 21. 1805.* Signed on exergual line: *K.*

Edge: (sunk in small capitals): *TO THE HEROES OF TRAFALGAR FROM M: BOULTON.*

COLLECTIONS: Originally Emma Hamilton's and from her descended via Horatia to Nelson's great-grandson, Maurice Suckling Ward. Presented by his widow to the Victory Museum in 1957. There are, two other gold examples at the NMM: one from the Admiral Sir Thomas Louis Collection and one on loan from the Walter Collection. The medal was issued in silver and pewter and numerous examples exist in all the main collections - some of them engraved (unofficially) with the recipient's name.

LITERATURE: LL27; Mayo pp.182-3; Milford Haven 493 - Gordon p.20; Pollard pp.260-318; Hattersley 1974 p,197; Warner 1975 p.217, Brown 1980 584A-B; McCarthy 1995 No 67.

REPRODUCTIONS: Hattersley 1974 p.197 (Monmouth); Warner 1975 p.217 (Portsmouth), Brown 1980 584A-B.

COMMENTS: pages 166-170.

ILLUSTRATED: page 165.

211: *'The Death of Nelson' by A W Devis, 1807*

ANDRAS 1805-06

NELSON BY CATHERINE ANDRAS, 1805-06

214 *London: Westminster Abbey*

Wax and wood effigy 166.5cm (5ft 5½in) high, the body of carved wood, the head and hand modelled in wax, WL standing in vice-admiral's full-dress uniform said to have been Nelson's own; ribands of the Bath and St Ferdinand, stars of the Bath (above), St Ferdinand, the Crescent (in reverse), St Joachim (below); one medal (a gilt bronze cast of Davison's Nile medal) on a white ribbon edged with blue; the right sleeve is fastened to the riband of St Ferdinand and Merit by a narrow bow made of the same material (blue with a cream border). Nelson's undress cocked hat is displayed in an adjoining showcase together with Messrs Lock & Company's hatter's account book showing several bills for Nelson's hats with green eyeshades 1800-05; the last entry, *10 September 1805 Cocked Hat Green Shade £2.2.6.*, is followed by the account's settlement shortly before Trafalgar, *Paid Sept 13 1805 £11.19.6.*

COLLECTION: Westminster Abbey since 1806.

CONDITION: clumsily repaired mid 19th century; cleaned and repaired in 1933; stored during the 1939-45 war in a London Underground station and re-dressed afterwards by Lady Tanner and Miss Marjory Usher; cleaned and repaired by the Victoria Museum conservation staff in 1951 (*The Times* 12 May 1951 4b).

LITERATURE: Lawrence Tanner, letter to *The Times*, 8 November 1932 10d; Tanner & Nevinson 1935, pp.197-202; *Illustrated London News*, 15 June 1935, pp.1055-7, for illustrations after cleaning at the V & A Museum; Callender 1941, pp.307-13; Sir Lawrence Tanner, *Recollections of a Westminster Antiquary* (1969), pp.135-7; Pyke 1973, pp.5-6; Pocock 1987, fig.51; Anthony Harvey & Richard Mortimer, *The Funeral Effigies of Westminster Abbey* (1994), pp.175-87; Hibbert 1994, pl.34 (colour).

COMMENTS: pages 170-5.

ILLUSTRATED: page 168 and detail page 171.

FLAXMAN 1805 - 1818

NELSON BY JOHN FLAXMAN, 1805

215 *London: Ministry of Defence*

Marble bust 75 cm (29½in) high, no inscription, head and shoulders facing forwards in rear-admiral's full-dress uniform, ribands of the Bath and St Ferdinand, stars of the Crescent Bath and St Ferdinand, two Naval gold medals worn from the neck (St Vincent above, the Nile below incised: NILE / AUGUST / 1 / MDCCXCVIII), below the stars Davison's Nile medal as in Thaller & Ranson's Vienna bust (107; *p.102*); the cuff buttons set horizontally.

COLLECTIONS: bought by the United Service Club in 1840 possibly from the collection of Nelson's prize agent, Alexander Davison, who is known to have commissioned Flaxman to make a 'copy from the great bust' in 1805-06 (see p.175).

CONDITION: the Nile medal is slightly chipped at 5 o'clock.

REPRODUCTION: Russell Grenfell *Nelson the Sailor* (1949) republished as *Horatio Nelson* (1969), frontispiece.

COMMENTS: pages 175-8. ILLUSTRATED: page 174.

216 *Greenwich: National Maritime Museum (SCU 0090)*

Marble bust as above except for the star of the Crescent being worn below and in reverse. The cuff anchor buttons are diagonal.

COLLECTIONS: Viscount Bridport, then his daughter Lady Mary Cook who married Sir Frederick Cook of Doughty House; she died in 1943 and the bust was bought by the NMM in 1948 from her nephew, the 3rd Viscount Bridport. Another version (or perhaps the same) was in Lord Bridport's sale, Christie's 11 July 1895 (103).

217 *Greenwich: National Maritime Museum (SCU 1014)*

Marble bust as above, scratched on the back: *By Flaxman*.

COLLECTIONS: W C Renshaw, Bencher of Lincoln's Inn, then his daughter and son-in-law Colonel W J Fernie of Old Bursledon and given by him in 1946. Colonel Fernie in an extensive correspondence with Professor Callender said that a similar bust belonged to Mrs Nelson Weekes, a grand daughter of Horatia, and

219: *Detail of marble statue by John Flaxman, 1807-08*

that there was a family tradition that the bust might be a copy by Henry Weekes though there is no mention of a Nelson in Weekes's sitter-book (letters in NMM archive). Inquiries among the Weekes family today (1980) have elicited no knowledge of this bust.

218 *Portsmouth Royal Naval Museum*

Copeland Parian bust 29cm (11½in) high including the socle, incised on incluse: *Copyright Reserve, Copeland M-91.* The medal arrangement corresponds to the marble busts except that only the stars of the Crescent and St Ferdinand are worn. Another copy, in the Monmouth Museum, is incised: *COPELAND* with an arrow.

COLLECTIONS: Lily Lambert McCarthy 1975, no.187.

LITERATURE: Alterbury 1989, p.136, fig.613.

ILLUSTRATED: right.

NELSON BY JOHN FLAXMAN, 1807-08

219 *London: St Paul's Cathedral*

Marble monumental group, Nelson standing in uniform, the Turkish sable-lined pelisse over his right shoulder, his left hand on an anchor and coil of cable,

the capstan-shaped plinth decorated with sea-gods and the names of his victories and supported by a half-couchant lion and Britannia indicating the admiral to two midshipmen. The rectangular pedestal is incised in front. The monument is unsigned.

COLLECTIONS: commissioned by the Dean and Chapter of St Paul's in 1807 and paid for by public subscription. It was erected in May 1818.

ENGRAVING: line engraving by S Rawle in *The European Magazine* 73 (1818) frontispiece.

LITERATURE: *The Times* 14 May 1818 3d; E Croft Murray 'An Account Book of John Flaxman' *Walpole Society Journal* XXVIII (1939-40) pp.51-94; T S R Boase *English Art 1800-1870* (1959) p.133; Margaret Whinney *Sculpture in Britain 1530-1830* (1964) pp.190-1 and plates 147-8; David Bindman *John Flaxman* (1979) pp 119 (for the Nile Britannia); White's *Companion*, pp.134-5.

COMMENTS: page 175-8.

ILLUSTRATED: page 177 and detail left.

218: *Copeland parian bust, c.1855, after Flaxman*

TASSIE 1805

NELSON BY WILLIAM TASSIE, 1805

220 *Greenwich: National Maritime Museum*

Oval white paste medallion 11.5cm (4¹/₂in) high, HS profile to left in vice-admiral's uniform, riband and star of the Bath, one Naval gold medal, hair in queue with a lock over the forehead; incuse on truncation: *Admiral / Lord Nelson / died in the / Glorious Battle / off Trafalgar / Oct. 21 1805*, and signed *Tassie F. 1805*.

COLLECTIONS: acquired from Trafalgar House 1948. Many other copies exist in the NMM and in other collections.

ENGRAVING: possibly the line engraving published by W. B. Daniel in 1808 (BM Catalogue No. 77).

LITERATURE: John M Gray *James and William Tassie* (1894); Duncan Thomson 'Two Medallists in Georgian London' in *Country Life* 27 January 1972, pp.214-9; McCarthy 1995 no. 199.

COMMENTS: page 178. ILLUSTRATED: page 153.

221 *Norwich: Castle Museum (93.639)*

Wax cameo 2.5cm (1in) high, damaged near the signature lower-left which reads: ...ASS... / 180- (last numeral illegible).

COLLECTIONS: a note inside the case reads: 'A gift for little Mary Ann...from...(illegible) March...1817'. Given to the Castle Museum by the Misses K. and E. Williams.

NELSON attributed to WILLIAM TASSIE

222 *Monmouth: Nelson Museum*

Hard yellowish wax medallion 24.5cm (9⁵/₈in) diameter no inscription, head in profile to left.

COLLECTIONS: acquired by Lady Llangattock, probably shortly before the Nelson centenary in 1905 and bequeathed to the town of Monmouth with the rest of her large collection of Nelson manuscripts and relics at her death in 1923.

THOMAS WEBB 1805

MEMORIAL MEDAL BY THOMAS WEBB, 1805

223 *Greenwich: National Maritime Museum*

Circular bronze gilt medal 5.3cm (21/8in) diameter, head and bare shoulders in profile to left engraved around: *HOR VICE COM NELSON OB PATRIAM MORI OCT XXI . MDCCCV*; reverse: a winged Victory bearing a thunderbolt engraved around: *IPSE BELLI FULMEN*

ILLUSTRATED: opposite, above.

224 *Portsmouth: Royal Naval Museum*

A variant of the above medallion engraved, obverse: *ADM. VISC NELSON K.B.D.: of BRONTE*, and below: *Webb. F. / Mudie Dir.* Reverse: *NILE 1. 1798 COPE* (thunderbolt) *NHAGEN 28* (sic) *APR 1801. TRAFALGAR 21 OCT 1805*, and below: *Droz del fec / Mudie. D.*

ENGRAVING: line engraving by John Landseer (*opposite, below*) from a design by Richard Smirke in the manner of an antique cameo on a sarcophagus and surrounded by an uroboros, palm leaves on either side and his motto, PALMAM QUI MERUIT FERAT, published by Cadell & Davies 1809 as tailpiece to Clarke & M'Arthur vol II - 'The Likeness is principally taken from the Bolton medal' (vol I p.xlv), presumably a mistake for the Webb medal which it clearly resembles more closely.

LITERATURE: McCarthy 1995, no.197; NMM Medal Catalogue (in progress) LL.28; Milford Haven 507; Forrer p.401.

COMMENTS: Webb gives no source for his profile of Nelson but it seems to stem from one of the post-Nile busts by Gahagan (48; *p.59*). Two similar medals were designed by Webb, probably intended for Mudie's series of National Medals published *c*.1820 (Brown 1980 595-6).

223: *Memorial medal by Thomas Webb, 1805*

224: *Line engraving by John Landseer after Webb's medal*

THOMAS WYON 1805

TURTON'S MEMORIAL MEDAL BY THOMAS WYON 1805

225 *Portsmouth: Royal Naval Museum*

Circular bronze medal, *Obverse:* profile head and shoulders of NELSON to left in vice-admiral's full-dress uniform, stars of Crescent (above), St Ferdinand and the Bath, two Naval gold medals, hair in queue, around: *NELSON ET BRONTI . VICTOR TRAFALGAR ET VICTIMA . PERIIT ET PERIIT OCT 21 1805.* Signed on truncation *T. Wyon Sc.*

Reverse: view of the Battle of Trafalgar lettered around: *MEMORIAE CONSECRAVIT . GUL . TURTON M.D. F.L.S. ESTO PERPETUA*

COLLECTIONS: Examples exist in most of the main Nelson Collections, including a version in silver at the NMM.

LITERATURE: NMM (MED 1257-8)
Milford Haven 496; Forrer VI p.640; Brown 1980 586.

POST-1805

Many different likenesses of Nelson have been produced since his death. Here are a few of the more interesting examples.

NELSON BY JAMES GEORGE BUBB, c.1810

226 *Greenwich: National Maritime Museum (SCU 0089)*

Marble bust 54.5cm (21¹/₂in) high, incised on base scroll *NELSON,* and on reverse *J.G. BUBB Sculpᵗ.*

COLLECTIONS: Nelson Ward family until 1955; Rupert Gunnis and bequeathed by him in 1965.

EXHIBITIONS: RA 1810 (871) and 'British Portraits' RA, 1956-57 (317).

LITERATURE: Gunnis 1964, p.68.

COMMENTS: page 185. ILLUSTRATED: page 186.

COADE STONE BUST

227 *Portsdown Hill, Hampshire*

Colossal Coade Stone bust crowning the monument on Portsdown Hill, the result of Collingwood and the captains' decision after Trafalgar in a Fleet Order dated 2 November 1805. The bust is sometimes attributed to John Bacon the Younger.

COMMENTS: pages 188-9.

ILLUSTRATED: page 188 and inscription page vi.

NELSON BY THOMAS R. POOLE

228 *Portsmouth: Royal Naval Museum*

Coloured wax bust signed on back: *Pool fecit,* 16cm (6¹/₄in) high, head facing, rear-admiral's full-dress uniform, ribbon of Bath, three stars (Bath, Crescent, St Ferdinand), hair brushed forward on forehead, flesh coloured face, ribbon and uniform blue, gold lace (KB ribbon should be red).

COLLECTIONS: Poole (sometimes Pool) specialised in wax profile medallions describing himself on his trade labels as 'Medallion modeller to his Royal Highness the Prince of Wales' of whom Pyke lists eight portraits as Prince and King. The earliest profile seems to be that of Burke 1791 and the NPG has a double profile of the Prince and the Duke of York dated 1795. The bust of Nelson is unusual for Poole, being in three dimension, but it does not relate closely to any other bust or portrait though it may owe something to Catherine Andras's wax effigy in Westminster Abbey. It is also unusual in the treatment of the hair and the absence of Naval gold medals. Another version is in the Lloyd's Nelson Collection.

LITERATURE: Reilly 1953, pp.93-4, for a comparable wax by William Cuming. Pyke 1973, pp.112-3; McCarthy 1975, no. 182.

COMMENTS: page 185. ILLUSTRATED: opposite, left.

NELSON BY SAMUEL PERCY, c.1810

229 *Brighton: Brighton Art Gallery*

Coloured wax relief deriving from Gahagan and Andras.

ILLUSTRATED: page 184.

NELSON BY UNKNOWN SCULPTOR

230 *Norfolk: Paston College, North Walsham*

Elmwood bust of uncertain date, formerly polychrome and with bullet holes in the back.

ILLUSTRATED: top, right.

NELSON AFTER FLAXMAN, *c.1815*

231 *Portsmouth: Royal Naval Museum*

Davenport caneware wine cooler, unglazed, with a half-length figure of Nelson deriving from Flaxman's monument in St Paul's Cathedral.

LITERATURE: McCarthy 1995, no.224.

ILLUSTRATED: bottom, right.

230: *Elm wood bust, c.1810*

228: *Coloured wax bust by T R Poole, c.1810*

231: *Davenport wine cooler c.1815*

271

NELSON BY SIR FRANCIS CHANTREY, 1835

232 *London: National Portrait Gallery (4309)*

Marble bust 96.5cm (38in) high, incised on left side: *SIR FRANCIS CHANTREY, / SCULPTOR 1835.* and on right side: *AUSPICE GULIELMO IV^to.*

HS facing in rear-admiral's full dress uniform (one shoulder star), two broad ribbons over right shoulder (Bath and St Ferdinand), stars of Bath (above), St Ferdinand and the Crescent, (not St Joachim), two Naval gold medals, St Vincent above overlapping the Nile which is incised *MDCCXCVIII / NELSON / NILE*; hair thick, brushed forwards and parted in centre, no queue.

COLLECTIONS: commissioned by William IV and worked up by Chantrey from his 1809 bust for the Royal Naval College, Greenwich; in the Guardroom at Windsor Castle; presented by King Edward VII to the Royal United Service Museum 1901; presented to the NPG by the RUSI in June 1962.

EXHIBITION: 'Sir Francis Chantrey RA' NPG 1981(9).

LITERATURE: Windsor Castle Catalogue (1851), no.83; Beresford & Wilson 1897-8, p.214, with an illustration showing it in the Guardroom on the foremast pedestal surrounded by cannon-balls; Official Catalogue of the RUSI (1924), no.2017; Walker 1985/2, pp.364-5; Walpole Society LVI (1994), p.286.

COMMENTS: pages 185-7, 191 note 5.

ILLUSTRATED: page 187.

STATUE BY E.H. BAILY, 1839-43

233 *London: Trafalgar Square*

COMMENTS: page 190

ILLUSTRATED: page 182 and 190.

POTTERY BUST OF NELSON, *c*.1850

234 *Portsmouth: Royal Naval Museum*

Faience bust from the Veuve Perrin pottery, the Bath riband yellow.

LITERATURE: McCarthy 1995, no.193.

ILLUSTRATED: page 183.

POTTERY BUST OF NELSON, *c*.1850

235 *Portsmouth: Royal Naval Museum*

Faience bust from the Rouen Delft pottery, the Bath riband blue.

LITERATURE: McCarthy 1995, no.192.

ILLUSTRATED: page 183.

NELSON BY CHARLES LUCY 1853

236 *Portsmouth: Royal Naval Museum*

Oil on canvas signed C. Lucy. Nelson is shown, seated at his desk in the *Victory* on the morning of the battle of Trafalgar. He is wearing a vice admiral's undress uniform with his four stars of knighthood on the left breast and the Bath ribbon underneath his coat. He is not wearing neck medals. The face most closely resembles the Hoppner portrait, the Andras waxwork and the Thaller and Ranson bust. The famous codicil to his will, leaving Emma Hamilton as a legacy to his country, lies on the desk, together with his hat and telescope. His sword leans against a chest in the left foreground.

COLLECTIONS: Private owner, presented to the Royal Naval Museum in 1994.

ENGRAVINGS: Line engraving by C.W. Sharpe, 1853. This engraving was published together with a testimonial (*opposite*) signed by a number of Nelson's surviving officers and associates, declaring that "...the likeness of his Lordship is highly characteristic and true."

LITERATURE: White's *Companion* 152.

ILLUSTRATED: page 274.

NELSON BY ROBINSON & LEADBEATER, after 1885

237 *Portsmouth: Royal Naval Museum*

White Parian bust on a square stand impressed *R&L* in an oval. 20.5 cm (8 in) high, head facing and inclined slightly downwards, full dress uniform, Bath ribbon, 3 stars and neck medal. It is almost identical to the wax bust by Poole (228; *p.271*), the only significant difference being the addition of the neck medal.

COLLECTIONS: Lily Lambert McCarthy, 154/73. This is a fairly common piece of Nelsonia and there are numerous examples in all the main collections.

LITERATURE: Shinn 1971, pp. 100-2; McCarthy 1995, no. 181.

COMMENTS: Messrs Robinson and Leadbeater of Stoke specialised in good quality but cheap moulded Parian figures and ornament of which they produced vast quantities from 1864 onwards. From about 1885 they used the imprint *R&L* in an oval surround. Examples of this bust also exist in black basalt and copper - some of the latter were produced in 1905 in aid of the BFSS, using copper from HMS *Victory*.

NELSON BY JOSEPH PITTS, 1853

238 *Portsmouth: Royal Naval Museum*

Polychrome bust in Parian ware, inscribed: *Jos^b PITTS - Sc. / London 1853 / Model^d under the direction of / Admiral Sir William Parker K.C.B. / from the painting by Whichelo in his possession.*

COLLECTION: Lily Lambert McCarthy 184/73.

LITERATURE: Shinn 1971, pp.101, 103; Dennis 1990, pp. 263, 266; McCarthy 1995, no.183.

COMMENTS: page 154.

ILLUSTRATED: page 181.

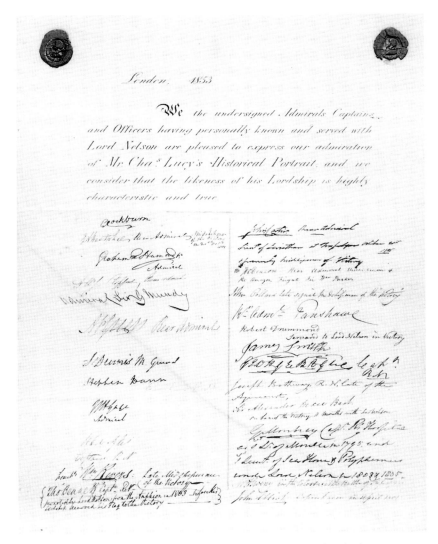

236: *Testimonial accompanying the Sharpe engraving of the portrait by Charles Lucy, 1853*

236: *Oil by Charles Lucy, 1853*

C H R O N O L O G Y

1758	29 September, birth of Horatio Nelson	
1771	1 January, midshipman on HMS *Raisonnable* August, to the West Indies in a merchant ship	
1773	HMS *Carcass* to the Arctic HMS *Seahorse* to the East Indies	
1775	invalided home with malaria War of American Independence	
1776	acting lieutenant; another bout of malaria	
1777	HMS *Lowestoffe* to the West Indies	Rigaud
1778	September, first lieutenant of HMS *Bristol* December, in command of HMS *Badger*	
1779	post captain in command of HMS *Hinchinbroke*	
1780	Nicaraguan expedition, invalided home with dysentry, manchineel poisoning, and pains in the chest; recuperating in Bath with the 'most excruciating tortures'	Rigaud (second sitting)
1781	HMS *Albemarle*; scurvy and foul breath	
1782	North American squadron, Quebec, New York and West Indies	
1783	War of American Independence ends; learning French in Boulogne	
1784	HMS *Boreas* to the West Indies; malaria and a yellow wig	Collingwood
1786	ADC to Prince William	
1787	11 March marries Frances Nisbet at Nevis. HMS *Boreas* pays off and Nelson ashore on half pay for five years, 'fit for any quarter of the globe'	
1793	HMS *Agamemnon* and the Mediterranean	
1794	right eye injured at Calvi, 'very painful at times'	Leghorn miniaturist
1795	action against *Ça Ira* off Genoa; ill with 'flux and fever'	
1796	commodore, HMS *Captain* and HMS *La Minerve*	
1797	14 February, Battle of Cape St Vincent, wounded by a shell splinter; promoted Rear Admiral of the Blue, Knight of the Bath; HMS *Theseus* 24 July, loses his right arm at Santa Cruz September, returns to England in HMS *Sea Horse*	Unknown artist (Monmouth)
1797-8	winters in Bath and London recuperating from the amputation and loss of teeth	Edridge, Abbott, Orme, Singleton, Gahagan

275

1798	HMS *Vanguard* to the Mediterranean	
	1 August, Battle of the Nile; wounded in the head	Unknown Italian artist
	22 September, arrives at Naples	Damer
	6 October, 'Extirpation' satirical print	Gillray
	6 November, created Baron Nelson of the Nile	De Vaere (Wedgwood)
	1 December, 'Hero of the Nile' satirical print	Gillray
	13 December, chelengk arrives from Turkey	Unknown artist
	22-6 December, evacuates royal family to Palermo	(?Head)
1799	14 February, Rear Admiral of the Red	Guzzardi, Head,
	8 June, HMS *Foudroyant*	Grignion
	August, receives Order of the Crescent; Duke of Bronte	Palermo miniaturist
	Davison's Nile medals arrive in Palermo	Boulton & Küchler
	symptoms of Da Costa's syndrome, 'soldier's heart'	
1800	1 April, Order of Ferdinand & Merit	
	August-September, returns home via Vienna, Prague,	Füger, life mask,
	Dresden and Hamburg; 'my health is better but you	Thaller and Ranson
	will see an old man'	Schmidt
	6 November, lands at Great Yarmouth	Rowlandson, Keymer
	9 November, arrives in London and sits to various	Beechey, Hoppner,
	artists	De Koster, Andras,
		Bowyer, Coade
1801	1 January, Vice Admiral of the Blue, HMS *San Josef*	
	in command of the Channel Fleet	
	1 February, birth of Horatia	
	February-March at Great Yarmouth; heart pains, 'my head,	
	my head... my eye is like blood'	Keymer
	2 April, Battle of Copenhagen	
	6 May, succeeds Admiral Parker as Commander-in-Chief	
	22 May, created Viscount Nelson of the Nile and Burnham Thorpe	
	June returns home	
	July-August, commanding naval forces in the Channel	
	18 September, buys Merton Place	
	22 September, arrival at Merton Place	
1802	February, Order of St Joachim	Rising
	22 March, Peace of Amiens	Downman,
	July-August, West Country tour with the Hamiltons	Edridge
		Caulfield
1803	20 March, Declaration of War	
	6 April, death of Sir William Hamilton	
	16 May, Declaration of War	
	18 May, hoists flag in HMS *Victory* as C-in-C Mediterranean	
	'my shatter'd carcase is in the worst plight of the whole fleet'	

276

1804	Vice Admiral of the White, blockading Toulon 14 December, Spain declares war on Britain	
1805	April-July, follows Villeneuve to the West Indies and back August-September, at Merton; left eye deteriorating 14 September hoists flag in HMS *Victory* 20 October, Battle of Ulm; 'my battered old hulk is very crazy - indeed not seaworthy', aged 47 21 October, Battle of Trafalgar and death of Nelson 6 November, news of Trafalgar arrives in England first monuments erected in County Cork and Taynuilt, Argyll 5 December, *Victory* arrives at Spithead autopsy carried out by Dr Beatty	Bowyer, Andras, Whichelo Craig Devis, Andras, Flaxman, etc
1806	9 January, state funeral in St Paul's Cathedral effigy by Catherine Andras installed in Westminster Abbey	
1807	7 July, monument on Portsdown Hill, foundation stone laid, monument in St Paul's Cathedral commissioned	Coade / Bacon Flaxman
1808	monument erected in Montreal	Coade
1843	monument in Trafalgar Square completed	Baily

The Chelengk presented to Nelson by the Sultan of Turkey

THE CHELENGK

The Chelengk was presented to Nelson by the Sultan of Turkey in recognition of the victory of the Nile and its delivery of the Ottoman Empire from the onslaught of Napoleon's armies.[1] It was the highest honour he could bestow, never having been awarded before to anyone, however distinguished, outside Islam. Chelengks were given in 1801 to George III, Lord Keith, C-in-C Mediterranean (in Lord Shelburne's collection at Bowood) and to Admiral Sir Sidney Smith, defender of Acre, but Nelson's was certainly the first in Christendom. It arrived in Naples aboard the *Alcmene* (Captain Hope) on 13 December 1798, a few days before the evacuation to Palermo, but the British plenipotentiary in Constantinople, Spencer Smith, had already dispatched to the Foreign Office a translation of the message of congratulation from the Sublime Porte together with an account of its significance in the Islamic world and a rough drawing of the jewel itself :

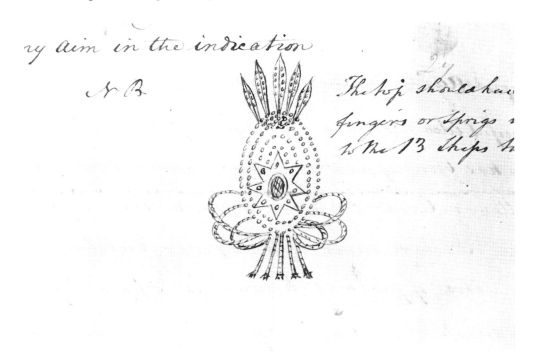

Drawing of the Chelengk by Spencer Smith

Memorandum

Constantinople October 3. 1798
Lord Grenville's Office
November 3, 1798

A superb *aigrette* (of which the marginal sketch gives but an imperfect idea) called a chelengk or plume of triumph, such as has been upon very famous and memorable successes of the Ottoman Arms conferred upon victorious Seraskers (I believe never upon a disbeliever) as the 'ne plus ultra' of personal honour as separate from official dignity. The one in question is indeed rich of its kind; being a blaze of brilliants crowned with a vibrating plumage; and a radiant star in the middle, turning upon its centre by means of watch work which winds up behind. This badge was absolutely taken from one of the imperial turbans and can hardly, according to the ideas annexed to such insignia here, be considered as less than equivocal to the first order of Chivalry in Christendom -such at least was my aim in the indication.

The note was forwarded to Nelson himself who sent it on to his wife. It is endorsed: 'This was sent me by Lord Nelson. FRANCES H. NELSON AND BRONTE'.[2] Nelson's letter of thanks to the Sultan was sent from Naples on 16 December:

Words are entirely inadequate to my feelings for the exalted mark of approbation   bestowed on me by the Imperial Grand Signior, which I must ever attribute to his goodness, not to my deserts. As it is my duty, so I shall always pray to the God of Heaven and Earth to pour down his choicest blessings on the Imperial Head, to bless his Arms with success against all his Enemies, to grant health and long life to the Grand Signior, and for ever to consider me his grateful and devoted servant

NELSON

Requested to be received in hand of the most Sublime Imperial Grand Signior.[3]

The chelengk was a plume of triumph made of diamonds. It consisted of a central revolving rose of sixteen petals with leaves and buds on either side and bound below with a true-love knot; above it a fan of five rays vibrated as the wearer walked. These rays were later fitted with extras in accordance with the Sultan's command to commemorate the thirteen ships captured or destroyed at the Battle of the Nile.[4] The artists' interpretations of the jewel vary considerably. Guzzardi's renderings, (77; *p.82*) pai[...] [...] show the original format with fi[...] the Sultan and now in the D[...] central rose and the true-love [...] andably satirical

and Abbott's version (16; *p.31*) was a concoction painted from hearsay, Nelson still being in the Mediterranean when M'Arthur commissioned it. But there is very little excuse for the Palermo miniaturist's wild inaccuracy (98; *p.97*). Here the rays have increased to seven, the revolving rose has been replaced with a group of four large stones and the true-love knot has totally disappeared. In Burke's engraving of this the rays have become ten, the rose has become a crescent and the true-love knot is still absent. Keymer's copy of the Guzzardi, painted in Yarmouth late in 1800, follows the original portrait but gives the chelengk eight rays and the group of four stones in the centre. Beechey in the Norwich whole-length of 1800-01 (137; *p.123*) is the first to give it the thirteen rays, stipulated by the Sultan to commemorate the ships at the Nile, but omits the revolving centre altogether. Only De Koster in the Scottish National Portrait Gallery version (see 166) has painted the chelengk to agree with the jewel we know from the photograph taken at its presentation to the National Maritime Museum in 1929 (see *p.278*).

The clockwork mechanism mentioned in Spencer Smith's memorandum was removed at some unspecified date, possibly when the extra rays were fitted. Nelson wore the chelengk frequently and even though it had the King's approval it was looked on with suspicion and irritation by his brother officers who regarded it as an alien eccentricity and not part of naval uniform. It was ridiculed ruthlessly, as indeed were all Nelson's vanities, by the political and social satirists of the day. After his death it passed to his brother, the first Earl Nelson, then to his daughter Charlotte, Duchess of Bronte, who had married Samuel Hood, second Lord Bridport. She died in 1873 and it was sold by her son, the third Lord Bridport, in 1895.[5] Much of the collection of Nelson relics in the sale was bought by the government for the Royal Naval College, Greenwich, and most of the remainder was bought by a private benefactor, J A Mullens, who presented them to Greenwich and the Royal United Service Institution. The chelengk itself was bought by Constance Eyre-Matcham whose husband was descended from Nelson's sister Catherine. It remained with Mrs Eyre-Matcham until she was obliged to put it up for sale and it was bought in 1929 by Lady Barclay and presented to the nation in memory of her husband the Right Hon Sir Colville Barclay, KCMG, His Majesty's Ambassador to Portugal 1928-29.[6] It was stolen in a carefully planned smash-and-grab raid on

11 June 1951. A Parliamentary Question in the House of Lords asked about the burglary and it transpired that although the chelengk was of untold historic value in fact the diamonds were shallow-cut Brazilians and intrinsically only worth £150.[7] It was described by Lady Minto, in Vienna in 1800, as 'very ugly and not valuable, being rose diamond'.[8] The chelengk has never been recovered, though the burglar, George Chatham (Taters), confessed his crime in a television programme some forty years later, and even achieved an obituary in *The Independent*.[9]

NOTES TO APPENDIX I, THE CHELENGK

1. *Nicolas* III p. 82; Clarke & M'Arthur 11 pp. 94-5.
2. Naish *Letters* p. 405.
3. *Nicolas* III pp. 202-3.
4. Society for Nautical Research *Annual Report* (1929) pp. 37-44.
5. Christie's 12 July 1895 (120) bought Haws £710 for Mrs Eyre-Matcham; see also John Knox Laughton *The Nelson Memorial* (1896) pp. 328-9 where there is a photograph of Nelson's orders, medals and relics as arranged for Viscount Bridport, Duke of Bronte,
6. National Art-Collections Fund 26 Report (1929) No.720, p. 48.
7. *The Times* 12 June 1951 4f and 27 June 1951 4a.
8. Minto III, p.147.
9. Obituary by Dick Hobbs, *The Independent* 10 June 1997, and Supplement by Dr Pieter van der Merwe, ibid. 14 June 1997.

APPENDIX II

TRANSCRIPT OF AUSTRIAN DOCUMENTS HELD IN THE NATIONAL PORTRAIT GALLERY ARCHIVE.

(1)   Oestereich. Der Adm. Nelson und die schöne Lady Hamilton lassen sich
gegenwärtig in Lebensgrösse von dem berühenten Füger malen. Da viele
Menschen sich drängen um den Adm Nelson zu sehen so pflegt er wenn
eine gewisse Anzahl von Neugirigen vorhanden er sich denselben zu
präsentiren. (*Allgemeine Zeitung*, Montag 1 Sept 1800. No.244 p 1023).

(2)   Vienna Sep.t 23.d 1800
Whenever Mr Füger delivers to Mr Hertz the Banker three Pictures Viz.
One full length of the Queen of Naples. One full length of Lady
Hamilton & one quarter of a length of Lord Nelson of the Nile.
        Then Mr Hertz is to pay Mr Füger the sum of two hundred & fifty
Pounds Sterling, for which Mr Hertz will have the goodness to draw
bills on Lord Nelson in London
                (signed) Bronte Nelson of the Nile

(3)   Erklärung   (undated)
        Ich endesgefertigter Heinrich Füger erkläre hiermit feierlich dass
das an Herrn Moritz von Tschoffen überlassen Porträt des Engl. Adm
Nelson von meinem verstorbener Vater Heinrich Füger Direktor der
Kaiserlich und Königlich Bilder Gallerie und Praeses der K K Akademie
der Bildenden Künste in Wien gemalt wurde. Adm. Nelson wurde von
meinem Vater in Jahre 1800 bei der ersten aussenthalt in Vien in
Lebensgrösse Porträtirt wozu ihm der Adm. persönlich sass. Aus interesse

für den grossen Mann, mahlte mein Vater dessen Brustbild für sich selbst wo es bis zu des Vaters Todte als Zierde in seinem Atelier hängt. Es ist nie eine Copie desselben genommen worden. Im Jahre 1823 überliess ich dieses Porträt dem Herrn Moritz von Tschoffen von welcher Zeit mir die fernernen Schicksale dieses Gemäldes unbekannt sind.

(Witnesses)   Franz Eggendorfer   Heinrich Füger

Dr Ernst Leyrer

(4)   Ich endesgefertigter Moritz Edler von Tschoffen erkläre hiermit feierlichst dass das oben-erwähnte Portrait des Engl Admirals[ls] Nelson gemalt von Heinrich Füger, sich seit dem Jahre 1823 in meinem Besitz befindet, und niemals aus meine Händen kamm. Eben so versichere ich das niemalen eine Copie desselben genommen worde.

Moritz Edler von Tschoffen

Declared before me at Leipzig

in the Kingdom of Saxony this

third day of March 1859,

J Ward

Her Britannick Majesty's

Consul-General.

APPENDIX III

THE DARTMOUTH GUZZARDI PORTRAIT
(Catalogue Number 90)

There are three main possibilities for the origin of this portrait before its acquisition by the Royal Naval College in 1916. The first view, held by Sir Robert Harmsworth and his advisers, is that it is one of the original versions painted by Guzzardi in Palermo in 1799. This was supported by Sir Lionel Cust, Director of the National Portrait Gallery, who had reported to his cousin, Admiral Purey Cust, that he had 'happened upon the original portrait by Guzzardi' in the parsonage at Great Weldon, Northamptonshire, in 1913. He admitted however that he saw it on a dark day and by artificial light which was too deceptive for assurance. Harmsworth himself also admitted that he had shown the picture to the National Gallery with a view to presenting it there but had been advised that it was only an excellent copy. In 1942 the College suffered heavily from enemy air attack and the picture was badly damaged. It was restored after the war by Messrs Frost & Reed whose technical report is in the College library dated 11 February 1964:

> We have come to the conclusion during cleaning that there is little doubt of it being an original i.e. of the date purported, 1799. From this one would think that it is highly probably another version by the Neapolitan painter, Guzzardi. All the pigments and conditions suggest that this is the answer, though of course the picture has suffered very much at some period in the past and there is a considerable amount of damage in various spots.

This makes an interesting point in Harmsworth's favour but in general the report should be treated with considerable caution as evidence.

The second view was cogently argued by Sir Geoffrey Callender, naval historian and the first Director of the National Maritime Museum. He believed the Dartmouth picture to be the copy painted by Keymer in Yarmouth, basing his argument mainly on the curiously misspelt *PNIX* in the inscription, a mistake which he thought could have been easily perpetrated by an obscure Norfolk artist but unlikely to have escaped the eye of Guzzardi himself. Callender put forward his theory in a long letter to the Captain of the College but making several suppositions which cannot be supported by later research and furthermore brushing aside the equally plausible possibility that the spelling mistake could also have been made by another English copyist or even a restorer.

This brings us to the third possibility which, in this author's view, is the most likely and was supported by the Admiralty at the time of Harmsworth's presentation, namely that the Dartmouth version is the copy made by Beetham for the Milford Hotel as part of the agreement when Greville presented the original Guzzardi portrait to the Admiralty in 1848 (see pp.88-9). A number of factors strengthen this view. The first is that Beetham's copy was seen hanging in the hotel in September 1856 by a visitor, Frederick Manning, who recorded it in his *Journey in Wales*, sending an extract to the National Portrait Gallery in June 1859:

> Milford Haven Sept 1856. The Nelson Hotel was much frequented by Lord Nelson, the steps to the Water were made for him or by him. In the House near a Portrait of him by a foreign artist, and considered extremely like. The Admiralty desiring to possess it, Mr Greville the owner of the Hotel, permitted the removal provided it was copied by a good and first rate artist; that has been done and it is very fairly executed. It represents a full length figure in a Naval uniform, no white facings, broad gold lace, 2 epaulettes, with a Star of the Honourable Order of the Bath, Red Ribbon and a Gold Medal Victory crowning Britannia, a large cocked Hat with a splendid Diamond feather rising from a large Star - short white Breeches 4 buttons above the Knee, Knee buckles & shoe ditto. The Figure standing by a Gun near which is a chair with a Red Cloak thrown over it; the left arm is raised and pointing towards the background where a Naval action is being (fought), of a grey or neutral color - at the Bottom of the Picture is - Leonardus Guzzardi Pinxt. Panor.[mi] 1799.

Manning does not give the size of the picture which was presumably the same as the original, and indeed the measurements of the Dartmouth version and the original Admiralty canvas (the lines of the extensions can clearly be seen) are roughly the same, allowing a few inches leeway to account for the turnovers on the stretcher. Manning's transcription of Guzzardi's signature and date copied at the bottom on the rim of the targe, if correct, is certainly an obstacle to the third theory, but various possibilities could account for this; perhaps he felt it necessary to correct Beetham's spelling mistake; or perhaps he copied it exactly and the mistake was inserted during some later unrecorded cleaning operation. The fact remains that he recorded the basic principle of the picture being a copy.

This brings us to the next piece of circumstantial evidence namely the bequest of Colonel Greville who died on 12 September 1867 leaving in his Will, dated 7 September 1867, 'all his real and personal estate of every description' to his nephew Edward Finch Hatton. The bequest is corroborated in a letter from James Gambier Noel CB to the Admiralty chief clerk, Thomas Wolley, dated 23 April 1875:

> My dear Wolley, You may like to add to the history of the Nelson Picture in the Board Room here this fact with regard to the copy alluded to that was presented by the Admiralty to the late Colonel Greville viz:- that the said copy is now in the possession of his nephew and representative - Mr Edward H. Finch Hatton, of Weldon Northants, and is ... hanging in a house occupied by his mother - Lady Louisa Finch Hatton, St Elmo, Torquay. Believe me, Yours very truly, (signed) James G Noel.

Finally, when the picture was sold in 1916 Harmsworth was assured by the vendor, E H Finch Hatton of Great Weldon, that it was a genuine old painting inherited from his uncle, Colonel Greville, who had himself inherited it from the heir of Sir William Hamilton. However this statement was disbelieved by the Rev Nelson Ward, grandson of Horatia and owner of the only other full sized version of the Guzzardi portrait, the unsigned copy acquired from his family by the National Maritime Museum in 1946 (see 85). Mr Nelson Ward declared with some feeling that Harmsworth had offered it and some other pictures to the National Gallery as a memorial to his nephew. He had been asked by the National Gallery to identify the portrait and the general agreement had been that it was a copy. The National Gallery had then refused it and Harmsworth had presented it to the Royal Naval College, Dartmouth in 1918 in memory of his nephew, Lieutenant the Hon Victor Harmsworth, killed at the Battle of Beaumont Hamel in 1916, aged twenty-one.

COLLECTIONS

ROYAL COLLECTION

St James's Palace: Hoppner 1800-10
Windsor Castle: Hoppner (copy by Bone) - Damer 1827 - Bowyer

PUBLIC COLLECTIONS

BARLESTON
Wedgwood Museum: Shout 1798 - De Vaere 1798

BATH
Victoria Art Gallery: Gahagan 1804

BEAULIEU RIVER
Buckler's Hard Museum: Füger (copy 1905)

BECCLES
Lemar House: Thaller & Ranson (copy)

BOURNEMOUTH
Russell Cotes Art Gallery: Thaller & Ranson (copy)

EDINBURGH
Scottish National Portrait Gallery: Abbott, De Koster, Tassie

GREAT YARMOUTH
Town Hall: Keymer 1801

GREENWICH
National Maritime Museum:
   PICTURES: Rigaud 1777-81 - Collingwood 1784 - Leghorn miniaturist 1794 - Singleton
   1797 - Abbott 1797 and versions - Guzzardi 1799 (2) - Grignion 1799 - Palermo miniaturist
   1799 - Schmidt 1800 - Beechey 1800-01 - Hoppner 1800 (sketch) - Hoppner (copy by
   Shepperton) - De Koster 1800 (5) - Rising 1801 - Devis 1805 (3)
   SCULPTURES: Gahagan 1798, 1804, 1839 - Shout 1798 - De Vaere 1798 - Davison's Nile
   medal 1798-9 - Thaller & Ranson 1800 - life mask 1800 - Coade 1800 - Copenhagen badge
   1801 - Andras 1805 (4) - Flaxman 1805 (2) - Flaxman (Copeland) - Trafalgar medal 1805 -
   memorial medals 1805 - Tassie 1805 - Bubb c 1810 - Chantrey 1834 - Coffee
   (after Mrs Damer).

KING'S LYNN
Town Hall: Hoppner (copy by Lane)
Lynn Museum: Hoppner (sketch by Lane)

LEWES
Town Hall: Thaller & Ranson (copy by Turnerelli)

LONDON
Admiralty: Guzzardi 1799 - Beechey (modern copy)
Admiralty House: Thaller & Ranson (copy) - Flaxman (Copeland copy)
Apsley House: Beechey (copy *c.*1840)
British Museum: Shout 1798 - De Vaere 1798 - Davison's Nile medal - Andras 1805 -
   Trafalgar medal 1805 - memorial medals 1905 - Tassie 1805

Drapers' Company: Beechey (*c* 1805)
Government Art Collection: Guzzardi
Guildhall: Damer 1803 - Beechey *c* 1805
Ministry of Defence: Abbott - Beechey - Flaxman
National Portrait Gallery: Abbott 1797 - Gillray 1798 - Guzzardi (1888) - Head 1798-9 -
    Füger 1800 - Beechey 1800 - Edridge 1802 - Devis (copy by Bone) - Chantrey 1835
St Paul's Cathedral: Flaxman statue 1807-18
Victoria & Albert Museum: Shout 1798 - De Vaere 1798 - Andras 1805 - Tassie 1805
Westminster Abbey: Andras 1805-06

MONMOUTH

Nelson Museum: unknown 1797 - Shout 1798 - De Vaere 1798 - Palermo miniaturist 1799 -
    Andras 1805 - Flaxman (Copeland copy) - Copenhagen badge 1801 - Trafalgar medal 1805 -
    Tassie 1805

NORWICH

Castle Museum: Gahagan - Beechey 1800-01 - De Koster 1800 - Tassie 1805

PORTSMOUTH

Royal Naval Museum:

PICTURES: Abbott 1798 - Gillray - Palermo miniaturist 1799 - Füger 1800 -
Hoppner (sketch) 1800 - Hoppner (1875 copy) - De Koster 1800 (2) - Edridge 1802 -
Devis (copy by Cadogan) - Lucy

SCULPTURE: Gahagan 1798 - Shout 1798 - De Vaere 1798 - Davison's Nile medal 1798-9 -
life mask 1800 - Andras 1805 - Flaxman (Copeland copy) - Thaller and Ranson (Cardosi copy) -
Copenhagen badge 1801 - Trafalgar medal 1805 - memorial medals - Tassie 1805 - Poole

HMS *Nelson:* Guzzardi 1799
HMS *Victory:* Beechey (sketch) - Devis (sketch)
HMS *Dryad:* Towne 1836

PORT SUNLIGHT

Lady Lever Art Gallery: Abbott

PRIVATE COLLECTIONS

DALMENY: (Earl of Rosebery): Devis miniature 1805

DARTMOUTH: *Britannia Royal Naval College*: Guzzardi (1848 copy) - Hoppner

DORKING: Thaller & Ranson (Cardosi copy) - Coade 1800

DORSET: Palermo miniaturist (Hardy's)

ESSEX: Devis 1805

FYVIE CASTLE: Hoppner (Bridport's)

GUERNSEY: Schmidt (miniature)

HAMPSHIRE: Gahagan (Copeland copy) - Hoppner (collage) - Edridge 1802 - Devis 1805

HENLY-ON-THAMES: Abbott

HEREFORDSHIRE: Northcote - Guzzardi Miniature

HEYDON HALL: Beechey (sketch)

HOLBROOK: *Royal Hospital School:* Edridge 1797

HOLKHAM: Hoppner

JERSEY: Beechey

KING'S LYNN: Thaller & Ranson

KNOWSLEY: (Earl of Derby): Hoppner (copy by Derby)

LEICESTERSHIRE: Downman 1802

LINCOLNSHIRE: Whichelo 1805

LONDON
Army and Navy Club: Abbott
Covent Garden Gallery: Coffee (after Mrs Damer)
Lloyd's: Abbott (Westminster's)
Maritime Club: Hoppner
Royal College of Defence Studies: Thaller & Ranson
Ten Downing Street: Hoppner (copy 1910)
Private collections: Abbott 1797 (2) Guzzardi 1799, 1800 - Gahagan 1805, 1814 -
   Andras 1805 - Devis

NEWCASTLE-ON-TYNE, *University:-* Gahagan

NORFOLK: Palermo miniaturist 1799 (Lady Hamilton's)

ROMSEY: Thaller & Ranson (Nollekens copy)

RUDDING PARK (formerly): Gahagan

SALISBURY: Orme 1797-98

STROUD: Abbott

ABROAD

BOSTON, *Museum of Fine Arts*: Hoppner

ISTANBUL, *Dolmabahce Palace*: Guzzardi (1799)

NAPLES, *Museo di San Martino*: Guzzardi (1799)

VANCOUVER ISLAND, *Esquimault Naval College*: Thaller & Ranson (copy)

VERSAILLES, *Château de Versailles:* Hoppner (copy *c.*1835)

USA, private collection: Abbott (Bridport's)

ABBREVIATIONS

Alterbury	Paul Alterbury (ed.) *The Parian Phenomenon* (Richard Dennis, Somerset 1989).
Barras 1986	T.C. Barras, 'Vice-Admiral Nelson's Lost Eye', *Trans. Ophthalmological Society U.K.* (1986), pp.351-5.
Barras 1987	T.C. Barras, 'I have a right to be blind sometimes', *Nelson Dispatch II* (1987).
Beatty 1807	Sir William Beatty, *The Authentic Narrative of the Death of Lord Nelson* (1807), with Devis-Scriven frontispiece.
Bennett 1972	Geoffrey Bennett, *Nelson the Commander* (1972).
Berry 1798	Sir Edward Berry, *An Authentic Narrative . . . to the Conclusion of the Battle of the Nile 1798* (1798).
Beresford & Wilson 1897-8	Lord Charles Beresford and H.W. Wilson, *Nelson and his Times* (1897-8), copiously illustrated.
BL / BM	British Library / British Museum .
BM Guide 1905	*A Guide to the Manuscripts, Printed Books, Prints and Medals Exhibited on the Occasion of the Nelson Centenary* (British Museum 1905).
Bosanquet 1952	Captain H.T. A. Bosanquet R.N., 'Lord Nelson and the loss of his arm', *Mariner's Mirror* 38 (1952), pp.184-95 with full references.
Bosanquet 1955	H.T. A. Bosanquet, *The Naval Officer's Sword* (ed. John May 1955).
Bowyer Memorials	A manuscript compiled by Mrs Asquith from Mrs Stratton's 'Reminiscences'; A copy, made by Alice Hesterdale in 1908, was very kindly lent to me by one of Bowyer's descendants, Miss Emily Wolstencraft. Typescript in NPG archive.
Brenton 1823	Captain Edward Brenton, *The Naval History of Great Britain* (1823).
Broadley 1906	A.M. Broadley, *Three Dorset Captains at Trafalgar* (1906).
Brown 1980	Laurence Brown, *British Historical Medals* (3 vols 1980-95).
Bryant 1970	Sir Arthur Bryant, *Nelson* (1970).
Callender 1912	Sir Geoffrey Callender, *The Life of Nelson* (1912).
Callender 1914	Callender, *The Story of H.M.S. Victory* (1914).
Callender 1928	Callender, 'The Death Mask of Lord Nelson', *SNR Annual Report* 1928.
Callender 1941	Callender, 'The Effigy of Nelson in Westminster Abbey', *Mariner's Mirror* 27 (1941).
Callender 1943	*The Illustrated London News*, 20 March 1943, on the Schmidt portraits.
Callender Papers	Callender's papers deposited in the NMM.
Chaloner Smith 1883-1925	John Chaloner Smith, *British Mezzotinto Portraits* (4 vols 1883 and continued by Charles Russell 1925).

Charnock 1806   John Charnock, *Biographical Memoirs of Lord Viscount Nelson* (1806).

Churchill 1808   T.O. Churchill, *The Life of Lord Viscount Nelson* . . . (1808), illustrated
                   by W. Bromley and W.H. Worthington, published by R. Bowyer.

Clarke & M'Arthur James Clarke & John M'Arthur, *The Life and Services of Horatio,*
1809   *Viscount Nelson, K.B. from his Lordship's Manuscripts* (2 4° vols 1809),
                   illustrated mainly by Westall, Pocock and West; 1810 8° reprint has
                   'Immortality of Nelson' by West-Heath and the Abbott-Golding print of
                   15 November 1808.

Collingwood 1837   G.L.N. Collingwood, *Selections from the Public and Private*
                   Correspondence of Vice-Admiral Collingwood (1837).

Connell 1957   Brian Connell, *Portrait of a Whig Peer* (1957).

Cowie 1990   L.W. Cowie, *Lord Nelson 1758-1805: a Bibliography* (1990).

Croft Murray 1970 Edward Croft Murray, *Decorative Painting in England* (2 vols 1970).

Dennis 1990   Richard Dennis, *The Parian Phenomenon* (Somerset c.1990).

DNB   *Dictionary of National Biography.*

Edwards 1808   Edward Edwards, *Anecdotes of Painting* (1808).

Farington   Joseph Farington, *Diary 1793-1821* (16 vols ed. K. Garlick,
                   A. Macintyre & K. Cave, Yale 1978, no index).

Forrer   L. Forrer, *Dictionary of British Medallists* (8 vols 1904-30).

Foskett 1987   Daphne Foskett, *Miniatures: Dictionary and Guide*
                   (Antique Collectors' Club 1987).

Fraser 1987   Flora Fraser, *Emma, Lady Hamilton* (New York 1987).

Fraser 1995   Flora Fraser, 'If You Seek His Monument', White's *Companion*, chapter VI.

George 1942   M.D. George, *Catalogue of Political and Personal Satires...in the British*
                   Museum (vol VII 1942).

Gill 1987   Edward Gill, *Nelson and the Hamiltons on Tour* (Gloucester 1987).

Gordon 1962   Major Lawrence L. Gordon, *British Battles and Medals* (Aldershot 1962).

Grant 1910   M.H. Grant, *The Makers of Black Basaltes* (1910).

Gunnis 1964   Rupert Gunnis, *Dictionary of British Sculptors* 1660-1851 (1953 revised
                   1964).

Harrison 1806   James Harrison, *The Life of the Right Honorable Horatio, Lord*
                   Viscount Nelson of the Nile . . . (1806), with Beechey-Cook frontispiece.

Hattersley 1974   Roy Hattersley, *Nelson* (1974), copiously illustrated with colour plates.

Hibbert 1994   Christopher Hibbert, *Nelson: A Personal History* (1994), with excellent
                   bibliography.

Hill 1836   Benson Earle Hill, *Recollections of an Artillery Officer* (1836).

Hough 1980	Richard Hough, *Nelson* (1980).
Howarth 1969	David Howarth, *Trafalgar: the Nelson Touch* (1969).
Howarth 1988	David and Stephen Howarth, Nelson: *The Immortal Memory* (1988).
ILN	*The Illustrated London News* (1842 in progress)
Isaacson 1991	Cecil J. Isaacson, *Nelson's Five Years on the Beach* . . . (Fakenham 1991).
James 1837	William James, *The Naval History of Great Britain 1793-1820* (1837).
James 1948	Admiral Sir William James, *The Durable Monument: Horatio Nelson* (1948).
Keate 1939	E.M. Keate, *Nelson's Wife* (1939).
Keigwin 1985	K.P. Keigwin, 'Lord Nelson's Journey through Germany', *Mariner's Mirror* XXI (1985).
Kelly 1990	Alison Kelly, *Mrs Coade's Stone* (1990).
Kemble 1933	James Kemble FRCS, 'The Medical Life of Lord Nelson', *Idols and Invalids* (1933).
Kemp 1976	Peter Kemp, ed., *The Oxford Companion to Ships and the Sea* (O.U.P. 1976).
Kennedy 1975	Sir Ludovic Kennedy, *Nelson's Band of Brothers* (1951, revised 1975), with many illustrations and diagrams.
Knight 1861	Cornelia Knight, *The Autobiography of Miss Knight* (1861, ed. Roger Fulford 1960).
Knight 1977	R.J.B. Knight, *Guide to the Manuscripts in the National Maritime Museum* (1977).
Kosegarten 1801	Thomas Kosegarten, *Meine Freuden in Sachsen* (Leipzig 1801).
Laughton 1905	Sir John Knox Laughton, *The Nelson Memorial: Nelson and his Companions in Arms* (1896 and 1905), with good bibliography.
LeQuesne 1955	Leslie P. LeQuesne, 'Nelson's Wounds', *Middlesex Hospital Journal* 55 (1955).
Letters	see Nicolas and Naish.
Letters 1814	*The Letters of Lord Nelson to Lady Hamilton ...* (ed. anonymous, 2 vols 1814).
Lewis 1960	M.A. Lewis, *The Social History of the Royal Navy 1793-1815* (1960).
Lloyds 1932	W.R. Dawson, *The Nelson Collection at Lloyd's* (1932).
MacDougall 1955	Katherine Lindsay-MacDougall, 'Nelson Manuscripts at the National Maritime Museum' *Mariner's Mirror* 41 (1955).
Magazine of Art 1898	Douglas Sladen, 'The Nelson Centenary: how Nelson looked in the Year of the Nile', *Magazine of Art* (1898), pp.529-34.

Mahan 1897	Captain A.T. Mahan, *The Life of Nelson* (2 vols 1897, revised 1899).
Marcus 1971	G.J. Marcus, *A Naval History of England: the Age of Nelson* (1971).
May 1972	John May & Jennifer May, *Commemorative Pottery 1780-1900* (1972).
May 1995	John May, 'Nelson Commemorated', White's *Companion*, chapter IV.
Mayo 1897	J.H. Mayo, *Medals and Decorations of the British Army and Navy* (2 vols 1897).
McCarthy 1995	*Remembering Nelson; A Record of the Lily Lambert McCarthy Collection at the Royal Naval Museum, Portsmouth, England* (1995).
McKay & Roberts	W. McKay & W. Roberts, *John Hoppner R.A.* (2 vols 1909-14).
Medallic Illustrations	Hawkins, *Medallic Illustrations of the History of Great Britain and Ireland* (compiled F. Hawkins and others, British Museum 1885, 1904-11).
Milford Haven	Marquess of Milford Haven, *British Naval Medals* (1919).
Millar 1969	Sir Oliver Millar, *The Later Georgian Pictures in the Collection of Her Majesty the Queen* (1969).
Millett 1995	Timothy Millett, 'The Nelson Medallions' section in White's *Companion*, chapter III.
Minto 1874	Countess of Minto, ed., *The Life and Letters of Sir Gilbert Elliot, First Earl of Minto 1751-1806* (3 vols 1874).
Mollo 1965	John Mollo, *Uniforms of the Royal Navy During the Napoleonic Wars* (1965).
Morrison 1893-4	Alfred Morrison, *The Hamilton and Nelson Papers* (2 vols 1893-4).
Munday 1995	John Munday, 'The Nelson Relics', White's *Companion*, chapter III.
Naish 1958	G.P.B. Naish, ed., *Nelson's Letters to his Wife and other Documents 1785-1831* (1958).
Naish 1972	G.P.B. Naish, *Horatio Nelson* (Pitkin Pictorials 1972).
Nash 1985	Michael Nash, 'Young Nelson: some little known portraits', *Nelson Dispatch* II (April 1985).
Nash 1993	Michael Nash, ed., *The Nelson Masks* (Hoylake 1993).
Nash 1995	Michael Nash, 'Building a Nelson Library', White's *Companion*, chapter VIII.
Naval Chronicle	*The Naval Chronicle* (40 vols 1799-1818).
Nelson Dispatch	*Journal of the Nelson Society* (1981 - annually).
Nicolas 1844-6	Sir Nicholas Harris Nicolas, ed., *The Dispatches and Letters of Vice-Admiral Lord Viscount Nelson* (7 vols 1844-6).
NMM	National Maritime Museum, Greenwich.

NMM 1988   *Concise Catalogue of Oil Paintings in the National Maritime Museum* (1988).

Noble 1908   Percy Noble, *Anne Seymour Damer* (1908).

Northcote   *Conversations of James Northcote R.A. with James Ward on Art and Artists* (ed.Fletcher 1901).

NPG   National Portrait Gallery, London.

O'D 1908-25   F.O. O'Donoghue and Henry Hake, *Catalogue of Engraved British Portraits... in the British Museum* (6 vols 1908-25).

Oman 1947   Carola Oman, *Nelson* (New York 1946, London 1947), copiously illustrated and re-published 1950.

Orme 1806   F.W. Blagdon, *Orme's Graphic History of the Life, Exploits, and Death of Horatio Nelson...* (folio 1806), copiously illustrated with coloured engravings and a stipple frontispiece by Godby after Mrs Damer's marble bust in the Guildhall.

Palmer 1872   C.J. Palmer, *Perlustration of Great Yarmouth* (2 vols 1872).

Parsons 1843   G.S. Parsons, *Nelsonian Reminiscences, Leaves from Memory's Log* (1843 and ed. Long 1905).

Pavière 1950   S.H. Pavière, *The Devis Family of Painters* (1950).

Pettigrew 1849   T.J. Pettigrew, *Memoirs of the Life of Vice-Admiral Lord Viscount Nelson* (2 vols 1849), with frontispieces engraved by Skelton after Guzzardi and Devis.

Pocock 1968   Tom Pocock, *Nelson and his World* (1968, 1974), copiously illustrated with colour plates.

Pocock 1980   Tom Pocock, *The Young Nelson in the Americas* (1980).

Pocock 1987   Tom Pocock, *Horatio Nelson* (1987).

Pocock 1995   Tom Pocock, 'In Nelson's Footsteps', White's *Companion*, chapter V.

Pollard 1970   J.G. Pollard, 'Matthew Boulton and Conrad Heinrich Küchler', *Numismatic Chronicle* X (1970).

Pryor 1995   Felix Pryor, 'Nelson the Letter-Writer', White's *Companion*, chapter VII.

Pugh 1968   Admiral P.D. Gordon Pugh, *Nelson and his Surgeons* (1968), based on the Nelson exhibition at Haslar in 1967.

Pugh 1970   P.D. Gordon Pugh, *Staffordshire Portrait Figures* (1970).

Pugh 1971   P.D. Gordon Pugh, *Naval Ceramics* (Bath 1971).

Pyke 1973   E.J. Pyke, *A Biographical Dictionary of Wax Modellers* (1973).

RA   Royal Academy, Royal Academician.

Rathbone 1973	Philip Rathbone, *Paradise Merton: the Story of Nelson and the Hamiltons at Merton Place* (Windlesham 1973).
Reilly 1953	D.R. Reilly, *Portrait Waxes* (1953).
Reilly 1989	Robin Reilly, *Wedgwood* (2 vols 1989).
Reilly & Savage	Robin Reilly & George Savage, *Wedgwood: the Portrait Medallions* (1973).
Rigaud 1854	Stephen Rigaud, 'Memoir of John Francis Rigaud Esq. R.A.' (1854), ed. William L. Pressly, *Walpole Society* 50 (1984).
RNM Portsmouth	Royal Naval Museum, HM Naval Base, Portsmouth.
Roberts 1907	W. Roberts, *Sir William Beechey R.A.* (1907).
Robinson 1930	Commander Charles N. Robinson, 'The Engraved Portraits of Nelson', *The Print Collector's Quarterly* XVII (1930).
Rule Britannia 1986	Sotheby's loan exhibition, *Rule Britannia* (1986).
Russell	see Chaloner Smith.
Sandwich 1937	Earl of Sandwich, *British and Foreign Medals relating to Maritime Affairs* (NMM 1937 and Supplement 1939).
Sewter 1955	A.C. Sewter, 'Some new facts about Lemuel Abbott', *Connoisseur* 135 (1955).
Shinn 1971	Charles & Dorrie Shinn, *Victorian Parian China* (1971).
Sitwell 1936	Sacheverell Sitwell, *Conversation Pieces* (1936).
SNR	Society for Nautical Research.
Southey 1813	Robert Southey, *The Life of Horatio Lord Nelson* (2 vols 1813 expanded from *The Quarterly Review* February 1810). Callender's edition of 1922 corrects Southey's errors and is used here. See also Michael Nash, *Trafalgar Chronicle* I (1991).
Tanner & Nevinson	Lawrence Tanner & John Nevinson, 'On some Later Funeral Effigies in Westminster Abbey', *Archaeologia* 85 (1935).
TH 1948	An inventory of the contents of Trafalgar House compiled at the time of transfer to the NMM in 1948.
Thiemer-Becker	Thiemer-Becker, *Allgemeines Lexicon der Bildenden Kunstler* (37 vols 1907-50 and Supplements, and new edition in progress).
Trafalgar Chronicle	The Year Book of the 1805 Club (1991 annually).
Van der Merwe 1995	Pieter van der Merwe (ed.), *Nelson: An Illustrated History* (1995).
Walder 1978	David Walder, *Nelson* (1978).

Walker 1977   Richard Walker, 'Nelson as Romantic Hero', *Country Life* (17 Feb 1977).

1980   'Nelson's Masks - Life or Death', *Mariner's Mirror* 66 (1980).

1985/1   'The Guzzardi Portraits of Nelson', *Country Life* (18 July 1985).

1985/2   *Regency Portraits* (NPG 1985).

1986   'Foreign Impressions of a British Hero', *Country Life* (25 Sept 1986).

1992   *Miniatures in the Collection of Her Majesty the Queen...* (C.U.P. 1992).

1994   'Nelson as Painted by Lemuel Abbott', *Trafalgar Chronicle* (1994).

1995   'The Nelson Portraits', White's *Companion*, chapter II.

Warner 1955   Oliver Warner, *Lord Nelson: Guide to reading with a Note on Contemporary Portraits* (1955).

1958   Warner, *A Portrait of Lord Nelson* (1958), with appendix listing the contemporary portraits, based on articles in *History Today* (1955), *Connoisseur Year Book* (1956), *Country Life* (2 August 1956, 8 May 1958), and *Connoisseur* (August 1958).

1971   Oliver Warner, *Nelson's Last Diary* (1971).

1975   Oliver Warner, *Nelson* (1975), copiously illustrated.

Waterhouse 1953   Ellis Waterhouse, *Painting in Britain 1530-1790* (1953).

Waterhouse 1981   Ellis Waterhouse, *Dictionary of British 18th Century Painters* (1981).

Westwood 1926   A. Westwood, *Matthew Boulton's Medals on the Reconquest of Naples in 1799* (1926).

White's *Companion*   Colin White ed., *The Nelson Companion* (Portsmouth 1995).

White 1995   Colin White, 'The Immortal Memory', White's *Companion*, chapter I.

Whitley I-IV   William T. Whitley, *Artists and their Friends in England 1700-1799* (C.U.P. 2 vols 1928) and *Art in England 1800-1837* (C.U.P. 2 vols 1928-30).

Wilkinson 1931   Clennell Wilkinson, *Life of Nelson* (1931).

Windsor Mag.1904   Rt Hon Horatio Nelson (third) Earl, 'Nelson Relics and Relic Hunters', *Windsor Magazine* 1904.

PICTURE ACKNOWLEDGEMENTS

The illustrations are reproduced with the kind permission of the following:

The Trustees of the Royal Naval Museum
vii, xiv, 11, 16, 21, 22, 28, 35, 42, 47, 51, 59, 62, 63, 65 (both), 66, 67, 75, 98 (both), 106, 109, 111,126, 133, 135, 139, (both), 152, 153, 164, 165, 181, 183 (both), 188, 196 (both) , 198, 202, 205, 216 (both), 218, 220, 221, 224, 229, 231 (top), 234, 241, 247, 251, 253, 256, 263, 267 (bottom), 269 (bottom), 271 (bottom), 273, 274.

The Trustees of the National Maritime Museum
iii, xx, xvi (top) 18, 19, 24, 26, 31, 45, 56, 64, 81, 95, 102, 108, 116, 117, 130, 131, 144, 151, 158, 161, 163, 186, 195 (top), 204, 211, 215, 233, 239, 242, 265, 269 (top),278.

The Trustees of the National Portrait Gallery
ii, xvi (middle), 30, 32, 72, 87, 90, 118, 122, 149, 169,187, 195 (bottom), 201, 209, 217, 236, 243, 244, 246.

Clive Richards Collection
xiii, xv, 43, 83

Sotheby's
199, 206 (bottom), 231 (bottom), 261

The Nelson Museum, Monmouth
8, 230, 279

Royal Collection: By Gracious Permission of Her Majesty the Queen
127, 138.

Courtauld Institute
177, 182, 267 (top)

Royal Navy
4, 82

Norfolk Museums Service
60, 123.

Dean and Chapter of Westminster Abbey
168, 171.

Victoria Art Gallery, Bath
210.

London, Guildhall
79

Trustees of the Wedgwood Museum
77

Royal Institute of British Architects
190

Great Yarmouth Town Council
86

Christie's
258

Crown Estate Commissioners
174

Brighton Art Gallery
184

Paston School, North Walsham
271 (top)

Newcastle University
213

Paul Hopper Collection, Sydney
23

Holman Potterton Collection, New York
212

Dolmabahce Palace, Istanbul
225

Thanks are also due to a number of private owners who have most kindly made their portraits available for this book, but who have indicated that they wish to remain anonymous:

xvi (bottom), 25, 37, 39, 85, 96, 97, 147, 155, 201, 248, 249, 255, 262.

LIST OF ILLUSTRATIONS

INDEX

The index covers the Introduction, Prologue, Catalogue, Chronology and the
Appendices as well as the main text.
All images are of Nelson unless stated otherwise.
Page numbers of illustrations are in italic.